CRUSADER hymns
and hymn stories

BOOKS BY BILLY GRAHAM

Peace with God
Cloth $3.50   Paperback 75¢

Secret of Happiness
Cloth $2.95   Paperback 50¢

My Answer
Cloth $3.50

BOOKS ABOUT BILLY GRAHAM

Billy Graham *by John Pollock*
Cloth $4.95   Paperback 95¢

Those Who Came Forward *by Curtis Mitchell*
Cloth $3.95

The Making of a Crusader *by Curtis Mitchell*
Cloth $3.95

The London Crusade Story *by Curtis Mitchell*
$1.50

THE BILLY GRAHAM EVANGELISTIC ASSOCIATION

Box 779 (1300 Harmon Place), Minneapolis, Minnesota 55440
Box 841 (414 Graham Avenue), Winnipeg 1, Manitoba, Canada
Bush House, Aldwych, London, W.C. 2, England
820 Caltex House, Sydney, New South Wales, Australia
Box 870, Auckland, New Zealand
Decision, 102 Avenue des Champs-Elysees, Paris 8, France
Entscheidung, Postfach 16309, 6 Frankfurt/M, Germany
Casilla 5055, Buenos Aires, Argentina
Decimex, Apartado 10742, Mexico 1, D.F., Mexico
Apartado 13098, Santurce, San Juan, Puerto Rico

CRUSADER
hymns
and
hymn stories

Crusade Hymn Stories *edited by Cliff Barrows*
Hymn studies and personal stories *by Billy Graham
and the Crusade Musicians*

Crusader Hymns *compiled and edited by
Cliff Barrows and Donald Hustad*

Special Crusade Edition

Used by permission of Hope Publishing Company
Chicago, Illinois 60644.
THE BILLY GRAHAM EVANGELISTIC ASSOCIATION
Box 779, Minneapolis, Minnesota 55440

preface

I love to hear the great choirs sing at our Crusades around the world — often in languages I cannot understand — but God can. I love the Gospel songs of George Beverly Shea and the other soloists on our Team who travel with us. I love the final verse in the Psalms (the greatest hymn collection of all time) that tells us, "Let every thing that hath breath praise the Lord."

God put a song into man, but sin garbled it, distorted it, and brought discord into his life. When a person repents and puts his trust unreservedly in Jesus Christ, God gives him back the melody that was almost muted. That is the secret of the Christian life.

Cliff Barrows and Don Hustad, two Team musicians who have been my close associates, have made a priceless gift to the church by writing and compiling this volume of hymn stories. Not many people know that the greatest Christian hymns and songs have often come out of the deep wells of life: wells of adversity, of suffering, of tragedy. It is inspiring to know that when events have turned dark and somber, these men and women have been able to tune their souls to a pitch unheard apart from the mind of Christ. The result has been a multiplied blessing to all mankind.

"Is any among you merry?" asked the Apostle James. "Let him sing psalms." "Be filled with the Spirit," wrote the Apostle Paul, "speaking to yourselves in psalms and hymns and spiritual songs, singing and making melody in your heart to the Lord, giving thanks always for all things unto God and the Father in the name of our Lord Jesus Christ."

I commend unreservedly this book with its companion volume, *Crusader Hymns* (here specially bound together), to our millions of televiewers, listeners, readers, and friends around the world. May God bless you as you read of what He can do through the power of music; and may you join the mighty choir of the faithful by lifting your own voice in heartfelt praise to the King of kings and Lord of lords who loved us and gave Himself for us.

Billy Graham

FOREWORD

One of the greatest contributions to the spiritual development of my life has come from the influence of sacred songs. As a young boy I learned to love our Gospel songs and hymns, as well as the Bible, at my mother's knee.

And now, for over twenty years of Crusade evangelism, we of the Billy Graham Team have witnessed the lasting appeal of these hymns and their power to unite the hearts of a congregation. Wherever Christians gather, the singing of these hymns and songs has been a vital and meaningful part of worship.

The stories behind the hymns have always fascinated me. I believe they provide some of our most inspiring devotional literature. CRUSADE HYMN STORIES brings together some of the favorites of Billy Graham, and of the members of our music staff. Of course, not all our favorites — or yours — are here, but there are enough to give you a hymn a week for a full year — to study, to memorize, to make your very own.

Try using them for your personal worship or for family devotions. We believe you will find that one of the purposes of this book — to help you sing "with the spirit and with the understanding also" — is being fulfilled.

In writing CRUSADE HYMN STORIES there has been an honest attempt to present the facts concerning the hymns, their origins, and their significance in the Billy Graham Crusades as we have known them. We do not claim that these are all the facts. Wherever we have erred or omitted something others may deem important, we ask indulgence.

I am indebted to all the members of the Team who have shared their favorite hymn stories along with their personal experiences and observations. Lee Fisher, a gifted musician and Bible scholar, who has been an intimate friend and associate of Dr. Graham, gave invaluable help in checking the manuscripts.

foreword con't

A special word of thanks goes to my beloved colleague, Don Hustad, whose fellowship and musicianship has been a great source of inspiration to me. His unique gifts and abilities have well qualified him for the task of research and writing which he has untiringly pursued.

If the song of the Lord resounds more assuredly from your heart and life as a result of this little volume, all of the time and effort put into it will be worthwhile.

Yours, in the glad song our Savior brings,

Cliff Barrows

table of contents

table of contents con't

i with thee would begin

[*Crusader Hymns*, No. 279]

A Hymn Story by Cliff Barrows

What a wonderful thing it is to be able to "begin again!" What if, having made a bad start in a subject in school or with a project at work, we were doomed to receive a failing grade or to be dismissed from our job? How much more tragic life would be if we could never recover from the bad starts we all make in moral and spiritual ways. In his poem "Birches" Robert Frost says: "I'd like to get away from earth awhile and then come back to it and begin over." The first part of his wish will never be realized; but we can all stay right where we are and begin over again.

This is one of the benefits that salvation brings. We can forget our old sins and failures because God has forgotten them. Through the prophet Jeremiah, God has said, "I will forgive their iniquity and I will remember their sin no more" (Jer. 31:34). The Bible talks about "books" (Dan. 7:10; Rev. 20:12) and suggests that all our shortcomings are recorded from the day of our birth. But when we accept Christ's offer of forgiveness, our embarrassing and condemning record is blotted out. In a past generation they would have said, "The slate was wiped clean."

More than this, we are given a completely new nature — the nature of God — so that we need not be dominated by our weaknesses as we were before. In *Living Letters*, II Corinthians 5:17 reads this way: "When someone becomes a Christian he becomes a brand new person inside. He is not the same any more. A new life has begun."

Of course, we continue to make occasional "bad starts" throughout life. Even after Christ dwells within us, we may be tempted to err and spoil our record. But Christians too can "begin again." I John 1:7, 9 (*LL*) says: "If we are living in the light of God's presence, just as Christ does, then we have wonderful fellowship and joy with each other, and the blood of Jesus His Son cleanses us from every sin... If we confess our sins to Him, he can be depended on to forgive us our sins and to cleanse us from every wrong." Remember that John is writing here to Christians, to those who "are living in the light of God's presence."

Sometimes we hear the idea mentioned that, after a certain age, a person cannot change. It is true that our patterns of behavior are pretty well established when we are young. But it is also true that a man can change and be changed at any age, with the help of God. At any time in life, we can win victory over an attitude or a habit, and we can begin again. The Apostle Paul was probably thinking of some old failures of his own when he said, near the end of his life; "Forgetting the past and looking forward to what lies ahead, I strain to reach the end of the race" (Phil. 3:13, 14, *LL*).

Some folk talk about "turning over a new leaf" at the beginning of a new year. Others seem to be cynical about New Year's resolutions because they are often forgotten by the 5th of January. When this happens, it is either because we did not really mean to keep them or because we tried to do so in our own human strength. Only God can give us the power to change and to be changed.

Each morning is a good time to begin again. In our period of personal worship, we can ask God for strength and grace to live that day in victory, accomplishing all that we would like to do. And, if we find that we have failed by noon, even then we can begin again.

In its original form, this is a Swedish hymn whose author is unknown. Because the translation is literal, you may find that the sentence structure is occasionally inverted and the meaning is a bit obscure. But if you make the effort to understand, you will find that it is a prayer that we may start anew — right now — in the strength of Christ and with guidance from His Word. And if you take the trouble to sing it, you will enjoy its "Swedish style" melody.

[Read or sing the entire hymn.]

I with Thee would begin, O my Saviour so dear,
    On the way that I still must pursue;
I with Thee would begin every day granted here,
    As my earnest resolve I renew
To be and remain Thine forever.

I with Thee would begin and go forth in Thy name,
    Which alone doth salvation bestow;
Fold me close to Thy breast where found joy all who came,
    There is refuge for me too, I know,
Though all in this world is confusion.

Let Thy Word all-divine be my lamp, in whose light
    I may constantly keep to Thy way;
And each day wouldst Thou cleanse me anew, make me white
    In the blood shed for me on that day
The cross Thou didst suffer, Lord Jesus.

I with Thee would begin — yea, and hear one more prayer,
    I would close with Thee too my brief day,
And when daylight has failed, let me sleep in Thy care,
    Until waking Thy child Thou dost say,
"Come, live with me ever in heaven."

From the Swedish, anon.
Tr. by A. Samuel Wallgren (1885-1940)

Amazing grace! how sweet the sound,
    That saved a wretch like me!
I once was lost, but now am found,
    Was blind, but now I see.

'Twas grace that taught my heart to fear,
    And grace my fears relieved;
How precious did that grace appear
    The hour I first believed!

Through many dangers, toils and snares,
    I have already come;
'Tis grace hath brought me safe thus far,
    And grace will lead me home.

When we've been there ten thousand years,
    Bright shining as the sun,
We've no less days to sing God's praise
    Than when we first begun.

John Newton, 1-3 (1725-1807)
John P. Rees, 4 (ascribed) (1828-1900)

amazing grace! how sweet the sound

[*Crusader Hymns*, No. 108]

A Hymn Story by Billy Graham

One Sunday in 1966 during the Earls Court crusade in London, we were driving between speaking engagements in the university towns of Oxford and Cambridge. Suddenly I noticed that we were passing through the village of Olney and I remarked to my wife, "There's a famous church and graveyard here. Let's stop to visit them."

Riding through the Olney village square, we passed the former home of William Cowper. It is now a museum that houses the personal effects of that great English poet, to whom we are indebted for classic poetry as well as for some of our finest hymns. This village is also famous as the place where the Shrove Tuesday pancake races originated.

The Olney parish church of Saints Peter and Paul was built in the fourteenth century, but much of the original beauty and dignity remains. In the corner of the churchyard, almost overgrown with tall grass, we found what we were looking for — a large tombstone with these words inscribed:

> John Newton, Clerk; once an infidel and libertine, a servant of slaves in Africa, was by the rich mercy of our Lord and Saviour Jesus Christ preserved, restored, pardoned, and appointed to preach the faith he had long labored to destroy.

Newton was the son of a sea captain who was engaged in the Mediterranean trade. His mother died when he was six, and after only two years of formal schooling he joined his father's ship at the age of eleven. His early life was one of immorality, debauchery and failure. He was rejected by his father, in trouble with all his employers, and finally jailed and degraded. In later years he served on slave ships, where he so incurred the hatred of his employer's negro wife that he became virtually a "slave of slaves."

This miserable seaman was brought to his senses by reading Thomas a Kempis's book, *Imitation of Christ.* His actual conversion was the result of a violent storm in which he almost lost his life. At the age of thirty-nine, John Newton became a minister and gave the rest of his life to serving God in the church. During the fifteen years he was the pastor at Olney, he wrote many hymns. Together with William Cowper, he published a hymnal which was widely used in Anglican churches.

7

It seems to me that "Amazing Grace" is really Newton's own testimony of his conversion and of his life as a Christian. He might have begun the hymn with the first stanza of another of his poems, "He Died for Me," but these words have somehow dropped out of use:

> In evil long I took delight,
> Unawed by shame or fear,
> Till a new object struck my sight,
> And stopped my wild career.

"God's grace" has been defined as "His undeserved favor." It was this grace that reached out to John Newton. When he learned that Christ loved him and had died for him, he was amazed. It was this grace which made him conscious that he was a sinner ("grace taught my heart to fear") and then assured him that his sins were forgiven ("grace my fears relieved"). So it is with all of us. We are all "great sinners" not only because of transgressions committed, but also because we fall short of God's standard for our lives. And this "amazing grace" is available to all of us.

[Read or sing stanzas 1 and 2.]

As Christian believers we continue to experience God's undeserved love and favor throughout all of life. Every day He forgives our shortcomings, if we confess them. Every day He supplies all our needs.

John Newton never ceased to marvel at God's mercy and grace that had been granted to him. Over the mantelpiece in the Olney vicarage he had placed an inscription which still remains:

Since thou wast precious in my sight, thou hast been honourable (Isa. 43:4). But thou shalt remember that thou wast a bondman in the land of Egypt, and the Lord thy God redeemed thee (Deut. 15:15).

He never forgot the sea. Late in life, when he was pastor of St. Mary, Woolnoth in London, Newton entered the pulpit in the uniform of a sailor, with a Bible in one hand and a hymnbook in the other. His mind was failing then, and he sometimes had to be reminded what he was preaching about. When someone suggested that he should retire, he replied, "What, shall the old African blasphemer stop while he can speak?" On another occasion, he said, "My memory is nearly gone, but I remember two things: that I am a great sinner, and that Christ is a great Saviour."

They tell us that the last stanza of this song was not written by John Newton. But I think he would agree that it is a fitting climax to his testimony. After he — and we — have been in heaven for ten thousand years worshipping our Lord, we will still have endless time to sing of His amazing grace!

[Read or sing stanzas 3 and 4.]

8

how great thou art

[*Crusader Hymns*, No. 1]

A Hymn Story by George Beverly Shea

During the London crusade at Harringay Arena in 1954, my friend, Mr. Andrew Gray, of the publishing firm Pickering and Inglis, Ltd., handed me a little four-page leaflet containing a "new hymn." We receive many contributions of this kind and at first I did not examine it closely. But I did notice that it had words in both English and Russian, and that it had a very strong and worshipful title, "How Great Thou Art."

A few weeks later I learned that this "new hymn" by S. K. Hine was the final result of almost seventy years of literary activity, involving several different writers and translators. It had first been written in Sweden in 1885 or 1886 by Rev. Carl Boberg, a well-known preacher and religious editor, who also served for fifteen years as a senator in the Swedish parliament. The original title was "O Store Gud" (O Great God).

An earlier translation into English was published in 1925 under the title "O Mighty God," but it never really caught on. "How Great Thou Art" arrived in America by a much more devious route! Retracing its history will allow the reader to share an interesting bit of hymn research.

The German version "Wie gross bist Du" had been translated from the original Swedish by Manfred von Glehn, a resident of Estonia, in 1907. Five years later, in 1912, the Rev. Ivan S. Prokhanoff — known as the "Martin Luther of modern Russia" — published the hymn in St. Petersburg in his own language, probably translating it from von Glehn's German poem. It is included in a booklet entitled *"Cymbals"* — "a collection of spiritual songs translated from various languages." The interesting title was derived from Psalm 150:5, "Praise him upon the loud cymbals: praise him upon the high sounding cymbals."

In 1922, several of Prokhanoff's hymn-booklets, including *Cymbals*, were combined in a large volume, *The Songs of a Christian*. It was published (in Russian) in New York City, by Prokhanoff's friends of the American Bible Society. Finally, in 1927, this larger book was reprinted in Russia, again through the assistance of Prokhanoff's American supporters. This new release of Russian evangelical hymns brought "How Great Thou Art" to the attention of an English missionary couple, Mr. and Mrs. Stuart K. Hine, and it was widely used by them in evangelism in the western Ukraine. After singing it for many years in Russian, Mr. Hine translated three verses into English. When the Second World War broke out, the Hines returned to Britain, where the fourth stanza was added in 1948.

The completed song was printed in 1949 in a Russian gospel magazine published by Mr. Hine. Reprints were requested by missionaries all over the world, and it was one of those leaflets that was given to us in 1954. We first sang "How Great Thou Art" in the Toronto, Canada Crusade of 1955. Cliff Barrows and his large volunteer choir assisted in the majestic refrains. Soon after, we used it on the "Hour of Decision" and in American crusades. In the New York meetings of 1957 the choir joined me in singing it ninety-nine times! It became a keynote of praise each evening.

Reading the first verses of this song of worship, we think of the opening words of Psalm 19: "The heavens declare the glory of God and the firmament showeth his handiwork." Carl Boberg once said that the inspiration for his original hymn was the beauty of the Swedish meadows and lakes, after a summer thunderstorm.

Stuart Hine has also written* that the first verse of his English version came to life after a memorable thunderstorm in a Carpathian mountain village in Czechoslovakia, where he had to seek shelter for the night. On a later occasion, he visited the mountain country of Bukovina in Romania, and in the grandeur of the "woods and forest glades" heard a group of young Christians burst instinctively into song, accompanied by their mandolins and guitars. The hymn they sang was "How Great Thou Art" with Prokhanoff's Russian text, and it was this experience which moved Hine to pen his second stanza.

[Read or sing stanzas 1 and 2.]

Yes, God talks to us through His creation — the heavens and the earth declare His glory. But the greatness of God is shown even more completely in the salvation He has planned and provided for us. What wisdom it reveals! What love it discloses! As the third stanza confesses, this greatness is more than I can understand; "I scarce can take it in."

Mr. Hine also says* that his final verse was written just after the Second World War, when many refugees from eastern Europe were streaming into England. Although they had found greater safety and freedom in their adopted land, their incessant question

*By permission. The author's complete and fascinating story of his writing of this hymn: *The Story of How Great Thou Art*, by Stuart K. Hine, "Carpathia", Coast Road, Berrow, Burnham-on-Sea, Somerset (England). Price: $.80

was "When are we going home?" It is only when we reach our heavenly home that we will fully comprehend the greatness of our God. As the Apostle Paul reminds us: "Now we see only puzzling reflections in a mirror, but then we shall see face to face. My knowledge now is partial; then it will be whole, like God's knowledge of me." (I Cor. 13:12, *New English Bible*). In that day we shall "bow in humble adoration" and say, "My God, how great Thou art!"

[Read or sing stanzas 3 and 4.]

O Lord my God, when I in awesome wonder
    Consider all the worlds Thy hands have made,
I see the stars, I hear the rolling thunder,
    Thy pow'r thro'out the universe displayed.

When through the woods and forest glades I wander
    And hear the birds sing sweetly in the trees,
When I look down from lofty mountain grandeur,
    And hear the brook and feel the gentle breeze.

And when I think that God, His Son not sparing,
    Sent Him to die, I scarce can take it in,
That on the cross, my burden gladly bearing,
    He bled and died to take away my sin.

When Christ shall come with shout of acclamation
    And take me home, what joy shall fill my heart!
Then I shall bow in humble adoration,
    And there proclaim, my God, how great Thou art.

Refrain:

Then sings my soul, my Saviour God, to Thee;
    How great Thou art, how great Thou art!
Then sings my soul, my Saviour God, to Thee:
    How great Thou art, how great Thou art!

Stuart K. Hine (b. 1899)

(This important song copyright has been handled in the United States by Mr. Tim Spencer, our longtime friend who was for many years president of the Hollywood Christian Group. Mr. Spencer has provided thousands of free copies of "How Great Thou Art" for use by Crusade Choirs and as souvenir editions for our radio and television audiences. *Editor.*)

All creatures of our God and King,
Lift up your voice and with us sing,
  Alleluia! Alleluia!
Thou burning sun with golden beam,
Thou silver moon with softer gleam!
  O praise Him, O praise Him,
Alleluia! Alleluia! Alleluia!

Thou rushing wind that art so strong,
Ye clouds that sail in heav'n along,
  O praise Him! Alleluia!
Thou rising morn, in praise rejoice,
Ye lights of evening, find a voice!
  O praise Him, O praise Him,
Alleluia! Alleluia! Alleluia!

Dear mother earth, who day by day
Unfoldest blessings on our way,
  O praise Him! Alleluia!
The flow'rs and fruits that in thee grow,
Let them His glory also show!
  O praise Him, O praise Him,
Alleluia! Alleluia! Alleluia!

And all ye men of tender heart,
Forgiving others, take your part,
  O sing ye! Alleluia!
Ye who long pain and sorrow bear,
Praise God and on Him cast your care!
  O praise Him, O praise Him,
Alleluia! Alleluia! Alleluia!

Let all things their Creator bless,
And worship Him in humbleness.
  O praise Him! Alleluia!
Praise, praise the Father, praise the Son,
And praise the Spirit, Three in One!
  O praise Him, O praise Him,
Alleluia! Alleluia! Alleluia!

St. Francis of Assisi (1182-1226)
Tr. by William H. Draper (1885-1933)

all creatures of our god and king

[Crusader Hymns, No. 16]

A Hymn Story by Tedd Smith

One of my favorite hymn tunes, and one that I often play in sacred concerts, is associated with what has been called "Nature's Hymn of Praise"—namely, "All Creatures of Our God and King." It was written by Francis of Assisi, one of the most interesting figures in all church history. The melody is of unknown origin, but was first published in a Roman Catholic hymnal in 1623.

Francis was born into the carefree life of a wealthy Italian family in 1182. At an early age he was converted to Jesus Christ. Renouncing his life of ease, he became an itinerant evangelist who roamed through the countryside, working with the peasants and preaching to them. He gathered about him a large group of followers with whom he toured the Mediterranean lands for fourteen years. The message he proclaimed was that love for Christ leads to a life of sacrifice and of brotherly love among men.

This "patron saint of animals" came to love God's world of nature, probably because he lived a simple life so close to it. His hymn expresses the truth that all creation praises its Creator. It may have been based on Psalm 145:10, 11: "All thy works shall praise thee, O Lord . . . They shall speak of the glory of thy kingdom, and talk of thy power."
[Read or sing stanza 1.]

The hymn is similar in form to the *Benedicite*, a traditional church canticle which is taken from the *Septuagint* version of the Scriptures. The *Benedicite* calls upon "showers and dew," "frost and cold," "lightnings and clouds," as well as "green things" and "fowls of the air" — to "bless the Lord." It begins with the words: "O all ye works of the Lord, bless ye the Lord; praise him and magnify him forever."

All earth's creatures derive life from God and depend on Him for the continuance of their existence. Inferior animals are not capable of knowing the Almighty, yet the Bible says that they "wait upon God" because they seek their food according to natural instinct. "That thou mayest give them their meat in due season...thou openest thine hand, they are filled with good" explains Psalm 104:27, 28. It is said that Saint Francis wrote these words during the hot summer of 1225 when he was very ill and losing his sight. To add to his discomfort, a swarm of

13

field mice were trying to take over his little straw hut. No doubt he encouraged even the mice to praise God!

O all ye beasts and cattle: bless ye the Lord! (Benedicite)

It is not difficult to see that the cosmic universe shows the power and glory of God. As Psalm 97:6 says, "The heavens declare his righteousness, and all the people see his glory."

In our day, the telescope reveals much about space that was not known before. We are told that if our sun were hollow, it could hold more than a million worlds the size of our earth. But some of the remote stars are so vast that they could hold half a billion of our suns! There are about 100 billion stars in the average galaxy, and at least 100 million galaxies in *known* space. And many scientists believe that we have probed only one billionth of "theoretical space!"

O ye Sun and Moon, bless ye the Lord.

O ye stars of heaven, bless ye the Lord.

The microscope reveals that ours is a God of *little* things, as well. The ocean is teeming with tiny living forms called plankton. One variety of plankton is the *diatom,* a form of life related to seaweed. The diatom is so small that it would take 15 million to fill a thimble, yet each one is a marvel of beautiful and intricate design. Like the snowflakes, it seems that no two are alike!

O ye Whales and all that move in the waters: bless ye the Lord.
[Read or sing stanzas 2 and 3.]

And what of man, the crowning achievement of the creative acts of God? Is not human personality the outstanding marvel in a world of wonders? God has lavished more love and care on man than on all the rest of His world. Jesus said, "Are not two sparrows sold for a farthing? and one of them shall not fall on the ground without your Father ... Fear ye not therefore, ye are of more value than many sparrows" (Matt. 10:29, 31).

Unlike the rest of God's creation, man has been given a soul and spirit with which he may know his Creator. He praises God in a way that is denied the rest of the universe — by responding to the love of God with his entire being!

O ye children of men: bless ye the Lord.

O ye holy and humble men of heart: bless ye the Lord. Praise Him and magnify Him forever!
[Read or sing stanzas 4 and 5.]

14

guide me, o thou great jehovah

[*Crusader Hymns*, No. 213]

A Hymn Story by Don Hustad

The Welsh people may well be the most enthusiastic singers in the world. Their centuries-old tradition, that everybody loves to sing, has been perpetuated in the International Eisteddfod which is held at Llangollen each year.

The Welsh miners customarily sang on their way to work in the coal pits. In the great spiritual revivals which have come to Wales several times during the past two hundred years, music was often more important than preaching. Their pastors and evangelists were never disturbed if the sermon was interrupted by a spontaneous outburst of congregational song. For it was often through singing that the Spirit of God moved the congregation to repentance and faith in Christ.

One of Wales' greatest hymn writers in the late eighteenth century was the layman-preacher William Williams. During forty years of ministry he traveled almost 100,000 miles, on foot and on horseback, preaching and singing. The best known of his 800 hymns is "Guide Me, O Thou Great Jehovah."

During a choir concert I conducted in Cardiff in 1954, we invited the congregation to join us in singing this hymn. After we had finished the stanzas we knew in English, someone in the audience led out in the Welsh version. On and on they sang, hymn after hymn, until we were almost unable to finish the choral program. Today, as in much of the world, the folk in Wales do not attend church as faithfully as they once did. But you will still hear them sing this hymn — just as we sing our national anthem — at the beginning of outdoor athletic events!

[Read or sing stanza 1.]

From the words of the first line, we understand that this is a prayer for God's care and guidance throughout life. It recalls incidents from the forty-year journey of Israel through the desert, after they had left Egypt for their trek to the promised land of Canaan. Although they were delayed in reaching their new home because of sin and unbelief, God continued to lead them and to provide for their needs each day of those forty years.

We too are pilgrims in a journey from the cradle to the grave, and many times our lives will seem like a "barren land," a wilderness. Many times in our weakness we call upon the mighty God to sustain us with His powerful hand. As He fed the children of Israel each day with manna — a supernatural "bread from heaven" — so He has promised to "supply our every need" (Phil. 4:19). We are nourished by the Word of God, which another hymn calls the "bread of life;" and it is God's written Word which tells of the "Word made flesh," Jesus Christ.

[Read or sing stanza 2.]

Twice, during the Hebrews' years of wandering, they became faint because they had no water. At the command of God, Moses struck a large rock with his wooden staff and out of it flowed a pure, crystalline stream which saved their lives. The apostle Paul once told the story and drew the same spiritual lesson as the hymn presents:

> And by a miracle God sent them food to eat and water to drink there in the desert; they drank the water that Christ gave them. He was there with them as a mighty Rock of spiritual refreshment (I Cor. 10:3,4, *Living Letters*).

God supplied the basic physical needs of the Hebrews. He also led them miraculously, day by day and step by step. During the day they followed a cloud which moved before the marching column; at night, the cloud appeared to be a "pillar of fire" which hung over the camp to remind them that God was there, watching over them. Even so, the Christian believer today may experience God's guidance in all the little things, as well as in the major decisions of life.

[Read or sing stanza 3.]

When the ancient Jewish pilgrims finally reached the Jordan river which formed the boundary of the promised Canaan, there too God was with them. Joshua 3:14-17 tells us that, when the people moved forward in faith, the river parted so that they could walk over "dryshod." At the end of our life's journey, death may appear to be a river we dread to cross. But when Christ is our Lord, He walks with us through the waters of death and leads us with great happiness to the other side — our Canaan, our eternal home.

One of the joys of the Christian life is the consciousness that God is with us each moment, guiding, protecting, and providing. This is why we love to sing, with our brothers in Wales:

Songs of praises, songs of praises
I will ever give to Thee.

Guide me, O Thou great Jehovah,
　　Pilgrim through this barren land;
I am weak, but Thou art mighty;
　　Hold me with Thy powerful hand;
Bread of heaven, Bread of heaven,
　　Feed me till I want no more.

Open now the crystal fountain,
　　Whence the healing stream doth flow;
Let the fire and cloudy pillar
　　Lead me all my journey through;
Strong Deliverer, strong Deliverer,
　　Be Thou still my strength and shield.

When I tread the verge of Jordan,
　　Bid my anxious fears subside;
Death of death, and hell's destruction,
　　Land me safe on Canaan's side;
Songs of praises, songs of praises
　　I will ever give to Thee.

From the Welsh
Tr. by Peter Williams (1722-1796)
and William Williams (1717-1791)

Stand up, stand up for Jesus,
  Ye soldiers of the cross;
Lift high His royal banner,
  It must not suffer loss:
From victory unto victory
  His army shall He lead,
Till every foe is vanquished,
  And Christ is Lord indeed.

Stand up, stand up for Jesus,
  The trumpet call obey;
Forth to the mighty conflict,
  In this His glorious day:
"Ye that are men, now serve Him"
  Against unnumbered foes;.
Let courage rise with danger,
  And strength to strength oppose.

Stand up, stand up for Jesus,
  The strife will not be long;
This day the noise of battle,
  The next, the victor's song:
To him that overcometh,
  A crown of life shall be:
He with the King of glory
  Shall reign eternally.

Refrain:

Stand up for Jesus,
  Ye soldiers of the cross;
Lift high His royal banner,
  It must not suffer loss.

George Duffield (1818-1888)

stanð up, stanð up foR jesus

[*Crusader Hymns*, No. 225]

The hymn "Stand Up, Stand Up for Jesus" was written by a Presbyterian minister, Rev. George Duffield, Jr., in memory of the heroic life and the early, tragic death of an Episcopalian rector, Dudley Tyng.

The year was 1854. At the age of twenty-nine, Dudley Tyng had already become rector of the Church of the Epiphany in Philadelphia. Behind him was a rich heritage of churchmanship. His grandfather had been an Episcopal bishop. His father was the distinguished pastor of the famous St. George's parish in New York City; before this, the elder Mr. Tyng had himself served the Epiphany congregation in Philadelphia. Dudley succeeded his father in the pulpit, well-trained both by tradition and by education at the University of Pennsylvania and the Episcopal Seminary at Alexandria, Virginia.

But Dudley Tyng was not a typical "fashionable church pastor." He believed firmly the doctrine that all men are sinners who need to repent and be converted if they are to be accepted by God. He also was convinced that slavery was immoral and unchristian, and he said so from the pulpit of his plush sanctuary. By the end of the second year in this ministry, Tyng's bold and straight-forward denunciation of sin so disturbed his cultured, wealthy parishioners that some were demanding his removal.

Supported by younger members of the congregation, he resigned from Epiphany and formed the "Church of the Covenant," which gathered to worship in a little meeting hall. The family went to live in their country home outside Philadelphia.

In addition to his responsibilities at the new church, young Dudley began giving noon lectures at the Philadelphia Y.M.C.A. Interest grew and thousands were converted to Christ. On Tuesday, March 30th, 1858, there was held an especially noteworthy service. Over five thousand men were gathered in Jayne's Hall, and Tyng preached from Exodus 10:11, "Ye that are men...serve the Lord." It was an eloquent, passionate and moving challenge that those present would never forget. Because he spoke so strongly, he asked pardon for anything that had offended his hearers. But he added, "I must tell my Master's errand, and I would rather that this right arm (placing his left hand on his right arm near the shoulder) were amputated at the trunk, than that I should come short of my duty to you in delivering God's message." Over one thousand men confessed Christ that day!

His words were strangely prophetic. The next week, while home on the farm, he stopped studying for a few moments and went out to the shed where a horse-powered corn sheller was working. Reaching out to stroke the animal, his clothing was caught in the cogs of the machine, severely mangling his arm. A few days later it was necessary to amputate.

The following week it became obvious that Tyng would not recover from the severe shock to his body. According to a Philadelphia newspaper, the dying man, with the same heroic spirit which never forsook him through all his sufferings, received the solemn announcement with the utmost resignation, answering only, "Then it is well, it is very well; God's will be done."

In the next few moments he urged his doctor to become a Christian, and begged his wife to encourage their boys to be ministers. Taking his venerable father, Dr. Stephen H. Tyng, by the hand, he said, "Stand up for Jesus; father, stand up for Jesus; and tell my brethren of the ministry, wherever you meet them, to stand up for Jesus!" And so he died.

The following Sunday, in the Temple Presbyterian Church, Tyng's friend George Duffield, Jr. preached on Ephesians 6:14, "Stand therefore, having your loins girt about with truth." At the end of the sermon he read the stanzas of this hymn, which he had written after the funeral.

As the thrust of the song implies, we Christian soldiers must wage a defensive, as well as an offensive warfare. It is often necessary to "stand fast" against evil as we seek to honor God. This is especially true today in view of the prevalent "relativity" in morals and waning faith in the Word of God. A faithful Christian must take the banner of absolute truth and absolute holiness, because this is the standard of God Himself.

The second stanza of the hymn paraphrases the text of Dudley Tyng's eloquent sermon in that memorable YMCA noonday meeting, in these words: "Ye that are men, now serve Him." It takes *real men* to stand up for Jesus in the office and the factory! It takes courageous women to stand up for Christ in the neighborhood and in the social club! It takes brave boys and girls to stand up for Jesus in the classroom and on the sports field!

[Read or sing the entire hymn.]

love divine, all loves excelling

[Crusader Hymns, No. 170]

A Hymn Story by Cliff Barrows

all of us have experienced the "lift" that comes with singing a great hymn together. Uniting our hearts and voices in Christian song gives us a sense of release over our fears and weaknesses.

This has been my experience over and over again. One of the instances which is still vivid to me happened in 1961, during the Manchester, England crusade. Just as the meetings were about to start, Billy Graham became quite seriously ill. Leighton Ford was called to be his substitute for the first week of crusade services.

Billy had been scheduled to speak to the ministers of London just before the crusade opened. You can imagine my feelings when he sent word that I should represent him and speak at that meeting. The British pastors are themselves thorough scholars and often brilliant preachers. And they were expecting to hear Billy Graham, not me!

At the beginning of that meeting in Westminster's Central Hall, the ministers joined in singing this great hymn of Charles Wesley. Most of these British clergymen were also well acquainted with hymn texts and hymn tunes, and they sang gloriously. Accompanied by the grand piano and the great pipe organ and using the Welsh tune "Blaenwern," these familiar words lifted our hearts in praise and prayer to God. I felt God's strength evident through the singing; He blessed our meeting together, despite my fears and their disappointment.
[Read or sing stanza 1.]

This is perhaps one of our most familiar hymns, and yet I fear that most Americans have only a vague notion of what it says. Reading only the title or the first line, we assume that it is a hymn extolling the love of God. But its message is far more specific than that.

Who is the "Joy of heaven, to earth come down?" It is Jesus Christ who comes to make our hearts His humble dwelling. The third line of the first stanza makes it clear. Jesus is "pure, unbounded love" — the love of God made manifest — the love of God incarnate, in the flesh. The hymn, then, is really a prayer to Christ who is Love Divine.
[Read or sing stanza 2.]

But there are still other obscure phrases in the hymn. What is "that second rest" that we are asking to find? Here it helps to know some-

21

thing of the doctrinal emphasis of the Wesleys and of all the early Methodists. They believed that after conversion there is a second experience for the Christian — that when one totally consecrates himself to Christ, his heart is cleansed from all sin. The experience is called "entire sanctification." They believe that an individual who is sanctified — "made holy" — experiences a relief from the struggle with sin in his life, and finds a new "rest" or liberty in Christ. This is the "second rest" mentioned in the hymn and it is derived from Hebrews 4:9, "There remaineth therefore a rest to the people of God." This also helps us understand the "Alpha and Omega" phrase in the second stanza. The two experiences of conversion and sanctification are thought of as the "*beginning* of faith" and the "*end* of faith."

We must admit that there are differences among Christians with regard to this doctrine of sanctification. But there is common agreement that when we reach the end of ourselves and yield our bodies and minds completely to God, we do find spiritual power and freedom that we cannot otherwise know. Many Christians of varied church backgrounds have witnessed that for them this was a single crisis experience that came after they first knew Jesus Christ as Saviour. Others would say that their act of consecration was repeated daily, and that, for them, "becoming holy" was a matter of progress and growth.

Of course, for all Christians, any experience should be only the beginning of Christian maturing, of "growing in grace." We must all be changed "from glory to glory" — knowing more about Christ and becoming more like Him, until we "take our place in heaven."

And, let us not be afraid of the expression "Christian holiness." Actually it means more than freedom from sin — this is a negative concept that only partly explains the phrase. "Holiness" is really "wholeness" — a balanced personality that possesses all virtues and strengths, in body, mind and spirit. Spiritual "wholeness" or maturity is something we should all desire and seek.
[Read or sing stanzas 3 and 4.]

22

Love Divine, all loves excelling,
    Joy of heav'n, to earth come down:
Fix in us Thy humble dwelling,
    All Thy faithful mercies crown:
Jesus, Thou art all compassion,
    Pure, unbounded love Thou art:
Visit us with Thy salvation;
    Enter every trembling heart.

Breathe, O breathe Thy loving Spirit
    Into every troubled breast!
Let us all in Thee inherit,
    Let us find that second rest.
Take away our bent to sinning,
    Alpha and Omega be;
End of faith, as its beginning,
    Set our hearts at liberty.

Come, almighty to deliver,
    Let us all Thy life receive;
Suddenly return, and never,
    Nevermore Thy temples leave:
Thee we would be always blessing,
    Serve Thee as Thy hosts above,
Pray and praise Thee without ceasing,
    Glory in Thy perfect love.

Finish then Thy new creation,
    Pure and spotless let us be;
Let us see Thy great salvation
    Perfectly restored in Thee:
Changed from glory into glory,
    Till in heav'n we take our place,
Till we cast our crowns before Thee,
    Lost in wonder, love and praise.

Charles Wesley (1707-1788)

My Lord has garments so wondrous fine,
  And myrrh their texture fills;
Its fragrance reached to this heart of mine,
  With joy my being thrills.

His life had also its sorrows sore,
  For aloes had a part;
And when I think of the cross He bore,
  My eyes with teardrops start.

His garments too were in cassia dipped,
  With healing in a touch;
Each time my feet in some sin have slipped,
  He took me from its clutch.

In garments glorious He will come,
  To open wide the door;
And I shall enter my heavenly home,
  To dwell forevermore.

Refrain:

Out of the ivory palaces,
  Into a world of woe,
Only His great, eternal love
  Made my Saviour go.

Henry Barraclough (b. 1891)

IVORY PALACES

[*Crusader Hymns*, No. 86]

A Hymn Story by Billy Graham

The famous gospel song "Ivory Palaces" was written very near to my home in the mountains of North Carolina. In the summer of 1915 the famous evangelist Dr. J. Wilbur Chapman was preaching at the Presbyterian conference grounds at Montreat. With him were the songleader Charles M. Alexander, soloist Albert Brown, and their pianist Henry Barraclough. Barraclough, the author of this hymn, was a twenty-four-year-old Britisher; he had met Chapman the previous year during a preaching mission in England.

During the conference, the evangelist spoke one evening on the forty-fifth Psalm. He believed, as I do, that this is a prophetic, "Messianic" psalm which speaks of the relationship of Christ, the bridegroom, to His bride, the Church.

The eighth verse of the psalm was Dr. Chapman's text: "All thy garments smell of myrrh, and aloes, and cassia, out of the ivory palaces, whereby they have made thee glad." The oriental spices and perfumes mentioned here were used for many purposes. They were often poured on clothing so that their delightful odor seemed to be part of the very texture of the cloth. Following the suggestions of these provocative phrases, Dr. Chapman developed his sermon on the symbolism of the perfumed garments of an oriental bridegroom.

"Myrrh" was an exotic perfume associated with ecstasy and joy; it represents the beauty of the person of Christ—that beauty which attracts us to Him. "Aloes" was a bitter herb used in embalming, which should remind us that our Lord had many sorrows during His lifetime, culminating in a shameful and painful death on the cross. "Cassia" was a spicy perfume that was also a medication; Jesus Christ is like a potion that heals us from the wounds of sin when we look to Him in repentance.

After the evening service, "Charlie" Alexander and Henry Barraclough drove some friends to the Blue Ridge YMCA Hostel a few miles away. Sitting in the front seat of the car, young Barraclough thought about the message and the four short phrases of the refrain began to take shape in his mind. When they stopped at a little village store, he quickly wrote them down on a "visiting card"—the only paper that was available. Returning to the conference hotel, he worked out the first three stanzas, using the outline of Chapman's message. The following morning Mrs. Alexander and Mr. Brown sang the new hymn in the Montreat conference session.

Later, Dr. Chapman suggested that Barraclough add a fourth verse, reminding us that one day Christ will come again wearing the same glorious garments. I believe that through all eternity we will be reminded of the beauty of our Lord, of His suffering for us, and of the forgiveness and cleansing which He has made possible.

Henry Barraclough was not a prolific song writer. "Ivory Palaces" was his only masterpiece, but it has been sung around the world. After Dr. Chapman's death, Barraclough adopted the evangelist's country, America, as his own. He also became associated with Chapman's denomination and has served the Presbyterian Church (U.S.A.) for almost fifty years.

Our readers will be interested to learn that it was Albert Brown — one member of the duet that first sang "Ivory Palaces"—who first introduced Cliff Barrows to me in 1945. I was speaking at a youth night service at the Ben Lippen Conference Grounds in North Carolina. When the regular songleader could not appear, Mr. Brown suggested that we use two young musicians named Cliff and Billie Barrows who were visiting there on their honeymoon. That was the beginning of our many years of fellowship in God's service.

In our crusades today, "Bev" Shea often sings this hymn, sometimes accompanied by Cliff Barrows and the choir. We do not suppose that heaven actually consists of "ivory palaces;" this is merely the oriental imagery which is used to try to describe the beauty of our Lord's home, from which He departed to live among men on earth. Every time I hear this refrain, I am humbled by the truth that Jesus — the object of all the worship in heaven — willingly assumed all the limitations and suffering of a man. Why? Because He loved us so much.

> Out of the ivory palaces,
> Into a world of woe,
> Only His great, eternal love
> Made my Saviour go.

[Read or sing the entire hymn.]

holy, holy, holy

[*Crusader Hymns*, No. 8]

In the year that king Uzziah died I saw also the Lord sitting upon a throne, high and lifted up, and his train filled the temple. Above it stood the seraphims: each one had six wings; with twain he covered his face, and with twain he covered his feet, and with twain he did fly. And one cried unto another, and said, Holy, holy, holy, is the Lord of hosts: the whole earth is full of his glory. (Isaiah 6:1-3)

although the Christian doctrine of the Trinity was not clearly understood before the day of Pentecost, we believe that it is revealed in the Old Testament as well as in the New. In this record of the prophet Isaiah's vision of God, the Trinity is suggested in the triple repetition of the angels, "Holy, holy, holy." These words have become one of the historic songs of believers in worship. It is called the *Trisagion* or the *Tersanctus*, the "three holies."

A parallel scripture passage is Revelation 4:8-11, of which this is the central phrase: "Holy, holy, holy, Lord God Almighty, which was, and is and is to come." The historic hymn "Holy, Holy, Holy" is based on these words. It was written by Reginald Heber to be sung on Trinity Sunday in the parish of Hodnet in western England. He was vicar there in his family's church from 1807 to 1823.

Heber was an uncommon man. Born into a family of wealth and culture, he gave his life to the service of God both at home in England and far away in India. Though he possessed unusual literary gifts and was a friend of Britain's leading men of letters, his greatest ambition was to improve the hymn singing in his own church.

When Reginald Heber accepted the post of Bishop of Calcutta in 1823, it was the realization of a longtime, deep-seated interest in foreign missions. As a bishop, Heber served a diocese that included much of the south Pacific. For three years he traveled tirelessly from place to place, using his remarkable gifts to advance the work of the church in that distant area. On April 3rd, 1826, Heber preached on the evils of the caste system before a large audience at Trichinopoly. Afterward, he went to cool off in the swimming pool at the home where he was staying. Some time later, he was found drowned, the result of a stroke.

At the age of forty-three his brilliant life was ended, and he was buried in the Anglican church at Trichinopoly. In 1875 the Prince of Wales (later Edward VII) honored his memory by placing a tablet there.

Reginald Heber lived and worked at a time in history when his contemporaries of English literature were becoming aware of the beauty of words and of poetic structure. The romantic movement of that day added a new dimension of elegance and lyric grace to Christian worship. This characteristic is never more evident than in Heber's hymn "Holy, Holy, Holy" which Lord Tennyson said was the greatest in the English language.

The powerful phrases of the hymn declare the attributes of the Triune God—Father, Son and Holy Spirit. Heber shows his mastery of poetic design in composing each stanza to re-emphasize the doctrine of the Trinity by using a "trinity of words" to say something about God. Stanza one mentions three of the attributes of God; He is "holy, merciful and mighty."

The second stanza reminds us that God is worshipped in heaven by the saints who have already died, and by the angels—"the cherubim and seraphim." It closes with a "trinity of phrases" which says that God is eternal—"He was, He is, and He evermore shall be."

God is also perfect. Our understanding of Him is incomplete; He is partially hidden by the "darkness" of our sin and our ignorance. Yet we can see enough of His glory to know that He is perfect—"perfect in power, in love, and purity." That is the "trinity" of the third stanza.

The final verse borrows another idea from John's vision as recorded in Revelation 4:11—that God has created all things in the universe for "his own pleasure." Therefore, all creation—"the earth, the sky, and sea"—praises Him. This is Heber's final poetic trinity.

The tune commonly associated with these words was written by John B. Dykes, one of Britain's leading organists and composers, who was also an Anglican rector. When published in 1861, Dykes gave it the significant name "Nicaea." It was at the council of Nicaea in 325 A.D. that the church clearly enunciated its belief in the Trinity.

[Read or sing the entire hymn.]

Holy, Holy, Holy! Lord God Almighty!
  Early in the morning our song shall rise to Thee;
Holy, Holy, Holy! Merciful and Mighty!
  God in Three Persons, blessed Trinity!

Holy, Holy, Holy! All the saints adore Thee,
  Casting down their golden crowns around the glassy sea;
Cherubim and seraphim falling down before Thee,
  Which wert and art, and evermore shalt be.

Holy, Holy, Holy! Tho' the darkness hide Thee,
  Tho' the eye of sinful man Thy glory may not see,
Only Thou art holy; there is none beside Thee
  Perfect in power, in love, and purity.

Holy, Holy, Holy! Lord God Almighty!
  All Thy works shall praise Thy name, in earth, and sky, and sea;
Holy, Holy, Holy! Merciful and Mighty!
  God in Three Persons, blessed Trinity!

Reginald Heber (1783-1826)

"Great is Thy faithfulness," O God my Father,
　　There is no shadow of turning with Thee;
Thou changest not; Thy compassions, they fail not;
　　As Thou hast been Thou forever wilt be.

Summer and winter, and springtime and harvest,
　　Sun, moon and stars in their courses above,
Join with all nature in manifold witness
　　To Thy great faithfulness, mercy and love.

Pardon for sin and a peace that endureth,
　　Thy own dear presence to cheer and to guide;
Strength for today and bright hope for tomorrow,
　　Blessings all mine, with ten thousand beside!

Refrain:

"Great is Thy faithfulness! Great is Thy faithfulness!"
　　Morning by morning new mercies I see;
All I have needed Thy hand hath provided —
　　"Great is Thy faithfulness," Lord, unto me!

Thomas O. Chisholm (1866-1960)

GReat is thy faithfulness

[*Crusader Hymns*, No. 33]

A Hymn Story by George Beverly Shea

One of God's men who most influenced my life was **Dr. Will H.** Houghton, the late president of Moody Bible Institute. In **1938 when** I was working in an insurance office in New York City and **seeking** to know what God wanted me to do with my life, Dr. Houghton **asked** me if I would like to come to Chicago and sing on the Institute's **radio** station, WMBI. One of our programs was "Hymns From the Chapel" — fifteen minutes of hymns at the early hour of 8:15 every morning. Along about 1942, Don Hustad joined me on the program, playing **the organ.**

I learned afterward that the program was often heard **in those** days by a young man named Billy Graham who was attending **Whea**ton College, just west of Chicago. A short time later, Billy **asked me** to help him in a broadcast from the Village Church in Western **Springs** where he was student pastor; this association led to our **work together** in the evangelistic crusades. How I thank God for His **faithfulness** in leading me one step at a time into His plan for my life!

Looking back, I remember also Dr. Houghton's tall, dark, **command**ing presence as he led Moody's chapel services with a **wonderful com**bination of dignity, humor and song. He loved hymns and **especially** appreciated the song "Great Is Thy Faithfulness." Its music **had been** composed by William M. Runyan, who often appeared **in person at the** Institute in those days. Mr. Runyan later said that it was **Dr. Hough**ton's frequent use of the hymn which helped it to become **popular with** the general public.

It would be wrong to assume that every hymn has been **written** or has become well known as the result of some dramatic **experience.** Some authors have simply made it a habit to write poems **regularly,** perhaps one every day. Out of the hundreds that flow from **the pen,** only a few will be worthy of publishing.

Thomas Chisholm, a Methodist life insurance agent, gave us these inspiring words. He says that there were no special **circumstances** surrounding their writing. He simply penned the lines **from his im**pressions about God's faithfulness as told in the Bible and sent **them,** with several other poems, to his friend and collaborator William **Run**yan.

31

Our team had the privilege of introducing "Great Is Thy Faithfulness" to audiences in Great Britain in 1954; now the song is a favorite there too. It is often sung at British wedding services and was recently included in the new *Anglican Hymn Book* of 1965.

The opening stanza and refrain are taken directly from scriptural affirmations about God. "His compassions fail not. They are new every morning: great is thy faithfulness" (Lam. 3:22,23). "Every good gift and every perfect gift is from above, and cometh down from the Father of lights, with whom is no variableness, neither shadow of turning" (James 1:17). In other words, God is always like the bright sunlight characteristic of midday; there is never a shadow to cloud His complete and perfect faithfulness.

God's faithfulness derives from another attribute of His character—His immutability. This is our answer to a few so-called theologians in our day who proclaim that "God is dead." He *is* alive! He *is* eternal! He cannot change by so much as a shadow!
[Read or sing stanza 1 and refrain.]

In many ways nature shows us that God is faithful. Every sunset is followed by a sunrise. Every winter is followed by a summer. Whenever we plant seed, we can count on a harvest. In the sky we see innumerable stars all moving in patterns which can be charted by astronomers thousands of years in advance.

But even more clearly, through His dealings with mortal men, we have learned that God is faithful. He has promised in His Word to forgive our sins and to give us peace of mind and heart; when we accept Christ His Son as our Lord and Saviour, He fulfills His pledge. Morning by morning, day after day, we feel His presence in our hearts. Surely we can look forward with hope to His presence, even at the end of life's journey.

I am often reassured by these words of an unknown believer: "Fear not tomorrow, for God is already there!"
[Read or sing stanzas 2 and 3.]

Just as I am, without one plea

[*Crusader Hymns*, No. 57]

A Hymn Story by Billy Graham

When I was converted in 1937 under the ministry of the evangelist Mordecai Hamm, two invitation songs were used and a total of eight stanzas were sung. I did not respond to the invitation until the final verse of the second song, and I have always been grateful that the evangelist waited so patiently. One of these hymns was "Just As I Am, Without One Plea."

We use this hymn today in almost every one of our crusades. Some critics object to singing at the time of the invitation because they claim it has an excessive emotional impact on the audience. But on the occasions when we use no music at all, others complain about the "impressive, dramatic silence" that is broken only by the footsteps of those who are coming forward.

There are several reasons why we choose the hymn "Just As I Am" for use at this most important moment in a crusade service. For one thing, it rings with a strong, positive note. Other songs give Christ's invitation just as clearly, but this one keeps repeating the affirmative response, "O Lamb of God, I come." The choir sings it while the people are walking down the long aisle or across the turf of an outdoor stadium, and the hymn verbalizes just what each of them is doing.

This song also presents the strongest possible Biblical basis for the call of Christ. It repeats many of the reasons a person should respond when the Spirit of God speaks to him. The first stanza, like most great hymns, has captured the truth of the entire hymn. We should feel free to come to God because He has invited us to come, and because Jesus died on the cross in order to reconcile us to His Father.

All men who come into the world — whether in Christian or pagan, civilized or primitive cultures — have the same innate awareness of God. They want to approach God and to be accepted by Him. The book of Genesis tells us that Cain, son of Adam, came to God with an offering of fruit and grain produced through his own hard work, but God did not recognize him. His brother Abel's approach to worship was with the sacrifice of an animal, as God had decreed; he was welcomed and accepted by God.

Today as well, men cannot apparently give up the idea that God will accept them because they "are good and decent" or because they have done good works for others or for the church. But the Bible says that we have "no plea" before God — no claim on His love or His forgiveness — except that Jesus Christ shed His blood for us. God accepts the sacrifice made by His own sinless Son.

In coming to Christ we should not wait until we have straightened out our lives a bit. No small improvement we can effect will make us any more acceptable to Him. God loves us just as we are and we should come that way.

We should also come to Christ because He alone can solve the problems of our lives. Only He can free us from our sense of guilt and from our mental frustrations and anguish. Only He can pardon and cleanse us, in order to make us presentable before God.

We should come to Christ even though we don't understand all about salvation. I believe that God has designed His offer so it is necessary to take a final leap of faith to bridge the gulf of things we cannot comprehend. It is interesting to learn that Charlotte Elliott, author of this hymn, was an invalid during much of her life and that these words were written to express her victory over spiritual doubt.

The year was 1834 and Miss Elliott was living in Brighton in her native England. She was forty-five years old and had been a devoted Christian for many years. Even so, she was plagued with unhappiness because of her seeming uselessness, for everyone around her was busy in the service of God. In her extreme depression she was tempted to doubt the reality of her spiritual life.

Gathering strength and resolve, Charlotte Elliott deliberately wrote down the reasons for her trust in Christ. This hymn was the result. In the ensuing years, countless Christians have shared her experience and renewed their faith over and over through these familiar words.

[Read or sing the entire hymn.]

When I come to present my credentials at the gate of heaven, it will mean nothing that I have traveled around the world preaching the gospel. Then, as when I was first converted, I will say:

> Just as I am, without one plea,
> But that Thy blood was shed for me,
> And that Thou bidd'st me come to Thee,
> O Lamb of God, I come.

Just as I am, without one plea,
But that Thy blood was shed for me,
And that Thou bidd'st me come to Thee,
O Lamb of God, I come! I come!

Just as I am, and waiting not
To rid my soul of one dark blot,
To Thee whose blood can cleanse each spot,
O Lamb of God, I come! I come!

Just as I am, though tossed about
With many a conflict, many a doubt,
Fightings and fears within, without,
O Lamb of God, I come! I come!

Just as I am, poor, wretched, blind;
Sight, riches, healing of the mind,
Yea, all I need, in Thee I find,
O Lamb of God, I come! I come!

Just as I am, Thou wilt receive,
Wilt welcome, pardon, cleanse, relieve;
Because Thy promise I believe,
O Lamb of God, I come! I come!

Charlotte Elliott (1789-1871)

Make me a captive, Lord,
    And then I shall be free;
Force me to render up my sword,
    And I shall conqueror be;
I sink in life's alarms
    When by myself I stand;
Imprison me within Thine arms,
    And strong shall be my hand.

My heart is weak and poor
    Until it master find;
It has no spring of action sure —
    It varies with the wind;
It cannot freely move
    Till Thou hast wrought its chain;
Enslave it with Thy matchless love,
    And deathless it shall reign.

My pow'r is faint and low
    Till I have learned to serve:
It wants the needed fire to glow,
    It wants the breeze to nerve;
It cannot drive the world
    Until itself be driv'n;
Its flag can only be unfurled
    When Thou shalt breathe from heav'n.

My will is not my own
    Till Thou hast made it Thine;
If it would reach the monarch's throne
    It must its crown resign:
It only stands unbent,
    Amid the clashing strife,
When on Thy bosom it has leaned,
    And found in Thee its life.

George Matheson (1842-1906)

make me a captive, lord

[*Crusader Hymns*, No. 141]

A Hymn Story by Don Hustad

[Read or sing stanza 1.]

It may be that the opening phrases of this hymn are quite puzzling to some readers. "Make me a captive, Lord, and then I shall be free; Force me to render up my sword, and I shall conqueror be." One may ask, "How is it possible to be slave and free, winner and loser, at the same time?"

This kind of a statement is called a "paradox" — a declaration that is true, yet seemingly self-contradictory or absurd. A few years ago I wrote new music for these words. Remembering the message of the hymn I called the tune "Paradoxy."

There are many paradoxes in the Bible. "When I am weak, then am I strong" (II Cor. 12:10). "Whosoever will save his life shall lose it" (Matt. 16:25). "He that is least among you all, the same shall be great" (Luke 9:48). Perhaps each of these verses expresses a different aspect of the same spiritual truth.

I think this paradoxical idea can be illustrated by the relationship of marriage. At the wedding altar, two persons give themselves to each other. They promise to "forsake all others" and "to love and to cherish." They have obligated themselves "till death do us part" — almost like slaves, and we jokingly say that they have lost their freedom. Yet the poet Shelley calls human love "that sweet bondage which is freedom's self."

When two individuals share each other's lives in this way, giving and receiving true love, each finds greater fulfillment and self-expression than he could ever have known alone. In subjugating his own will to the desires of the other, each discovers that his own character has been developed. In the bondage of marriage, they both find freedom!

This truth about our relationship to God is illustrated in a more striking way in John 12:24: "Verily, verily, I say unto you, Except a corn of wheat fall into the ground and die, it abideth alone: but if it die, it bringeth forth much fruit." Here is one of nature's phenomena; a kernel of wheat must disintegrate and decompose in the ground in order to reproduce itself. It must die in order that it might continue to live! Of course, Jesus was referring here to His own death and the many new lives which it would produce.

However, in the next verse (John 12:25) He applies this truth to each of us. "He that loveth his life shall lose it; and he that hateth his life in this world shall keep it unto life eternal." We too must "die" to our own ambitions and desires if we are to produce spiritual fruit in our lives. This is what George Matheson says over and over in his hymn. We are weak human beings, and we gain strength only when Christ becomes our Master. We will rule over our own minds and bodies and find greatest self-fulfillment, only when we become His slaves.

No doubt the hymn's writer George Matheson learned this lesson, at least partly, through his own personal experience. As a brilliant young ministerial student of eighteen, he lost his sight almost completely. Because of his blindness, he eventually had to give up his research and scholarship in the field of apologetic theology, an activity which he dearly loved and for which he had great talent.

Instead, George Matheson gave his time and strength to devotional preaching and writing. During his lifetime as a minister in the Scottish Free Church, he had a profound influence on all who heard him preach, including Queen Victoria. Through his writings, God's truth has transformed the lives of many, right down to the present day.

Though he was physically sightless, Matheson could read the hearts of men and women. He could also see God in a way that few are able to do — and seeing God, he became more God-like. No doubt he would want to add another paradox to our list: "When I became blind, I really began to see!"

[Read or sing stanzas 2-4.]

what a fRienb we have in jesus

[*Crusader Hymns*, No. 185]

henry Brooks Adams (1838-1918) once said: "One friend in a lifetime is much; two are many; three are hardly possible." Does that seem to be a bit of an exaggeration? After all, if we are at all socially compatible, most of us have several friends. Or do we? Real friends, that is.

Begin with the definition, "A friend is a person who knows all about us, yet loves us just the same." That idea probably disqualifies a few. Because if we were to openly exhibit our inward selves — the thoughts which reveal our insecurities and prejudices — we would probably lose contact with many of the people we consider to be our "friends."

What if our home should be broken by divorce? Or what if we should suddenly be overtaken by temptation and commit some serious sin? Would the people we now call "friends" stand by us through disgrace?

How many of our friendships are dependent upon social position or financial status? We entertain and are entertained by the folk who live at our social level, who attend our church and live in our community. What if our financial situation should change — either for better or for worse — causing us to move to a different social and economic level? Would our old friendships bridge the gap of that change? Possibly not.

These questions are not intended to cause us to view all our present friendships with suspicion. But they should remind us of the gracious words Jesus spoke to His disciples, "Henceforth I call you not servants; for the servant knoweth not what his lord doeth: but I have called you friends; for all things that I have heard of my Father I have made known unto you (John 15:15).

Some of us Christians are tempted to believe that if a friend falls into sin — whether it be moral downfall or theological doubt — he must be dropped, lest our reputations be sullied by his failure. But Jesus proved Himself to be a "friend of publicans and sinners" (Luke 7:34). His is a friendship which reaches down and lifts us up from sin and brings us into His own heavenly family. "What a friend we have in Jesus — all our sins and griefs to bear!"

[Read or sing stanza 1.]

For most of us, continuing friendship depends on a delicate balance of "give and take." If our "friend" should snub us, or ask too often for a favor, or fail to reciprocate adequately, the relationship would be jeopardized. But not so with Christ; it is not possible to "presume on His friendship." He stands ever ready to forgive us, no matter how often we may slight Him. He is a Friend who hears every request, and answers each time in just the way that is best for us.

[Read or sing stanza 2.]

Joseph Scriven, author of this hymn, was a man who experienced the friendship of Christ during a life filled with trouble. As a young man in Ireland, about 1840, his intended bride was accidentally drowned the evening before their wedding. He had begun training as a military cadet, but poor health forced him to abandon his dreams of a career in this field.

Moving to Canada, he became a servant of the underprivileged, helping those who were physically handicapped and financially destitute. But tragedy continued to stalk his steps. Once again, the plans for a wedding were cut short when his second fiancee died following a brief illness. It seemed that Joseph Scriven was destined to go through life alone, knowing only the friendship of Jesus Christ.

Through much of his life he experienced loneliness, meager pay for menial work, and physical illness. This hymn is his testimony that prayer does not necessarily eliminate trouble from our lives. But, in the midst of tragedy, temptations and weakness, Christ will be our ever-present Friend who will give us peace, "take and shield us," and carry our "load of care."

[Read or sing stanza 3.]

After his death, in recognition of his sacrificial service to others, a monument was erected at Port Hope, Ontario in tribute to Joseph Scriven, an Irish immigrant who was a friend to many and who found a friend in Jesus.

Here is an interesting footnote to our song's story. Charles Converse, the composer of this familiar melody, was no "mere gospel song writer." In early life he had studied serious art music in Germany where he counted the great composers Franz Liszt and Louis Spohr among his friends. Later he became a very successful lawyer. Even though he had written symphonies and oratorios, Converse enjoyed writing simple melodies for gospel songs. This is one that is known and loved around the world.

What a Friend we have in Jesus,
　　All our sins and griefs to bear!
What a privilege to carry
　　Everything to God in prayer!
O what peace we often forfeit,
　　O what needless pain we bear,
All because we do not carry
　　Everything to God in prayer!

Have we trials and temptations?
　　Is there trouble anywhere?
We should never be discouraged,
　　Take it to the Lord in prayer.
Can we find a friend so faithful
　　Who will all our sorrows share?
Jesus knows our every weakness,
　　Take it to the Lord in prayer.

Are we weak and heavy-laden,
　　Cumbered with a load of care?
Precious Saviour, still our refuge —
　　Take it to the Lord in prayer.
Do thy friends despise, forsake thee?
　　Take it to the Lord in prayer;
In His arms He'll take and shield thee,
　　Thou wilt find a solace there.

Joseph Scriven (1819-1886)

All glory, laud, and honor
    To Thee, Redeemer, King,
To whom the lips of children
    Make sweet hosannas ring.

Thou art the King of Israel,
    Thou, David's royal Son,
Who in the Lord's name comest,
    The King and Blessed One.

The company of angels
    Are praising Thee on high,
And mortal men, and all things
    Created, make reply.

The people of the Hebrews
    With palms before Thee went;
Our praise and prayer and anthems
    Before Thee we present.

To Thee, before Thy passion,
    They sang their hymns of praise;
To Thee, now high exalted,
    Our melody we raise.

Thou didst accept their praises;
    Accept the prayers we bring,
Who in all good delightest,
    Thou good and gracious King.

Theodulph of Orleans (760-821)
Tr. by John Mason Neale (1818-1866)

all Glory, lauò, anò honor

[*Crusader Hymns,* No. 270]

On Palm Sunday morning, an interesting bit of pageantry takes place in some liturgical churches. As the opening processional moves around the sanctuary, it will pause in one corner, and a soloist or a small group of the choir will sing the ancient Latin canticle *Gloria, laus et honor* or its English equivalent "All Glory, Laud and Honor." When the song is completed, the processional moves on and the service continues. This tradition may be based only upon a legend, but it has been perpetuated for more than a thousand years.

It is said that in the year 821 King Louis the Pious, son of Charlemagne, was participating in the Palm Sunday procession through the streets of Angers in the region of Orleans. As the parade stopped near a prison tower, suddenly a melodious voice was heard singing "Gloria, laus et honor." The emperor learned that the vocalist was Theodulph of Orleans, a great pastor, bishop and poet whom he had jailed on suspicion of treachery against the crown. Whereupon, so the story goes, "the gentle and merciful monarch was moved with compassion, and from that hour he delivered and pardoned him, and sent him back to his church, quit and absolved of the crime whereof he had been accused."

There are puzzling aspects to the story of Jesus' "triumphal" entry into Jerusalem, the event we remember on this Sunday of the church year. Four hundred fifty years earlier the prophet Zechariah had written: "Rejoice greatly, O daughter of Zion; shout, O daughter of Jerusalem: behold, thy King cometh unto thee: he is just, and having salvation; lowly, and riding upon an ass, and upon a colt the foal of an ass" (Zech. 9:9). Yet it is quite probable that those who waved the palms never knew that they were fulfilling prophecy.

Jesus was offering Himself to the Jews as their promised Messiah and King. But they desired and expected a mighty deliverer who would rescue them from the legions of Rome and restore to them the glory of their ancient kingdom. Many of them were attracted by the miracles which Jesus had performed, and therefore were willing to join the shouting crowds that day. But when they were asked about His identity they said only, "This is Jesus, the prophet of Nazareth, of Galilee." No Messiah, no king, no promised deliverer; just Jesus, a prophet of Nazareth.

Of course, our Lord's disciples — at least some of them — had recognized Him. Several weeks earlier, Simon Peter had said to Him, "Thou art the Christ, the Son of the living God" (Matt. 16:16). It may be that it was the disciples (see Luke 19:37-38) who started the chant that day, "Hosanna to the son of David: Blessed is he that cometh in the name of the Lord; Hosanna in the highest" (Matt. 21:9). Many of the multitude joined in the cry, possibly without fully realizing what they were saying. Doubtless, some of the same people were part of another crowd which, only a few days later, shouted: "Crucify him! Crucify him!"

There will be many in our churches today, repeating these verses of praise, whose singing will be as meaningless as it was many years ago. If we are to praise Christ properly, He must be King in our hearts and Lord of our lives — sovereign over body, mind and spirit. Because the ancient Hebrews were not prepared to accept Him as "spiritual King," Jesus knew that it was not time to be their temporal ruler. But the day will come when He will return as a glorious Monarch. Revelation 19:11,16 pictures Him as seated on a white horse; and "he . . . was called Faithful and True . . . And he hath on his vesture and on his thigh a name written, KING OF KINGS, AND LORD OF LORDS."

Christ desires our praise and our adoration; He deserves it, and He knows that it is through worship that our lives are purified and made complete. When the Pharisees asked Jesus to restrain His disciples in their jubilant praise, He said, "I tell you that, if these should hold their peace, the stones would immediately cry out." Yes, Jesus must be praised; nature will do it if man will not!

Today, let us join with the children of that first Palm Sunday, with all those who truly accepted Him as Lord, with the angels on high, and with the saints of all ages, singing "All glory, laud and honor to Thee, Redeemer, King."

[Read or sing the entire hymn.]

when i survey the wondrous cross

[*Crusader Hymns*, No. 70]

A Hymn Story by Tedd Smith

One of the most important names in English hymnody is that of Isaac Watts. Born into a merchant's home in Southampton in 1674, Watts was sickly and rather unattractive as a child. At the same time by today's standards he was very precocious. Young Isaac began to study Latin at the age of four, and added Greek when he was nine, French at eleven and Hebrew at thirteen!

Watts was also interested in poetry, and it is said that much of his boyish talk came out in rhyme and meter. His father soon tired of conversation of this nature and outlawed the poetic improvising. But Isaac was irrepressible, and to enforce this prohibition, his father resorted to a spanking. Through his tears the boy cried:

"O father, do some pity take,
And I will no more verses make."

When he was fifteen, the young poet turned his talents to the service of the church. At that time, Christians in England sang nothing but strict and rather stilted versions of the Old Testament Psalms, introduced line after line by a "precentor" and repeated line after line by the congregation. Said Watts: "The singing of God's praise is the part of worship nighest heaven, and its performance among us is the worst on earth." Whereupon his father, a leading deacon in the Congregational church, charged him: "Young man, give us something better!"

Isaac Watts accepted the challenge and launched an avocation which earned him the title, "the father of English hymnody." As a Congregationalist minister he wrote over six hundred hymns, including the magnificent "When I Survey the Wondrous Cross."

Throughout the years this hymn has been acclaimed. It was ranked as "one of the four which stand at the head of all hymns in the English language" by John Julian, our greatest hymnologist. Many people would agree that it is the *very best* English hymn, a claim made by the nineteenth-century literary critic, Matthew Arnold.

In crusade services and in concerts, I often play two tunes which have been associated with these words. The tune "Hamburg" is best known in America and was written in 1824 by one of our own important musicians, Lowell Mason, when he was living in Savannah, Georgia. This simple yet solemn melody uses only five notes and is based on an ancient Gregorian "tone" or scale. I also enjoy playing the tune "Rockingham" which we sing more often in British crusades. This tune was published in 1790 by Edward Miller; its actual composer is not known. I believe that these two melodies bring out the different meanings of the words of the hymn's stanzas.

It seems to me that Isaac Watts wrote this text as if he were standing at the foot of Christ's cross, together with the disciple John, the faithful women, Jesus' mother, the Roman soldiers and the excited, shouting mob. When I play or sing the hymn, I try to make Watts' ideas and words my own. With him, I cannot help but marvel at the incredulity of the scene — the "Prince of heaven" nailed to a tree by sinful men. Jesus, dying for me! For it was my sins which He bore on that terrible day. Therefore, my voice was one of those which had cried, in Pilate's court, "Crucify him!" My hand — as well as the hand of the Roman soldier — had wielded the hammer which drove the nails into His body.

Then, in my mind's eye, I see the blood which flowed from His wounds, showing — as the hymn suggests — His sorrow because of my sins and also His great love for me. How can I fail to say, "God forbid that I should boast of anything but the cross of our Lord Jesus Christ, through which the world is crucified to me and I to the world" (Gal. 6:14, *New English Bible*).

It is difficult to understand the latter part of this scripture verse, but Watts explains it in the last stanza of his hymn. Our Lord does not want me to try to repay Him for His love and His sacrifice with my own sorrow, my good works, or with my material things. If I owned the "whole realm of nature," it wouldn't be enough to give Him in return. Christ wants *more* than this! He wants *me* — "my soul, my life, my all."

When you read this hymn, I hope that you will make the words and their meaning your very own, as I have done. If you sing it, I hope you will try both tunes. They are found on the same page in *Crusader Hymns*, numbers 70 and 71.

[Read or sing the entire hymn.]

When I survey the wondrous cross,
 On which the Prince of glory died,
My richest gain I count but loss,
 And pour contempt on all my pride.

Forbid it, Lord, that I should boast,
 Save in the death of Christ, my God;
All the vain things that charm me most
 I sacrifice them to His blood.

See, from His head, His hands, His feet,
 Sorrow and love flow mingled down;
Did e'er such love and sorrow meet,
 Or thorns compose so rich a crown?

Were the whole realm of nature mine,
 That were a present far too small;
Love so amazing, so divine,
 Demands my soul, my life, my all.

Isaac Watts (1674-1748)

I come to the garden alone,
　　While the dew is still on the roses;
And the voice I hear, falling on my ear,
　　The Son of God discloses.

He speaks, and the sound of His voice
　　Is so sweet the birds hush their singing,
And the melody that He gave to me,
　　Within my heart is ringing.

I'd stay in the garden with Him
　　Though the night around me be falling,
But He bids me go; through the voice of woe,
　　His voice to me is calling.

Refrain:

And He walks with me, and He talks with me,
　　And He tells me I am His own,
And the joy we share as we tarry there,
　　None other has ever known.

C. Austin Miles (1868-1946)

in the GARden

[*Crusader Hymns*, No. 196]

A Hymn Story by Don Hustad

Changing trends in church music was the discussion topic at a dinner party I attended a few years ago on a seminary campus. The wife of a theology professor complained that song leaders and choir directors seem to ignore many favorite hymns, such as "In The Garden."

"You don't sing the old favorites that we learned as youngsters," she said. "I've even heard some church musicians criticize 'In the Garden' as 'sentimental and meaningless'."

I couldn't resist the temptation. "What garden?" I asked.

"What difference does it make 'what garden'?" she retorted, with just a little heat.

The truth is — it makes quite a lot of difference. If the hymn is just a childhood favorite with pleasant phrases about gardens and birds and roses, it cannot be really meaningful in a vital worship experience today. This kind of an attachment for a song is a superficial emotion which is a good example of what we call "sentimentality."

But it doesn't have to be that way. There was a garden, and the hymn can be meaningful! C. Austin Miles, the composer, gives us the clue himself:

> One day in March, 1912, I was seated in the darkroom where I kept my photographic equipment and organ. I drew my Bible toward me; it opened at my favorite chapter, John 20 . . . That meeting of Jesus and Mary had lost none of its power to charm.
>
> As I read it that day, I seemed to be part of the scene. I became a silent witness to that dramatic moment in Mary's life, when she knelt before her Lord, and cried, 'Rabboni!' . . . Under the inspiration of this vision I wrote as quickly as the words could be formed the poem exactly as it has since appeared. That same evening I wrote the music. (From *Forty Gospel Hymn Stories*, by George W. Sanville).

The specific reference to a garden becomes much clearer when we learn that C. Austin Miles was writing about the first Easter morning and the garden in which Jesus was buried. It was here Mary Magdalene came alone very early, "while the dew was still on the roses." When Jesus first spoke to her, she thought it was the gardener; but when He called her by name, she recognized His voice.

It is difficult to imagine what Mary's feelings and actions were at that moment. She had seen Jesus die on the cross. She was now coming to anoint His dead body with spices. But there He was, standing before her and talking to her. He was alive! She may have been startled at first, but when His identity became clear, she was filled with joy — as the song says, like a melody ringing in her heart! No doubt Mary wanted nothing more than to stay there in the garden with Jesus, but He ordered her to go and tell His disciples what had happened.

Mary's experience is relived by every person who confronts the risen Christ and realizes His presence in the routine of daily life. We too can "walk and talk" with Christ and be assured that we belong to Him. This experience is very real to a believer and brings a joy that is beyond any other satisfaction. Indeed, it may sometimes seem that no one else has ever known as much delight as we experience, walking each day with Christ. At least, this was author Miles' conviction when he wrote: "The joy we share as we tarry there, None other has ever known."

When we take time to know Christ intimately through prayer and meditation, we too may feel that we want to stay in His presence forever. But He "bids us go" as He did Mary, to tell others of His death, His resurrection and ascension, and His promise of coming again. His command to go is, in a sense, a "voice of woe" because men must be warned to turn from their sins if they are to escape God's judgment. And we are the only messengers God has to take this news to the world. As Paul the Apostle said: "Woe is unto me, if I preach not the gospel!" (I Cor. 9:16).

"In the Garden" was a favorite song during the days Homer Rodeheaver led singing for the Billy Sunday campaigns. It can be just as significant today if we remember its true meaning as we sing.

[Read or sing the entire hymn.]

BLESSED ASSURANCE

[*Crusader Hymns*, No. 97]

A Hymn Story by Cliff Barrows

Several years ago I stood in a cemetery at Bridgeport, Connecticut and looked at an unpretentious gravestone marked "Aunt Fanny." I recalled the life of a remarkable woman blind almost from birth who was probably the most important gospel song writer of the last hundred years. How many people have been won to faith in Christ by the hymns of Fanny Crosby!

One of Miss Crosby's close friends was Mrs. Joseph Knapp, wife of the founder of the Metropolitan Life Insurance Company of New York. Mrs. Knapp was an amateur musician, and on one of her visits to the blind poetess she brought a melody she had composed.

"What does the tune say?" she asked Fanny Crosby, after playing it a few times. The blind woman responded immediately:

> Blessed assurance, Jesus is mine!
> Oh, what a foretaste of glory divine!
> Heir of salvation, purchase of God,
> Born of His Spirit, washed in His blood.

This method of composing words to an existing tune became a habit, and Miss Crosby used it in writing many of her seven thousand songs.

During the ministry of the crusades and the "Hour of Decision" broadcasts, several hymns have been used as "theme songs." "Blessed Assurance" is one that seems to have lasted longer than the others. It has always been a favorite of mine. It is an ideal song of testimony which tells the unending peace and joy of the person who knows that God has accepted him because of what Jesus Christ has done on his behalf.

As well as I can remember, we began to use this song with crusade choirs as early as 1948 in such places as Ocean City, New Jersey and Baltimore, Maryland. My wife Billie was playing the organ then — our family had not yet arrived to keep her at home — and together we worked out the changes of tempo and the high ending which have become a trademark of crusade music.

[Read or sing stanzas 1 and 2.]

Admittedly, "Blessed Assurance" does not seem to have a clear outline or progression of thought. It is not a strong doctrinal presentation. Rather, it is a succession of completely personal, almost rambling expressions by an individual who *knows* that he has found new life in Christ. In his happiness and freedom he sings "Blessed assurance, Jesus is mine!" He is convinced that he has experienced a sample of heaven — a "foretaste of glory."

Both the second and third stanzas begin with the reminder that when we truly accept Jesus as Lord, we submit our wills to Him. At first this may seem to mean that we have lost our personal freedom. But we soon discover that this yielded life brings peace and rest, "delight and rapture."

Some folk criticize our simple gospel songs by claiming that they are too selfish and personal in content. But becoming a Christian is a completely personal thing. I was converted when, as a teenager, it dawned on me that John 3:16 could be read this way: "For God so loved Cliff, that He gave His only begotten Son, that if Cliff would believe on Him, he would have everlasting life."

This is why I love to sing, "This is *my* story, this is *my* song, Praising *my* Saviour all the day long."
[Read or sing stanza 3.]

There is one short quotation on the side of Fanny Crosby's gravestone that is easily missed by the casual observer. It is a phrase that was spoken by Christ at Bethany after Mary the sister of Lazarus had anointed Him with a very costly perfume. When some objected to the "wasting" of the ointment, Jesus replied: "She hath done what she could."

I'm convinced that our Lord accepted the offering of Fanny Crosby in the same way. Her hymns contain the sweet aroma of her love for Christ. If she had written only this one song, it would have been enough to merit the approval of her Lord.

Blessed assurance, Jesus is mine!
  Oh, what a foretaste of glory divine!
Heir of salvation, purchase of God,
  Born of His Spirit, washed in His blood.

Perfect submission, perfect delight,
  Visions of rapture now burst on my sight;
Angels descending, bring from above
  Echoes of mercy, whispers of love.

Perfect submission, all is at rest,
  I in my Saviour am happy and blest;
Watching and waiting, looking above,
  Filled with His goodness, lost in His love.

Refrain:

This is my story, this is my song,
  Praising my Saviour all the day long;
This is my story, this is my song,
  Praising my Saviour all the day long.

Fanny J. Crosby (1820-1915)

The Son of God goes forth to war,
    A kingly crown to gain;
His blood-red banner streams afar:
    Who follows in His train?
Who best can drink his cup of woe,
    Triumphant over pain,
Who patient bears his cross below,
    He follows in His train.

The martyr first, whose eagle eye
    Could pierce beyond the grave,
Who saw his Master in the sky,
    And called on Him to save:
Like Him, with pardon on his tongue
    In midst of mortal pain,
He prayed for them that did the wrong:
    Who follows in his train?

A glorious band, the chosen few
    On whom the Spirit came,
Twelve valiant saints, their hope they knew,
    And mocked the cross and flame:
They met the tyrant's brandished steel,
    The lion's gory mane;
They bowed their necks the death to feel:
    Who follows in their train?

A noble army, men and boys,
    The matron and the maid,
Around the Saviour's throne rejoice,
    In robes of light arrayed:
They climbed the steep ascent of heaven
    Through peril, toil, and pain;
O God, to us may grace be given
    To follow in their train.

Reginald Heber (1783-1826)

the son of god goes forth to war

[*Crusader Hymns*, No. 223]

A Hymn Story by Billy Graham

One of my favorite melodies is the stirring hymn tune named "All Saints, New" which we used with "Macedonia," the theme hymn of the 1966 World Congress on Evangelism in Berlin. The tune was originally written for the text "The Son of God Goes Forth to War," a hymn about Christian martyrs, and that is why it is called "All Saints."
[Read or sing stanzas 1-3.]

The Apostle Paul often spoke of Christian life and service as a warfare. "Put on all the armour which God provides, so that you may be able to stand firm against the devices of the devil. For our fight is not against human foes, but against cosmic powers, against the authorities and potentates of this dark world, against the superhuman forces of evil in the heavens" (Eph. 6:11,12, *New English Bible*). In the verses that follow are listed the pieces of spiritual armor with which we fight this war: the belt of truth, the breastplate of integrity, shoes of the gospel of peace, the shield of faith, the helmet of salvation, and the sword of the Spirit — the Word of God.

In this hymn we see a picture of Jesus Christ at the head of a great battle column. Over and over the question is asked, "Who follows in His train, in His victory procession?" The answer is obvious; Christ's army is made up of men and women who "best can drink their cup of woe" and patiently "bear their cross below."

From the words of the second stanza, we discern that one of the prominent figures in this battle formation is Stephen, the first Christian martyr. Acts chapter seven *(NEB)* tells us that Stephen saw Jesus "standing at God's right hand" and that he prayed for his murderers, "Lord, do not hold this sin against them."

Behind Stephen in the procession, the third stanza mentions "twelve valiant saints," the Lord's twelve apostles. Tradition tells us that they too were martyrs, killed by the sword, by animals in the Roman arena, or by other brutal methods.

And who follows in their train? The hymn writer sees a noble army of "men and boys, the matron and the maid" who down through the years have given their lives for the cause of the gospel of Jesus Christ. Our own century has produced more martyrs than the entire 1900 years since Jesus' death. Included are Dr. Paul Carlson, who died in the Congo uprising of 1964, and the five missionaries murdered by Ecuador's Auca Indians in 1956.

But what kind of an army can this be, following in the train of Jesus Christ? It would seem that they are all casualties of war who lost their lives in battle. Can this be a victorious group?

The Bible records that the brilliant young Jew, Saul of Tarsus, was watching the stoning of Stephen and that the martyr's testimony in death profoundly influenced this persecutor of the church. Soon after, Saul was converted and became Paul the Apostle. Through his missionary journeys and those of all of Jesus' disciples, the gospel was spread throughout the known world and the Christian church was founded.

In our own times, because of the death of Dr. Paul Carlson, a medical foundation has been set up in the Congo; thus his ministry will be multiplied to those who murdered him. And in South America, almost the entire Auca Indian tribe has been won to faith in Jesus Christ as an end result of the death of those five young men. Two of the Aucas — including one who participated in the killing — attended the 1966 Berlin Congress on Evangelism!

I believe that in the days ahead we may experience even greater persecution because of our faith. Many more young men and women may become martyrs for the cause of Christ. Are we willing "to drink the cup which Jesus drank" — the cup of suffering, pain and death? We should remember these words of Paul, who also died a martyr:

> Take your share of hardship, like a good soldier of Christ Jesus... Remember Jesus Christ, risen from the dead, born of David's line. This is the theme of my gospel, in whose service I am exposed to hardship, even to the point of being shut up like a common criminal; but the word of God is not shut up. And I endure it all for the sake of God's chosen ones, with this end in view, that they too may attain the glorious and eternal salvation which is in Christ Jesus.
>
> Here are words you may trust: "If we died with him, we shall live with him; if we endure, we shall reign with him" (II Timothy 2:3, 8-12, *NEB*).

[Read or sing the final stanza.]

saved!

[*Crusader Hymns*, No. 110]

The idea that Christians should modernize their speech when talking about their faith is much discussed today. Some of these reactions to traditional language may reveal a bit of cynicism — as for instance the one ridiculing the soul-winner who grabs you by the lapels and says, "Brother, are you saved?"

It must be granted that such a frontal attack may not be the best way to introduce someone to Jesus Christ. We must use an appropriate approach and language that makes sense to our generation. But the word "saved" should be just as intelligible to modern minds as other Biblical words such as "salvation" and "Saviour." After all, this expression appears in some of our most significant scripture passages.

> For this is good and acceptable in the sight of God our Saviour; who will have all men to be saved, and to come unto the knowledge of the truth (I Tim. 2:3, 4).
>
> For whosoever shall call upon the name of the Lord shall be saved (Rom. 10:13).
>
> For by grace are ye saved through faith; and that not of yourselves; it is the gift of God: not of works, lest any man should boast (Eph. 2:8, 9).

The meaning of "saved" is not really obscure. Among other things, it signifies "rescued." We say that a person was "saved from drowning." Similarly, we affirm that through faith in Christ "a soul is saved from eternal loss, judgment and death," and that "a life was saved from frustration and meaninglessness."

The angel of God used this expression in telling Joseph about the son who was to be born to Mary: "Thou shalt call his name Jesus (Saviour); for He shall save His people from their sins." Preachers of the gospel agree that, through the death and resurrection of our Lord, we are "saved from sin" in a threefold way.

First, we are saved, or delivered, from the condemnation and the *penalty* of our sins. Romans 8:1 declares: "There is therefore now no condemnation to them which are in Christ Jesus, who walk not after the flesh, but after the Spirit."

We are also saved, or freed, from the *power* of sin in our lives. This is a progressive freedom. As we walk faithfully with Christ day by day, we experience increasing victory over the temptations and the defeats that are common to men. The Bible has this encouraging promise: "For sin shall not have dominion over you; for ye are not under the law, but under grace" (Rom. 6:14).

Finally, we will one day be saved from the very *presence* of sin. We are told in Revelation 21:27 that "there shall in no wise enter into it (heaven) any thing that defileth." We will also then be freed from all the results of sin. "And God shall wipe away all tears from their eyes; and there shall be no more death, neither sorrow, nor crying, neither shall there be any more pain" (Rev. 21:4).

[Read or sing stanzas 1 and 2.]

The author of this great salvation song is Dr. Oswald J. Smith, for many years pastor of The Peoples Church of Toronto, and one of our outstanding missionary statesmen. Dr. Smith recently wrote:

It was in Toronto in 1917, when I was twenty-seven years of age, that I wrote my hymn 'Saved.' At that time I was sending my hymns to the Tabernacle Publishing Company of Chicago. Arthur W. McKee, Paul Rader's great song leader, was the one with whom I corresponded. He sent a number of my hymn-poems to Roger M. Hickman, a Baptist musician and evangelist, and he was the one who wrote the inspiring music.

In the year 1919, Dr. Rader and Mr. McKee came to Toronto to hold an evangelistic campaign in Massey Hall. I had just resigned from Dale Presbyterian Church and was out of work. I tried to usher in the meetings but was turned down. I tried to do personal work but was ignored. Then I started selling hymnbooks in the aisles, praying and hoping that God would use me again.

Suddenly one night, Mr. McKee announced that they were going to sing a brand new hymn called 'Saved.' My heart was in my mouth. Pointing down to where I was selling hymnbooks McKee said, 'That young man down there wrote this hymn.' I turned my back and went on selling books.

Then they sang it — 3400 voices strong — sang it until it seemed as though they would lift the roof. I was hearing it introduced for the first time. Oh, how it stirred me! I had been fearfully discouraged, but that night God spoke to me again and I was inspired and elated. I knew God was not going to put me on the shelf.

Then came the Alliance Tabernacle on Christie Street, The Peoples Church and worldwide evangelism. And now, in all parts of the world, and in many languages, for more than fifty years my song has been sung. It is still my testimony, every word of it. May it long live after I am gone, to proclaim the great message of God's salvation.

[Read or sing the last stanza.]

Saved! saved! saved! my sins are all forgiv'n;
  Christ is mine! I'm on my way to heav'n;
Once a guilty sinner, lost, undone,
  Now a child of God, saved thro' His Son.

Saved! saved! saved! by grace and grace alone;
  Oh, what wondrous love to me was shown,
In my stead Christ Jesus bled and died,
  Bore my sins, for me was crucified.

Saved! saved! saved! oh, joy beyond compare!
  Christ my life, and I His constant care;
Yielding all and trusting Him alone,
  Living now each moment as His own.

Refrain:

Saved! I'm saved thro' Christ, my all in all;
  Saved! I'm saved, whatever may befall;
He died upon the cross for me, He bore the awful penalty;
  And now I'm saved eternally — I'm saved! saved! saved!

Oswald J. Smith (b. 1890)

And can it be that I should gain
    An interest in the Saviour's blood?
Died He for me, who caused His pain?
    For me, who Him to death pursued?
Amazing love! how can it be
    That Thou, my God, shouldst die for me?

'Tis mystery all! Th'Immortal dies!
    Who can explore His strange design?
In vain the first-born seraph tries
    To sound the depths of love Divine!
'Tis mercy all! let earth adore,
    Let angel minds inquire no more.

He left His Father's throne above,
    So free, so infinite His grace;
Emptied Himself of all but love,
    And bled for Adam's helpless race;
'Tis mercy all, immense and free;
    For, O my God, it found out me.

Long my imprisoned spirit lay
    Fast bound in sin and nature's night;
Thine eye diffused a quick'ning ray,
    I woke, the dungeon flamed with light;
My chains fell off, my heart was free;
    I rose, went forth, and followed Thee.

No condemnation now I dread;
    Jesus, and all in Him, is mine!
Alive in Him, my living Head,
    And clothed in righteousness Divine,
Bold I approach th'eternal throne,
    And claim the crown, thro' Christ my own.

Charles Wesley (1707-1788)

anò can it be that i shoulò Gain?

[*Crusader Hymns*, No. 74]

A Hymn Story by Cliff Barrows

One of the most gripping songs about salvation in all hymnody is "And Can it Be;" it is especially strong when sung to the thrilling tune "Sagina." The poem presents the drama of man's redemption in two parts: first, the Lord's sacrifice to provide our salvation; and second, our experience when we accept His offering for us.
[Read or sing stanzas 1-3.]

Not many hymns begin with a question as does this one. However, it is not an expression of doubt but of wonder and awe. How can it be that the shedding of Jesus' blood 1900 years ago is relevant to me today? How was it possible for the Son of God to have died for me? Why should our Lord empty Himself of all His divine glory and become a man, in order to save "Adam's helpless race?" It is said in stanza two that even the angels — including Gabriel, who is called the "first-born seraph" — try in vain to understand.

Charles Wesley, author of this hymn, may have been thinking of the earlier words of Isaac Watts:

> Alas, and did my Saviour bleed?
> And did my Sovereign die?
> Would He devote that sacred head
> For such a worm as I?

Watts' attempt to explain the mystery is also limited to an expression of wonder: "Amazing pity! grace unknown! and love beyond degree!"

It is Wesley's advice that we do not waste time in a fruitless attempt to understand in full. It is beyond the comprehension of angels. Let us simply accept the fact of God's love, and then lift our hearts in adoration to Christ.

This is the mystery of Christ's death. What does it mean in the experience of the individual believer?
[Read or sing stanzas 4 and 5.]

There is considerable evidence that this hymn was written by Charles Wesley soon after his own conversion. Looking back, he sees himself as a prisoner in a dark dungeon, chained by the *sins* which he had committed and even more made captive by the *sin* which was a part of his very nature. The gospel of Christ — the good news that Christ had died to meet his need — seemed to flood the dungeon with light, break the chains, and set him free. His feeling of guilt was gone. For the first time he seemed to be really alive, because he possessed the supernatural life of Jesus Christ! He could face the final judgment unafraid because he was clothed in the very righteousness of Christ.

It may sound as if this were the dramatic experience of one who was rescued from a life of terrible sin and degradation. But, at the time of his conversion, Charles Wesley had already been a rector in the Church of England for three years; he had just returned from a term as missionary to Georgia in the New World. Even before that, he and his brother John had earned the derisive name "Methodist" because of the disciplined life which they imposed on themselves and other members of the "Holy Club" at Oxford University. But, in all this religious activity, he had never found spiritual peace; he was not convinced that the life of Christ was really his!

When our evangelistic crusades are held in London, we often drive past the location on Aldersgate street where history says that the Wesleys found Christian assurance for themselves. Nearby is the Wesley home and the chapel they built for worship.

Charles Wesley's crisis experience occurred on May 20, 1738. He had been sick in body as well as in spirit. It seemed that God spoke to him through a vision. According to his *Journal*, this confrontation took place after reading the Bible for some time. Following is his account:

> At midnight I gave myself up to Christ: assured I was safe, sleeping or waking. Had continued experience of his power to overcome all temptations; and confessed, with joy and surprise, that he was able to do exceedingly abundantly for me, above what I can ask or think.

Nineteen hundred years ago, when Jesus said to Nicodemus, "Ye must be born again," he was talking to one of the leaders of the Jewish community, one of the most respected men of that day. I recently heard of a seventy-one-year-old minister who, after spending fifty years in the service of the church, had just come to know Jesus Christ as his Saviour.

Like the experience Charles Wesley describes in this hymn, the old minister learned personally to know God. He realized as we must also, that "doing good" means nothing to God. To accept Christ's love and sacrifice for himself was to find the source of the Christian life.

[Read or sing stanza 1 again.]

loRò, ı have shut the ÒooR

[*Crusader Hymns*, No. 164]

A Hymn Story by Don Hustad

[Read or sing stanza 1.]

> And now about prayer. When you pray, don't be like the hypocrites who pretend piety by praying publicly on street corners and in the synagogues where everyone can see them! Truly, that is all the reward they will ever get! But when you pray, go away by yourself, all alone. and shut the door behind you and pray to your Father secretly, and your Father, who knows your secrets, will reward you (Matthew 6:5,6, *Living Gospels*).

here's a good question to ask ourselves. Are we ever guilty of praying horizontally — for people, instead of vertically — to God? When we lead in prayer at home or in church, are we too concerned about the impression we are making on other people? Well, even if we do not indulge in "show off" prayer, this is still good advice: "When you pray, go away by yourself, all alone."

I must admit that this is very difficult for me to do nowadays. From the moment a day begins in our home, life is a bustle of activity: getting the girls off to school, answering the telephone, rushing to the airport, going to crusade meetings or to our own church, entertaining our friends, and keeping up with music practice and correspondence.

Even on the rare occasions when families are at home today, they are seldom really quiet. The noise of traffic, of jet airplanes, of telephone and television, of hi-fi phonographs and transistor radios bores in upon them. Someone has said that the hearing capacity as well as the spiritual tone of the present generation is bound to be harmed by the "high decibel" rate of life as we know it.

It may be that modern man doesn't really want to be quiet, because then he is forced into sober and serious thinking. He hides from his inner fears, his weaknesses and failures, by constant talking and doing. If he commits some sin — if he says an unkind word or thinks an evil thought — he shuts it out of his mind by rushing to some new task or to another chat on the telephone. We need often to "shut the door" and pray, in order that we might really know ourselves and understand our deepest problems.

It is also true that unless we pray in this manner prescribed by our Lord, we do not really find God! Do you remember the story of Elijah's flight from King Ahab and Queen Jezebel? He was on the mountain called Horeb waiting to hear from God. I Kings 19:11, 12 says that:

> a great and strong wind rent the mountains, and brake in pieces the rocks before the Lord; but the Lord was not in the wind; and after the wind an earthquake; but the Lord was not in the earthquake: and after the earthquake a fire; but the Lord was not in the fire: and after the fire a still small voice.

God is not going to shout at us over the noise and the busy-ness of our lives. His voice is a quiet one, but it can be heard if we follow the Psalmist's advice: "Be still, and know that I am God" (Psalm 46:10).

Every individual must solve for himself this problem of securing privacy so that he can think and pray. It may be that in your home, only the basement is out of the main stream of traffic. My wife complains that the children are always bursting in with some problem about clothes or dates, even into her bedroom at night. Some people find they can pray best in the early morning, before the telephone, radio and TV get into gear. Others can do it while riding the train or bus to work. (If you obey the command "watch and pray" in an ultra-literal sense, you may also commune with God while you're driving.) You can even pray while walking your dog late in the evening! However you or I work it out, every one of us needs to shut the door on our busy world if we are to really pray.

William M. Runyan, author of both words and music of this hymn, was the kind of person who had evidently learned this secret. I remember him as a charming, friendly man of great dignity who occasionally dropped in at the Moody Bible Institute while he was editing hymnals for the Hope Publishing Company. Earlier in life he had been a Methodist pastor and evangelist.

Our last visit together was during his retirement in Galveston, Texas, when the Moody Chorale sang there. His very manner and his conversation revealed that, although he knew much about the world in which he lived, his greater acquaintance with God had given him a serenity which is rare in these hectic days. The dynamic for personal poise and power in meeting life's problems is found in these words of scripture: "Go away by yourself, all alone, and shut the door behind you and pray to your Father secretly, and your Father, who knows your secrets, will reward you."

[Read or sing stanzas 2-4.]

Lord, I have shut the door; speak now the word
　　Which in the din and throng could not be heard;
Hushed now my inner heart, whisper Thy will,
　　While I have come apart, while all is still.

Lord, I have shut the door, here do I bow;
　　Speak, for my soul attent turns to Thee now.
Rebuke Thou what is vain, counsel my soul,
　　Thy holy will reveal, my will control.

In this blest quietness clamorings cease;
　　Here in Thy presence dwells infinite peace;
Yonder the strife and cry, yonder the sin:
　　Lord, I have shut the door, Thou art within!

Lord, I have shut the door, strengthen my heart;
　　Yonder awaits the task — I share a part,
Only through grace bestowed may I be true;
　　Here, while alone with Thee, my strength renew.

William M. Runyan (1870-1957)

Free from the law, O happy condition,
    Jesus hath bled, and there is remission;
Cursed by the law and bruised by the fall,
    Grace hath redeemed us once for all.

Now are we free — there's no condemnation,
    Jesus provides a perfect salvation;
"Come unto Me," O hear His sweet call,
    Come, and He saves us once for all.

"Children of God," O glorious calling,
    Surely His grace will keep us from falling;
Passing from death to life at His call,
    Blessed salvation once for all.

Refrain:

Once for all, O sinner, receive it;
    Once for all, O brother, believe it;
Cling to the cross, the burden will fall,
    Christ hath redeemed us once for all.

                                    Philip P. Bliss (1838-1876)

ONCE FOR ALL

[*Crusader Hymns*, No. 119]

A Hymn Story by Billy Graham

While we were ministering in Edinburgh, Scotland in 1955, our Association was able to give some financial assistance to the famous Carruber's Close Mission which was founded by D. L. Moody many years ago. In appreciation, the mission leaders helped us acquire the reed organ which had been used by the gospel singer Ira D. Sankey when he and Moody worked together in Great Britain. The little organ has been preserved and is now exhibited in our offices in Minneapolis, Minnesota.

Every time I see it there, I am reminded of Sankey's first appearance in Edinburgh. The Presbyterians in Scotland had long insisted that only the "psalms" should be sung in church, and these without any accompaniment. On an earlier occasion, one lady had walked out on a Moody-Sankey meeting, protesting that the devil was in his "kist (chest) o' whistles." Sankey's concern about the Scots' acceptance of his simple "gospel hymns" was increased when he saw the great preacher and hymnwriter Horatius Bonar in the audience. As he recounts it, this is the narrative from *My Life and the Story of the Gospel Hymns:*

> Of all men in Scotland he was the one concerning whose decision I was most solicitous. He was, indeed, my ideal hymn writer, the prince among hymnists of his day and generation. And yet he would not sing one of his beautiful hymns in his own congregation . . . because he ministered to a church that believed in the use of the Psalms only.
>
> With fear and trembling I announced as a solo the song, 'Free from the Law, oh, happy condition.' . . . Feeling that the singing might prove only an entertainment and not a spiritual blessing, I requested the whole congregation to join me in a word of prayer, asking God to bless the truth about to be sung. In the prayer my anxiety was relieved. Believing and rejoicing in the glorious truth contained in the song, I sang it through to the end.
>
> At the close of Mr. Moody's address, Dr. Bonar turned toward me with a smile on his venerable face, and reaching out his hand he said: "Well, Mr. Sankey, you sang the gospel tonight." And thus the way was opened for the mission of sacred song in Scotland.

The choice of song Ira Sankey made that night had truly been dictated by God's leading. Its statement of faith included the whole story of sin and death, of grace and salvation. What better appeal could be made to a people who prided themselves on their doctrinal scholarship!

This simple hymn contains the basis of our Christian theology, from the fall of man to his final redemption in heaven. The Bible says that the Devil, in the form of a serpent, tempted the first man and caused him to sin, to fall from his state of perfect fellowship with God. Genesis 3:15 teaches that Satan "bruised the heel" of man in this act. When the created being thus became estranged from his Creator, determined to work out his own destiny, God gave a set of laws to show that man cannot please Him in his own strength; neither can he find complete happiness in himself or in his relationships with other men.

The penalty for breaking God's law is death, as is stated in Romans 6:23: "For the wages of sin is death." Furthermore, God knew that nobody could keep the law perfectly; this failure must ultimately pass a death sentence on the entire human race. This universal judgment is confirmed in Galatians 3:10: "Cursed is every one that continueth not in *all* things which are written in the book of the law to do them."

In His great wisdom and because of His great love, God provided that His Son Jesus Christ would bear our penalty and make possible the restoration of fellowship. Now we are "free from the law of sin and death" (Rom. 8:2). Galatians 3:13 says that "Christ hath redeemed us from the curse of the law."

The title of this hymn comes from Hebrews 10:10, "By the which will we are sanctified (set apart, made holy) through the offering of the body of Jesus Christ *once for all.*" Jesus died on Calvary almost two thousand years ago, but His death provides salvation for all who have believed in Him, and for all who will believe in the years to come.

When we accept Christ's sacrifice for us, there is "no more condemnation." God forgives all our sins, and by so doing frees our consciences from a sense of guilt. The Bible testifies that then "the Spirit itself beareth witness with our spirit, that we are the children of God" (Rom. 8:16). We have "passed from death unto life" (John 5:24). In addition, we are given the promise that Christ will keep us from falling into sin again if we walk day by day as His Word teaches us. "Now unto him that is able to keep you from falling, and to present you faultless before the presence of his glory with exceeding joy; to the only wise God our Saviour, be glory and majesty, dominion and power, both now and ever. Amen." (Jude 24, 25)

All this information is contained in the gospel song "Once For All." This hymn is almost a century old, but its message is timeless. It is just as relevant today as the scriptures upon which it is based.

[Read or sing the entire hymn.]

holy spirit, breathe on me

[*Crusader Hymns*, No. 176]

A Hymn Story by Cliff Barrows

Both because of his size and accomplishment, B. B. McKinney stood out as a giant in the field of gospel music during the early twentieth century. McKinney was a big man — more than six feet tall and two hundred pounds in weight — with a large, warm-hearted personality to match. He was both a winsome and commanding figure, whether he was singing a solo, directing an evangelistic choir, or managing an office.

His contributions to the Southern Baptist ministry accorded him a title as "the father of church music among Southern Baptists." After teaching at Southwestern Seminary and serving as assistant pastor of the Travis Avenue Baptist Church in Fort Worth, Texas, he became secretary of the newly-organized Church Music Department at Baptist headquarters in Nashville, Tennessee. Here he edited the first hymnals to be widely used by Southern Baptists, and initiated the now-burgeoning ministry in church music.

Besides this educational ministry, he exercised a personal talent for composing. Among the 150 songs for which Dr. McKinney wrote both words and music, there are at least two which are adaptations of earlier hymns by other writers. One of these, "Holy Spirit, Breathe on Me" gives us McKinney's personal understanding of the hymn "Breathe on Me, Breath of God." The original was written in 1878 by Edwin Hatch, a professor at Oxford University.

Borrowing from earlier hymnic sources, as McKinney did in this instance, is a fairly common practice. Many of Isaac Watts' hymns are adaptations of the Jewish hymns we call "psalms;" for instance, "O God, Our Help in Ages Past" (Number 12, *Crusader Hymns*) is based on Psalm 90. Similarly, "Just As I Am, Thine Own to Be" (Number 66) is a youth version of "Just As I Am, Without One Plea" (Number 57). J. Wilbur Chapman's "Our Great Saviour" (Number 4) quotes many phrases from Charles Wesley's "Jesus, Lover of My Soul" (Number 79). I believe it should be regarded as a compliment to the earlier hymn when a subsequent writer wants to re-state its truth in his own words.

69

At first glance, both these titles, "Holy Spirit, Breathe on Me" and "Breathe on Me, Breath of God," may seem a bit odd. To personify and address diety so directly may appear presumptuous. However, in the original language of the New Testament the word for "spirit" is *pneuma*, which means "wind" or "breath." On the day of Pentecost, the Holy Spirit's coming was accompanied with "a sound from heaven as of a rushing mighty wind" (Acts 2:2). In anticipation of that day, John 20:22 *(Living Gospels)* says that Jesus "breathed" on his disciples and said, "Receive the Holy Spirit."

The verses of this hymn tell what the Holy Spirit does for the Christian, because He dwells in the believer's heart. The words "Breathe on me, until my heart is clean" in stanza one, remind us that it is God's Spirit who daily cleanses or "sanctifies" us, causing us to be more and more like Jesus Christ. Paul said to the Corinthians: "But ye are washed, but ye are sanctified, but ye are justified in the name of the Lord Jesus, and by the Spirit of our God" (I Cor. 6:11).

[Read or sing stanza 1.]

It is the Holy Spirit who also leads us to consecrate ourselves to Christ. "Holy Spirit, breathe on me, My stubborn will subdue," the stanzas continue. In the scriptures, Ephesians 5:18 reiterates this in another way, "And be not drunk with wine, wherein is excess; but be filled with the Spirit." A man who is under the influence of intoxicants does not have control over his own actions; he is dominated by the effects of the alcohol. When we are filled with the Holy Spirit we are under His complete control to do the perfect will of God.

[Read or sing stanza 2.]

The third stanza states that it is the Holy Spirit who gives us spiritual power to become mature personalities capable of serving God more effectively. So we sing in a spirit of prayer, "Holy Spirit, breathe on me, Fill me with pow'r divine." Christ promised his disciples, "Ye shall receive power, after that the Holy Ghost is come upon you: and ye shall be witnesses unto me." It was this power that enabled the early Christians to spread the gospel throughout the known world within their lifetimes. The same resource for effective ministry is available today.

As we live each day, the Holy Spirit wants to do these same things for us, and in the same order. First, He would cleanse us from sin; second, He wants to help us dedicate ourselves completely to God; and finally, He desires to give us all the resources of God so that we may live triumphantly.

[Read or sing stanzas 3 and 4.]

Holy Spirit, breathe on me
Until my heart is clean;
Let sunshine fill its inmost part,
With not a cloud between.

Holy Spirit, breathe on me,
My stubborn will subdue;
Teach me in words of living flame
What Christ would have me do.

Holy Spirit, breathe on me,
Fill me with pow'r divine;
Kindle a flame of love and zeal
Within this heart of mine.

Holy Spirit, breathe on me,
Till I am all Thine own;
Until my will is lost in Thine,
To live for Thee alone.

Refrain:

Breathe on me, breathe on me,
Holy Spirit, breathe on me;
Take Thou my heart, cleanse every part,
Holy Spirit, breathe on me.

Edwin Hatch (1835-1889)
Alt. by B. B. McKinney (1886-1952)

Thy Word is like a garden, Lord,
    With flowers bright and fair;
And every one who seeks may pluck
    A lovely cluster there.
Thy Word is like a deep, deep mine;
    And jewels rich and rare
Are hidden in its mighty depths
    For every searcher there.

Thy Word is like a starry host:
    A thousand rays of light
Are seen to guide the traveler,
    And make his pathway bright.
Thy Word is like an armory,
    Where soldiers may repair,
And find, for life's long battle-day,
    All needful weapons there.

O may I love Thy precious Word,
    May I explore the mine,
May I its fragrant flowers glean,
    May light upon me shine.
O may I find my armor there,
    Thy Word my trusty sword;
I'll learn to fight with every foe
    The battle of the Lord.

Edwin Hodder (1837-1904)

thy WORD IS LIKE A GARDEN, LORD

[*Crusader Hymns*, No. 204]

The Bible is an amazing book! Although parts of it are almost three thousand years old, it has for years been the world's best-seller, and it is constantly being translated into new languages. Throughout two centuries of "higher criticism" the scriptures have been under constant attack because of a few apparent discrepancies. Yet, apart from God, its unity is unexplainable, since it was penned in three different languages, by more than forty different individuals, over a period of a thousand years. Each year the archeologist's shovel confirms more of what the Bible has recorded about human history.

Unlike any other volume in the world's libraries, the Bible is a miracle book — the living Word of God. It has altered the patterns of society and changed the destiny of nations. It has transformed individual lives. This hymn tells us why this is so.

"Thy Word is like a garden, Lord" suggests first that the Bible is comparable to a landscape full of lovely flowers that bring delight with every glance. We pick up a paraphrase like *Living Gospels* or J. B. Phillips' *Letters to Young Churches* and read it easily like a novel, with both pleasure and profit. Most public gardens have signs posted which warn: "Please do not pick the flowers." But in the garden of God's Word we read "Help yourself!"

Richard Cecil, in his book *Remains*, uses this same idea to say that every word in the Bible is important. "The Bible resembles an extensive garden, where there is a vast variety and profusion of fruits and flowers, some of which are more essential or more splendid than others; but there is not a blade suffered to grow in it which has not its use and beauty in the system."

The Bible is also like "a deep, deep mine" containing priceless jewels. These treasures may not be picked up in a casual stroll through the garden. They require digging — long and careful study — and perhaps some mining tools, such as different versions, dictionaries and commentaries. But we will find that both the predictable and the unexpected prizes we turn up are well worth all the hard work required. As the late Dr. M. R. De Haan of the "Radio Bible Class" once said, "The 'fringe benefits' of Bible study may be more precious than the thing we started looking for originally."

Psalm 119:105 declares that the scriptures are like a lantern: "Thy word is a lamp unto my feet, and a light unto my path." Our hymn carries the analogy a little further and says that the Bible is like the star-filled heavens, lighting up the entire landscape. Navigators use the celestial bodies to secure a "compass fix" and to chart the route of a great ship or an airliner. So God's Word gives direction to the whole course of our life and lights each step we take.

Finally, the Bible is like an armory in which are stored all kinds of weapons for the warfare against sin and the devil. When Jesus was tempted in the wilderness by Satan, He used the scriptures to repel the subtle, insidious assaults of the wicked one. If we memorize passages from the Word of God, they will become ever-ready weapons of defense whenever we are threatened by evil thoughts and desires.

Ephesians 6:17 states that God's Word is also an offensive weapon — "the sword of the Spirit." When we would win a victory in our own character development or in doing the work of Christ here on earth, it is the Bible which strengthens us and makes it possible.

The Bible is all this and more, according to the testimony of some of the world's greatest men:

Immanuel Kant — "The Bible is the greatest benefit which the human race has ever experienced."

Abraham Lincoln — "Read this book for what on reason you can accept and take the rest on faith, and you will live and die a better man."

John Ruskin — "The Bible is the one Book to which any thoughtful man may go with any honest question of life or destiny and find the answer of God by honest searching."

[Read or sing the entire hymn.]

Some of our hymn writers were neither ministers nor professional poets, but ordinary people who loved to sing and to write new Christian songs. Edwin Hodder (1837-1904), author of "Thy Word Is Like a Garden, Lord," spent the early part of his working life in New Zealand, doing sociological research among the Maori aborigines. Later he became a civil servant in his native England. As a hymnist, he would probably be called an amateur, but in this hymn alone he has made a great contribution to our worship.

all my life long

[*Crusader Hymns*, No. 107]

A Hymn Story by George Beverly Shea

When I was a boy of eight our family moved from Winchester, Ontario to Houghton, New York. My father had been a pastor in Winchester for twenty years and was now beginning a brief period of ministry in evangelism and church pioneering.

Walking together in Houghton one day, Dad pointed out a tall, elderly lady moving slowly along the sidewalk. He told me that she was Mrs. Clara Tear Williams, a much loved and respected hymn writer — author of one of his favorite Christian songs, "Satisfied." From that time on, Mrs. Williams' appearance always reminded me of the classic painting of Whistler's mother. She had a regal and dignified bearing and yet she had the kindness and gentleness of Christ in her face. When I came to know her and often spoke with her, I enjoyed the soft, musical tones of her voice. Through her sweetness and graciousness to everyone, she became another wonderful proof to me of the reality of the Christian walk. Hers was a beautiful life exhibited not only to the whole community, but expressed also in the pages of hymnody.

Some time afterward I memorized this hymn. It became one of my first solos as I began to sing publicly in my late teens. At that time my father had a pastorate in Ottawa, Canada. Since then I have always loved to sing it because "All My Life Long" expresses the conviction of everyone who has found satisfaction in Jesus Christ.

Like my family, Mrs. Williams was a Wesleyan Methodist. The composer of the hymn's melody, Ralph E. Hudson, was associated with the older Methodist Episcopal Church. After serving as a male nurse during the Civil War, he became a music teacher and publisher in Ohio. He was often engaged as an evangelistic singer, and wrote many gospel hymn tunes.

[Read or sing stanzas 1 and 2.]

Clara Williams' hymn is as modern as the concerns of mankind. Psychologists today refer to a person's fundamental needs — a need for security, a need to be loved, and a need to find identity. In this hymn these inner longings are represented by metaphors of hunger, thirst and a desire for material riches. Many men and women pursue these elemental physical wants, thinking that they will meet their deeper needs. But, of course, they never do.

Others expect that happiness will result from gratifying the desires of the mind and the ego. A thirst for knowledge and a hunger for power characterizes many men, accompanied by a desire for status and recognition. But these ambitions, too, finally become futile; as the hymn says, they are only "dust which we gather around us."

King Solomon exemplified a person who relentlessly pursued satisfaction in many areas. As a young man, he enjoyed everything that could please the body: rich foods, exotic wines, and other sensual pleasures.

When he became king of Israel, Solomon experienced great power and glory. He was a connoisseur of the arts and built one of the world's most beautiful temples. He displayed great wisdom in his judgments and even practiced religion — but without true faith in God.

At the end of life, Solomon looked back over his long and fruitless quest for happiness, and exclaimed, "Vanity, vanity, all is vanity!"

The final stanza of our hymn says that Jesus Christ alone can meet the deepest longings of men. He becomes to us a "well of water," the "bread of life," and "untold wealth that never faileth." Recall these words spoken by Jesus himself:

"If any man thirst, let him come unto me, and drink" (John 7:37).

"I am the bread of life: he that cometh to me shall never hunger; and he that believeth on me shall never thirst" (John 6:35).

"Seek ye first the kingdom of God, and his righteousness; and all these things shall be added unto you" (Matt. 6:33).

The truth is, no man can ever find true happiness apart from Jesus Christ. As St. Augustine said in his prayer, long ago, "Thou hast created us for Thyself, and our heart cannot be quieted till it find repose in Thee."

[Read or sing stanzas 3 and 4.]

All my life long I had panted
    For a drink from some cool spring
That I hoped would quench the burning
    Of the thirst I felt within.

Feeding on the husks around me
    Till my strength was almost gone,
Longed my soul for something better,
    Only still to hunger on.

Poor I was, and sought for riches,
    Something that would satisfy;
But the dust I gathered round me
    Only mocked my soul's sad cry.

Well of water, ever springing,
    Bread of life, so rich and free,
Untold wealth that never faileth,
    My Redeemer is to me.

Refrain:

Hallelujah! I have found Him —
    Whom my soul so long has craved!
Jesus satisfies my longings;
    Thro' His blood I now am saved.

Clara Tear Williams (1858-1937)

How firm a foundation, ye saints of the Lord,
    Is laid for your faith in His excellent Word;
What more can He say than to you He hath said,
    To you who for refuge to Jesus have fled?

"Fear not, I am with thee; O be not dismayed,
    For I am thy God, and will still give thee aid;
I'll strengthen thee, help thee, and cause thee to stand,
    Upheld by my righteous, omnipotent hand.

"When through fiery trials thy pathway shall lie,
    My grace, all sufficient, shall be thy supply;
The flame shall not hurt thee; I only design
    Thy dross to consume, and thy gold to refine.

"The soul that on Jesus hath leaned for repose,
    I will not, I will not desert to his foes;
That soul, though all hell should endeavor to shake,
    I'll never, no, never, no, never forsake!"

K. in Rippon's
A Selection of Hymns, 1787; Alt.

how firm a foundation

[*Crusader Hymns*, No. 180]

When he left the presidency, Andrew Jackson retired to his famous home, the Hermitage, where his many friends often came to visit — the world's great from afar as well as his simple neighbors nearby. On one such occasion, General Jackson said to a local clergyman: "There is a beautiful hymn on the subject of the exceeding great and precious promises of God to His people. It was a favorite hymn with my dear wife till the day of her death. It commences thus: 'How firm a foundation, ye saints of the Lord!' I wish you would sing it now." And so, to please the ex-president, the visitors sang the entire seven stanzas.

Although this hymn has been a favorite in America ever since it appeared in 1787, its authorship is unknown. When first published by Dr. John Rippon, a Baptist minister in London, it was signed simply "K — ", and efforts to identify "K — " with certainty have been fruitless. The tune called "Foundation" has also been credited to various individuals, but without proof we can only call it an "American folk melody."

Andrew Jackson's request revealed that he knew the Bible as well as the hymn. When these verses first appeared, they bore the scripture text: "Whereby are given unto us exceeding great and precious promises" (II Peter 1:4). The hymnwriter sets forth his entire message in the first lines; God's Word, the Bible, tells us that our faith in God is not misplaced. We have been assured, in the words of Moses to the children of Israel: "Be strong and of a good courage, fear not ... for the Lord thy God, he it is that doth go with thee; he will not fail thee, nor forsake thee" (Deut. 31:6).

This particular promise appears several times in scripture, in almost these same words. God first said it to Abraham (Gen. 28:15) and later to Moses (Deut. 31:8) and then to Joshua (Josh. 1:5). King David repeated the promise to his son Solomon (I Chron. 28:20). As the songwriter asks: What more can God say?

The second stanza is taken directly from Isaiah 41:10, "Fear thou not, for I am with thee: be not dismayed, for I am thy God; I will strengthen thee; yea, I will help thee; yea, I will uphold thee with the right hand of my righteousness."

[Read or sing stanzas 1 and 2.]

A stanza of "How Firm a Foundation" that is not always included in hymnals reads this way:

When through the deep water I call thee to go,
The rivers of sorrow shall not overflow;
For I will be with thee thy trials to bless,
And sanctify to thee thy deepest distress.

These words, and those of the third stanza included here, come from Isaiah 43:2, "When thou passest through the waters, I will be with thee; and through the rivers, they shall not overflow thee: when thou walkest through the fire, thou shalt not be burned; neither shall the flame kindle upon thee."

Some people have the mistaken notion that a Christian is somehow free from trouble and sorrow. A few of our gospel songs may seem to give that impression, in such phrases as "Every burden of my heart rolled away" or "Jesus took my burdens all away." What these songs mean to say is that the oppressive load of sin and guilt is gone when we know Christ personally as Saviour.

But the ordinary problems and tragedies that are a part of mortal existence do not bypass the believer. In fact, he may often seem to have even more than his share, for these trials perform a special function in his life. Paul said in Romans 5:3,4: "Tribulation (or pressures) worketh patience, and patience, experience; and experience, hope." Our song declares that God uses these difficult experiences to help us become full orbed Christians — with the "dross of our lives burned away, and the gold refined."

In the Billy Graham motion picture "For Pete's Sake," the young minister says to Pete, when his world seemed to come crashing down around him, "Christ has promised you nothing — nothing but Himself!" And that is enough! For He is with us in all the experiences of life, and that is what makes all the difference.
[Read or sing stanzas 3 and 4.]

A missionary, Fidelia Fisk, was in feeble health, with aching head and tired body, and very much discouraged. The woes of life pressed upon her like a great burden and she was about to sink beneath them. Seeing her depression, a native woman came and sat down behind her on the mat and whispered, "Lean on me." Miss Fisk, unheeding, still longed for assistance in bearing her burden. Presently came again the insistent "Lean on me." This time she leaned gently, but that did not satisfy her pleading friend. In most earnest tones the voice urged again, "If you love me, lean harder."

Everyone at times is weighed down with a particular load of trouble, disappointment or sorrow. To each of us, in times like these, the final stanza of our hymn says, "Lean hard on Jesus Christ."

O Beautiful for Spacious Skies

[*Crusader Hymns*, No. 283]

A Hymn Story by Billy Graham

[Read or sing stanza 1.]

O n a summer day in 1893 Katharine Lee Bates, renowned author and professor of English at Wellesley College, stood on Pike's Peak in Colorado. On three sides of her — north, west and south — stretched the majestic rocky mountains dressed in the purple haze which is common to the western United States. To the east was the fruitful Colorado plain, and just beyond the amber-colored grain fields of Kansas and Nebraska.

As she stood on the windy mountain top, Miss Bates imagined she could see the settlers who had trekked across those grasslands decades earlier to find new homes and new opportunities in the west. She remembered also the pilgrims who had first come to America's shores, expecting and finding a new life of freedom.

She thought as well of those who had laid down their lives for their country in the Revolutionary and Civil Wars, because they loved freedom and mercy more than life itself. This was her beloved country — America the Beautiful — beautiful in nature's gifts and in the dedication of those who had been part of its history.

As Katharine Bates returned to her hotel in Colorado Springs, a poem began to take shape in her mind and she began to put it on paper. She recalled also that, on her trip west, she had visited the Columbian Exposition on Chicago's south side. There an "alabaster city" of classic beauty had been erected to show what America's "cities of the future" should be like. She closed her hymn with a prayer that our cities may be as beautiful as the landscape God has prepared for them.

[Read or sing stanzas 2-4.]

Throughout the hymn, with all of her gratitude and admiration for America, Katharine Bates shows that she is very much aware of our weaknesses. During the last part of her life, she began to see the social reforms which gave us our child-labor laws, anti-trust legislation, nation-wide education and universal suffrage. And yet our country has much to desire!

Today we have the highest standard of living in the world — but also the highest crime rate, the highest rate of divorce, the highest rate of suicide. We spend far more each year for liquor, tobacco and gambling than we do for all the work of the church, both at home and abroad.

Sometimes we wonder why our forefathers were so slow to recognize the sin of slavery, yet we are even slower to help the negro emerge from the poverty, ignorance and degradation into which he was forced against his own will. We may point the finger of scorn at the monopolists of yesterday, but we too are bowing to the god of gold in our own day, and at the same time piling up a staggering national debt. It is sobering to learn that the site of the beautiful 1893 Columbian Exposition is now adjacent to one of our country's worst ghettos!

This great national hymn has occasionally been criticized. It is said that the bland prayer "God shed His grace on thee" fails to recognize our individual spiritual responsibility under God. However, I believe Katharine Bates remembered that the star of hope which led the first pilgrims was a desire to worship God and serve Him in freedom. In terms of material prosperity and personal freedom, no nation in history has been blessed more than our own. I believe that this is true because America was established as a "nation under God" — with Christian faith as the cornerstone of liberty.

Today our nation is threatened as never before — threatened by enemies without, but especially by decadence within. In our day, there seem to be many who believe that "freedom of worship" means freedom *from* worship. If we are to survive as a great country — if we are to achieve brotherhood, self-control and "liberty in law" — we must return to the faith on which America was founded. God will again shed His grace on America, if we will turn to Him in repentance.

Willis Haymaker, a friend and associate through much of my ministry, often uses a certain scripture passage in challenging a city to prepare for an evangelistic crusade. I believe it is appropriate for all America.

If my people, which are called by my name, shall humble themselves, and pray, and seek my face, and turn from their wicked ways; then will I hear from heaven, and will forgive their sin, and will heal their land (II Chron. 7:14).

O beautiful for spacious skies,
    For amber waves of grain,
For purple mountain majesties
    Above the fruited plain!
America! America!
    God shed His grace on thee,
And crown thy good with brotherhood
    From sea to shining sea!

O beautiful for pilgrim feet,
    Whose stern, impassioned stress
A thoroughfare for freedom beat
    Across the wilderness!
America! America!
    God mend thine every flaw,
Confirm thy soul in self-control,
    Thy liberty in law!

O beautiful for heroes proved
    In liberating strife,
Who more than self their country loved,
    And mercy more than life!
America! America!
    May God thy gold refine
Till all success be nobleness
    And every gain divine!

O beautiful for patriot dream
    That sees beyond the years
Thine alabaster cities gleam,
    Undimmed by human tears!
America! America!
    God shed His grace on thee,
And crown thy good with brotherhood
    From sea to shining sea!

Katharine Lee Bates (1859-1929)

Brightly beams our Father's mercy
From His lighthouse evermore,
But to us He gives the keeping
Of the lights along the shore.

Dark the night of sin has settled,
Loud the angry billows roar;
Eager eyes are watching, longing,
For the lights along the shore.

Trim your feeble lamp, my brother;
Some poor sailor tempest-tossed,
Trying now to make the harbor,
In the darkness may be lost.

Refrain:

Let the lower lights be burning!
Send a gleam across the wave!
Some poor fainting, struggling seaman
You may rescue, you may save.

Philip P. Bliss (1838-1876)

let the lower lights be burning

[*Crusader Hymns*, No. 233]

A Hymn Story by Billy Graham

O. L. Moody, the great evangelist of the last century, often told this story to illustrate each Christian's responsibility to point others to our Lord.

> On a dark, stormy night when the waves rolled like mountains and not a star could be seen, a large passenger boat cautiously edged toward the Cleveland harbor. The pilot knew that, in the inky darkness, he could only find the harbor channel by keeping two lower shore lights in line with the main beacon.
>
> "Are you sure this is Cleveland?" asked the captain, seeing only one light from the lighthouse.
>
> "Quite sure, sir," replied the pilot.
>
> "Where are the lower lights?" he asked.
>
> "Gone out, sir," was the reply.
>
> "Can you make the harbor?"
>
> "We must or perish, sir!"
>
> With a strong hand and a brave heart, the old pilot turned the wheel. But alas! In the darkness he missed the channel, the boat crashed on the rocks, and many lives were lost.

D. L. Moody's closing words were: "Brethren, the Master will take care of the great lighthouse; *let us keep the lower lights burning.*" Later, the story became a poem set to music, both written by Philip P. Bliss, the song evangelist who worked with Moody and also with Moody's friend, Major D. W. Whittle. This was the favorite hymn of the early-twentieth-century evangelist, Billy Sunday.

[Read or sing stanzas 1 and 2.]

Many people seem to believe that their lives and their witness do not count for much in God's kingdom. But every one of us contacts certain people every day — our neighbors, a friend in the shop or the office, the paper boy or the garbage collector — and for those particular persons, we may provide the only opportunity to hear a personal witness of the gospel. Unless we tell them, they will not hear!

Father Keller of the Christopher Society was once presiding at a large rally in the Coliseum at Los Angeles, California. Suddenly, at a prearranged signal, a switch was pulled and the entire stadium was plunged into darkness. Then Father Keller struck a small match and encouraged each of the 100,000 people present to do the same. In a moment the light from those tiny, flickering matches illuminated the entire amphitheatre. Our light of Christian witness may be small, but it does count, especially when it is added to that of other believers.

In explaining the imagery found in this gospel song, we might say that the great beam of the lighthouse represents the Bible, a Christian magazine, a gospel broadcast, or some outstanding preacher in a historic church pulpit. But each of us is a "lower light" whose gleam is needed to point lost souls to the safety of the harbor, Jesus Christ.

The last stanza of this hymn may not be immediately understood by today's younger generation. It refers to the kerosene lamps and lanterns which were common in Bliss's day and which were still being used in our house and barn when I was a boy on the farm. I remember that it was important that the wick be trimmed regularly — that all the charred part be removed — so that the lamp would burn brightly and evenly and not smoke up the protecting glass.

Each of us has only one light to give to the world. So it is important that we keep it burning brightly, and that all the charrings of sin and selfishness be taken away. This is the same spiritual experience that Jesus talked about in John 15:2: "Every branch that beareth fruit, he purgeth it, that it may bring forth more fruit." Trimming the wick — like pruning a vine — may be painful, especially to our pride, but it results in a brighter witness and a more fruitful life.

The light of the life of Philip Bliss — author of this hymn — burned brightly, but only for a few years. At the age of thirty-eight, while traveling to Chicago for an engagement at the Moody Tabernacle, both he and his wife were killed in a train accident. Yet, through the many hymns he wrote, his lamp of Christian influence still shines and lights the way to faith in God.

"Let your light so shine before men, that they may see your good works, and glorify your Father which is in heaven" (Matt. 5:16).
[Read or sing the last stanza.]

BE thou my vision

[*Crusader Hymns*, No. 147]

the hymn "Be Thou My Vision" is a prayer that we may accept Christ as our pattern, our hero, our ideal. Our adoration is told in these names and phrases: "Lord of my heart," "my best thought," "my Wisdom," "my true Word," "my great Father," "mine inheritance," "my Treasure," and finally "Heart of my own heart."

The original version of this hymn was written by an unknown Irish Christian in the eighth century. The tune is an Irish folk melody. Only in the last few years have both the words and the music become widely known and loved, especially among young people.
[Read or sing stanza 1.]

One of the phrases that is quoted most frequently in political rallies, in sales promotion meetings, and even in the pulpit, is taken from the wise sayings of Solomon: "Where there is no vision, the people perish" (Prov. 29:18).

Idealism is one of the normal, yet remarkable qualities of human personality. Most men and women dream of better things than they now experience. For some, the goal is a better job with more pay, so they might be able to buy what we call the "good things" of life. Others plan for a better education, in order that life might be enriched through service in one of the professions. A scientist envisions a world that is free of killing disease, and so devotes his life to research. An artist dreams of new expressions of beauty, and goes on to create them. Without an ideal, a dream, a vision, a man will not have the incentive to work and to discipline himself in order to achieve these better things. An anonymous author has written:

> A vision without a task is a dream;
> A task without a vision is drudgery;
> A vision and a task is the hope of the world.

Most of us know *individuals* whom we idolize — those whom we consciously or unconsciously revere and would like to imitate. This may be the cheap type of hero worship which surrounds our entertainment "stars;" actually, we are simply impressed because we think they are "famous" or "talented" or "rich." If we really *knew* them, we might discover that, despite their apparent success, they are quite unhappy people who are basically unsuccessful in achieving personal peace and poise. They would then rather quickly cease to be our "heroes." As Ralph Waldo Emerson said, "Every hero becomes a bore at last."

However, there is a valid and valuable type of hero-worship. Those of us who have loving and wise parents hold them up as ideals, even though as teenagers we may have seemed to be "sparring" with them. We give this sort of recognition to the teachers and coaches who have participated in our educational and physical growth. When we read the biographies of great men of other eras, or share their artistic and philosophical achievements, we often admire and seek to emulate them as well.

If our heroes are really worthy persons of great accomplishment and high ideals, hero worship is a good thing because *we become like the things or the people we idolize.* But, as someone has said, "No man is a hero to his valet." Whether we are thinking of parents, of teachers and pastors, or of the great men of the present or past, sooner or later we find something in their lives which spoils the "hero image," something we would not want to copy.

There is one hero whom it is safe to worship and to imitate in every aspect of personality and behavior; He is Jesus Christ. Men of every generation have echoed the judgment of Pilate, the Roman governor who sent Him to death — "I find no fault in him." Every outward action of Jesus' life reflected only perfect love, personal peace and mature, balanced personality. And, if we were able to read His mind, we would discover that every thought and motive was also perfect. Not only was He free from all evil; He also possessed every good thing.

We have recently heard a lot of discussion about whether or not the "Beatles" are more popular than Jesus, as one of their members insisted. Long after the "Beatles" are only vaguely remembered as one of the youthful entertainment groups in the 1960's, young men and women will still declare their allegiance to Christ. He is a worthy and a lasting hero!

[Read or sing stanzas 2-4.]

Be Thou my Vision, O Lord of my heart;
    Nought be all else to me, save that Thou art —
Thou my best thought, by day or by night,
    Waking or sleeping, Thy presence my light.

Be Thou my Wisdom, and Thou my true Word;
    I ever with Thee and Thou with me, Lord;
Thou my great Father, I Thy true son;
    Thou in me dwelling, and I with Thee one.

Riches I heed not, nor man's empty praise,
    Thou mine inheritance, now and always:
Thou and Thou only, first in my heart,
    High King of heaven, my Treasure Thou art.

High King of heaven, my victory won,
    May I reach heaven's joys, O bright heaven's Sun!
Heart of my own heart, whatever befall,
    Still be my Vision, O Ruler of all.

Ancient Irish
Trans. by Mary E. Byrne (1880-1931)
Versified by Eleanor H. Hull (1860-1935)

Words used by permission of Chatto and Windus, Ltd.

Have Thine own way, Lord! have Thine own way!
    Thou art the Potter; I am the clay.
Mold me and make me after Thy will,
    While I am waiting, yielded and still.

Have Thine own way, Lord! have Thine own way!
    Search me and try me, Master, today!
Whiter than snow, Lord, wash me just now,
    As in Thy presence humbly I bow.

Have Thine own way, Lord! have Thine own way!
    Wounded and weary, help me, I pray!
Power — all power — surely is Thine!
    Touch me and heal me, Saviour divine!

Have Thine own way, Lord! have Thine own way!
    Hold o'er my being absolute sway!
Fill with Thy Spirit till all shall see
    Christ only, always, living in me!

Adelaide A. Pollard (1862-1934)

have thine own way, lord

[*Crusader Hymns*, No. 154]

as she sat in a prayer meeting service early in this century, Adelaide Pollard was so depressed that she could hardly concentrate on what was being said. She had felt a heavy burden on her heart for the continent of Africa and was convinced that God wanted her to go as a missionary. She had been on the verge of preparing to sail, but now it was evident that the necessary funds could not be raised and her plans had to be canceled. Into her dark mood a few words filtered; it was part of the prayer of an old lady she knew: "It's all right, Lord! It doesn't matter what you bring into our lives; just have your own way with us!" Suddenly she found that her burden had lifted; in her own submission to the will of God she had found peace.

After returning home that evening, Miss Pollard meditated on the story of the potter, found in Jeremiah 18:3,4:

> Then I went down to the potter's house, and, behold, he wrought a work on the wheels.
>
> And the vessel that he made of clay was marred in the hand of the potter: so he made it again another vessel, as seemed good to the potter to make it.

The words seemed to describe the experiences of her own life. Born in Iowa in 1862, she had been well trained and for several years had taught in a girls' school. She was also a talented writer of both prose and poetry and produced many religious articles and some hymns. But her real interest was in evangelism, and soon she began a ministry of Bible teaching. Traveling widely throughout the United States, she spoke to numerous groups and churches.

Throughout her early life, Adelaide Pollard had a consuming interest in foreign missions. For a time, she taught at the Missionary Training Institute at Nyack, New York, hoping that she might herself serve as a missionary. And now it seemed that God, who had been molding her life all along, had suddenly deserted her. "But," she thought, "perhaps my questioning of God's will shows a flaw in my life, so God has decided to break me, as the potter broke the defective vessel, and then to mold my life again *in His own pattern.*"

The words of a poem took shape in her mind, even as her heart bowed in a new consecration — "Thou art the Potter, I am the clay. Mold me and make me after Thy will, While I am waiting, yielded and still."
[Read or sing stanza 1.]

As she continued to write, Miss Pollard acknowledged that the assertion of man's own will is the basic sin he commits before God. As unsaved men and women, we go our own way living as we please, assuming that God has no claim on us. And, even after we know Christ as Saviour, the sin which creeps into our lives is also centered in the ego — self-consciousness, self-centeredness, and self-will.

Sometimes we even sin while doing God's work, when we insist on doing it in our own way and according to our own time schedule. Perhaps this had happened in the planning of her trip to Africa, and in the frustration that arose when her plans fell through. And so, in contrition, she wrote again, "Search me and try me, Master, today! Whiter than snow, Lord, wash me just now, As in Thy presence humbly I bow."
[Read or sing stanzas 2 and 3.]

The life of selflessness which God desires is expressed in Paul's words, "I have been crucified with Christ: and I myself no longer live, but Christ lives in me" (Gal. 2:20, *Living Letters*). These words are the basis of the hymn's final stanza.
[Read or sing stanza 4.]

In God's own time He allowed Adelaide Pollard to minister in Africa. She also spent several years in England during the first World War, and then returned to her traveling ministry in America. She continued to speak publicly until she was 72 years of age when, on her way to yet another engagement, she was taken ill in a railroad station in New York City. Soon after, she died.

So ended the remarkable life of a frail, little woman who was so modest that her hymns were signed only by her initials. She had learned that God uses the person who will sincerely pray, "Have Thine Own Way, Lord."

to God Be the Glory

[*Crusader Hymns*, No. 3]

A Hymn Story by Cliff Barrows

If a hymn die, can it live again? The life-story of "To God Be the Glory" proves that the answer is "yes!" Originally composed in America sometime before 1875, it was almost immediately forgotten in its native land. In 1954, however, "To God Be the Glory" was rediscovered and acclaimed as a new favorite.

In Great Britain this same hymn never faded into oblivion as it did in the United States. I had heard it sung there in 1952 during one of our early visits. Later, it was suggested for inclusion in the songbook we were compiling for the London crusade of 1954. Because of its strong text of praise and its attractive melody, I agreed. We introduced the hymn during the early days of those meetings in Harringay Arena. As a result, Billy Graham asked that we repeat it often because he was impressed with the enthusiastic participation of the audience. In the closing weeks of the crusade it became our theme hymn, repeated almost every night. The words well expressed our praise to God, who was doing wondrous things in Britain.

Returning to America, we brought the hymn with us and used it first in the Nashville, Tennessee crusade of August, 1954. It was quickly adopted by many church groups and has recently been included in several new hymnals, including the *Baptist Hymnal* (Southern Baptist) and *Trinity Hymnal* (Orthodox Presbyterian).

Why "To God Be the Glory" was so late in achieving recognition in its homeland may always remain a mystery. It is not mentioned in the writings of either Fanny Crosby, author of the words, or W. H. Doane, composer of the music. Evidently the songleader Ira D. Sankey took it to Great Britain when he went there with evangelist D. L. Moody in 1873. Sankey included it in his *Sacred Songs and Solos,* a hymnbook first published in England in 1874 and still used today.

For some unknown reason, the song did not appear in the important *Gospel Hymns* series of books which Sankey published in America after his return from Britain in 1875. Through the years, "To God Be the Glory" *has* been included in several American hymnals. But until 1954, it failed to find its rightful place in the singing of our congregations.

Of all the songs that have been popularized through crusade activity, we are most happy about this one. Its testimony should rebound in the heart of every Christian; every area of a person's life should reflect this witness, "To God Be the Glory."

All men — Christian or non-Christian — try to find meaning in life. Modern existentialists, atheists and agnostics (and even a few who call themselves Christians) are trying to find this meaning *within man himself.* But the true answer to this quest is defined in the *Westminster Catechism:* "The chief end of man is to glorify God, and to enjoy Him forever." In other words, the reason for man's creation and the whole purpose of his living is to express praise of God, with his lips and with his life.

We give God glory because of His love, a love which provided redemption for mankind. The Apostle Paul exclaimed, "God forbid that I should glory, save in the cross of our Lord Jesus Christ" (Gal. 6:14). We bring nothing to our own salvation; it is all of God. Therefore we can take no credit for it. To God be the glory!

In another passage, Paul reminds us: "For ye are bought with a price: therefore glorify God in your body, and in your spirit, which are God's" (I Cor. 6:20). This is the Biblical answer to the seeking existentialist. Each day's experiences have ultimate meaning only if we acknowledge that we are God's, and that each act and each thought should glorify Him. To God be the glory!

Billy Graham often reminds us team members that this is especially true in the full-time Christian vocations. God has chosen to use *men* to spread His "good news," the gospel. Because we live in a Madison Avenue world of culture and communication, the names of preachers and evangelists are sometimes advertised widely. But we will be in serious trouble if we imagine that the crusade ministry is possible because of us or our talents. It is all of God, who has declared "My glory will I not give to another" (Isaiah 42:8). To God be the glory!

A challenge for each day of each Christian's life is found in Matthew 5:16: "Let your light so shine before men, that they may see your good works and glorify your Father which is in heaven." We should be thankful if others feel that we have been gracious and loving in our relations with them. But we dare not keep the praise for ourselves! It is God who enables us to be Christ-like. To God be the glory!

[Read or sing the entire hymn.]

To God be the glory, great things He hath done,
    So loved He the world that He gave us His Son,
Who yielded His life an atonement for sin,
    And opened the Lifegate that all may go in.

O perfect redemption, the purchase of blood,
    To every believer the promise of God;
The vilest offender who truly believes,
    That moment from Jesus a pardon receives.

Great things He hath taught us, great things He hath done,
    And great our rejoicing thro' Jesus the Son;
But purer, and higher, and greater will be
    Our wonder, our transport, when Jesus we see.

Refrain:

Praise the Lord, praise the Lord,
    Let the earth hear His voice!
Praise the Lord, praise the Lord,
    Let the people rejoice!
O come to the Father thro' Jesus the Son,
    And give Him the glory, great things He hath done.

Fanny J. Crosby (1820-1915)

For all the saints who from their labors rest,
    Who Thee by faith before the world confessed,
Thy name, O Jesus, be forever blest.
    Alleluia!

Thou wast their rock, their fortress and their might;
    Thou, Lord, their captain in the well-fought fight;
Thou, in the darkness drear, their one true light.
    Alleluia!

O blest communion, fellowship divine!
    We feebly struggle; they in glory shine.
Yet all are one in Thee, for all are Thine.
    Alleluia!

And when the strife is fierce, the warfare long,
    Steals on the ear the distant triumph song,
And hearts are brave again and arms are strong.
    Alleluia!

The golden evening brightens in the west;
    Soon, soon to faithful warriors cometh rest;
And sweet the calm of Paradise, the blest.
    Alleluia!

But lo! there breaks a yet more glorious day;
    The saints triumphant rise in bright array;
The King of Glory passes on His way.
    Alleluia!

From earth's wide bounds, from ocean's farthest coast,
    Thro' gates of pearl stream in the countless host,
Singing to Father, Son, and Holy Ghost.
    Alleluia!

William W. How (1823-1897)

fOR All the saints

[*Crusader Hymns*, No. 245]

A Hymn Story by Don Hustad

[Read or sing stanzas 1 and 2.]

Often in life, in order to avoid an error of one kind, we move so far in the other direction that we make an equally regrettable mistake. This principle may apply to our conception of sainthood. We are certainly right when we refuse to exalt departed Christians to such a degree that we would pray to them. However, we are wrong when we relegate God's men of the past to antiquity. We can learn much from them and should be thankful anew for the contributions that they have made. In our "forward-looking" twentieth century, we may be especially guilty of this error of neglect.

What then is the truth behind the phrase in the Apostles' creed, "I believe in the communion of saints"? Samuel J. Stone's hymn, "The Church's One Foundation," says that Christians today possess "mystic sweet communion with those whose rest is won." In the third stanza of Bishop How's memorial hymn "For All the Saints," it is expressed in these phrases: "O blest communion, fellowship divine! We feebly struggle; they in glory shine. Yet all are one in Thee, for all are Thine."

Some people insist that the citizens of heaven can observe what goes on in the world. But, can we be sure that bygone saints are sharing our specific problems and victories? As the hymn says, those in heaven are now resting from their labors. For them the struggle of life is over, and they now sing the song of triumph. Though we are all part of the Church — the body of Christ — ours is a mystic, a mysterious communion. Those who have died are the "church triumphant;" those of us who still live make up the "church militant."

The occupants of heaven must know that God is still working in the world through people like us, to further His kingdom. Certainly we can be encouraged by the examples and the wisdom they have left us from their earthly pilgrimage. This is the fellowship — the sharing — the communion of the saints — that the hymn is talking about.

The eleventh chapter of Hebrews has been called the "Westminster Abbey" of the scriptures. As many of the honored British dead are memorialized in that ancient church, so God's heroes are remembered in this chapter. When we review the lives of both Old Testament and New Testament saints, we are reminded over and over that God is faithful and all-powerful. He will be the final victor in the battle against evil.

There is another truth we should remember. Because God is faithful, Spirit-filled *men* can *also* be faithful and victorious, doing great things for God in spite of the temptations and persecutions which might beset them. As the writer infers in Hebrews 12:1, these saints are all witnesses to the power of the gospel. Because of their witness, we take fresh courage for the battle. Through their example, we are challenged to "lay aside every weight, and the sin which doth so easily beset us, and . . . run with patience the race that is set before us."

[Read or sing stanzas 3-5.]

Each of us will have a different group of "saints" to whom we give honor because of the contributions they have made to our lives. In addition to many of the Bible personalities, I have personally been challenged by the musicians and the hymnists who have given so much to the church. I owe a debt of gratitude to John of Damascus, Ambrose of Milan, Bernard of Clairvaux, Luther, Calvin, Sweelinck, Johann Walther, the Bach family, the Wesleys, Lowell Mason and many more.

The author of this hymn deserves to be noted for his contributions to God's work. William Walsham How, born into a wealthy Anglican family in 1823 and educated at Oxford, gave his entire life in sacrificial service to God. He was known as the "omnibus bishop" because he scorned the private coach he could afford, and rode public transportation alongside his poor parishioners in London's East End. How wrote about sixty hymns, of which twenty-five are still in use. Among them are the favorites "We Give Thee but Thine Own," "O Word of God Incarnate," and "O Jesus, Thou Art Standing."

In your prayers today, remember and thank God for the people, both living and dead, to whom you owe so much. In addition to my family heritage, I am grateful for the memory of preachers and Bible expositors who introduced me to Jesus Christ. Also influential in my life were others: a modest little piano teacher who encouraged me to begin practicing when I was four, a Primitive Methodist pastor who helped me go to college, and many music instructors who opened my mind and heart to the wonders of sound.

For whom do you give thanks to God?

[Read or sing stanzas 6 and 7.]

WhEREVER hE LEADS I'LL GO

[*Crusader Hymns*, No. 215]

A Hymn Story by Billy Graham

In January of 1936, the Southern Baptist songwriter B. B. McKinney was leading the music at the Alabama Sunday School Convention which was held that year in the town of Clanton. The featured speaker was the Reverend R. S. Jones, McKinney's friend of many years, who because of ill health had recently returned from missionary service in Brazil.

The two men were visiting over dinner one evening when Mr. Jones revealed to Dr. McKinney that his physicians would not allow him to return to South America. When asked about his future plans the missionary said, "I don't know, but wherever He leads I'll go." The words stuck in Dr. McKinney's mind, and before the convention's evening session began, he had written both the words and music of this song. At the close of Mr. Jones' message, Dr. McKinney related this story and sang "Wherever He Leads I'll Go" to the congregation. [Read or sing stanza 1.]

The opening words of the song, "Take up thy cross and follow me," contain one of Jesus' most penetrating challenges to his disciples — a statement so significant that it is found in each of the four gospels. Luke 9:23 states: "If any man will come after me, let him deny himself, and take up his cross daily, and follow me." In *The New English Bible* the same verse begins, "If anyone wishes to be a follower of mine, he must leave self behind." *Living Gospels* gives this paraphrase: "Anyone who wants to follow me must put aside his own desires and conveniences."

The original Greek New Testament has an even stronger inference than any of these. There the words used for "deny himself" can be translated "I don't even know that man!" This kind of selflessness is hard for most people to understand. Even when Christians understand it, performance is hard to achieve! Just how does this attitude manifest itself in everyday life?

A member of your church may be asked to teach a Sunday school class. Because of inborn timidity, his natural response is to refuse and even to believe that the refusal is a sign of humility. But, in the same situation, the dedicated Christian will accept the opportunity to serve, saying of himself, "Who is that shy and fearful 'self'? I don't know any such person!" This is "denying one's self" and it is a healthy attitude, psychologically and spiritually!

And what does it mean to "take up your cross?" Does this phrase suggest that the Christian should expect to carry heavy burdens? I believe it implies much more than that. The cross was an instrument of public execution. If Christ were speaking today, He would say, "Take up your gallows (or your electric chair) and follow me." The Apostle Paul explained this command when he said, "I have been crucified with Christ: and I myself no longer live, but Christ lives in me" (Gal. 2:20, *Living Letters*). It is our inner self-centeredness which dies when we yield to a higher will than our own. God's will replaces ours, and then Christ truly lives within us.

Living on this higher plane provides a new response to the situations of life. When a cruel and false accusation is made against us, our natural reaction is to fight back, to vindicate ourselves. If the story wasn't true, we feel justified in returning the insult. But to the person living on a Christ-centered level, the "self" who was criticized is dead — crucified. How can a dead "self" talk back?

The reality of the indwelling Christ is demonstrated by selflessness in all the important decisions of life. Such a dedication is what the hymn "Wherever He Leads I'll Go" is mostly all about. Of course, we may have a personal interest in one vocation or another or a preference to live in this location or that. But when we "follow Christ" we must ask ourselves, "What decision does He want me to make? Where does Christ want me to serve? And how?"

For some, it will be a glorious privilege to serve God as a pastor, a missionary, an evangelist, a teacher, or a church musician. This hymn is certainly a good one to sing when a challenge for missionary service is given. But don't forget that its inspiration came from a missionary who could not return to the field! Reverend Jones spent the rest of his life serving with the Southern Baptist Relief and Annuity Board.

Other Christians too will have the no-less-glorious honor of serving Christ as a homemaker, a doctor, a draftsman, or a farmer. In every instance, our life's work should be determined by God's call, not just our whims and desires. When this is true, even washing dishes becomes a sacrament, as proclaimed in the motto my wife has posted in her kitchen: "Divine services conducted here three times daily." [Read or sing stanzas 2-4.]

"Take up thy cross and follow me,"
   I heard my Master say;
"I gave my life to ransom thee,
   Surrender your all today."

He drew me closer to His side,
   I sought His will to know,
And in that will I now abide,
   Wherever He leads I'll go.

It may be through the shadows dim,
   Or o'er the stormy sea,
I take my cross and follow Him,
   Wherever He leadeth me.

My heart, my life, my all I bring
   To Christ who loves me so;
He is my Master, Lord, and King,
   Wherever He leads I'll go.

Refrain:

Wherever He leads I'll go,
   Wherever He leads I'll go,
I'll follow my Christ who loves me so,
   Wherever He leads I'll go.

B. B. McKinney (1886-1952)

Holy God, we praise Thy name;
    Lord of all, we bow before Thee;
All on earth Thy scepter claim,
    All in heav'n above adore Thee.
Infinite Thy vast domain,
    Everlasting is Thy reign.

Hark, the loud celestial hymn
    Angel choirs above are raising;
Cherubim and seraphim,
    In unceasing chorus praising,
Fill the heav'ns with sweet accord:
    Holy, holy, holy Lord.

Lo! the apostolic train
    Joins Thy sacred name to hallow;
Prophets swell the glad refrain,
    And the white-robed martyrs follow;
And, from morn to set of sun,
    Through the Church the song goes on.

Holy Father, Holy Son,
    Holy Spirit, Three we name Thee;
While in essence only One,
    Undivided God we claim Thee,
And adoring bend the knee,
    While we sing our praise to Thee.

From the *Te Deum*, 4th Century
German poem, 18th Century
Trans. by Clarence Walworth (1820-1900)

holy God, we praise thy name

[*Crusader Hymns*, No. 11]

One hymn that will always be used, whenever a crusade is conducted on the continent of Europe, is "Holy God, We Praise Thy Name." In Germany — and this is where, in the eighteenth century, the hymn as we know it first appeared — it begins "Grosser Gott, wir loben Dich." In France, it is "Grand Dieu, nous te benissons" and in Denmark, "Almagt Gud, velsignet vaer."

The original text is much older and is a part of the fourth century *Te Deum.* This ancient canticle has been called the "greatest of all non-scriptural hymns in Latin," and is sung around the world in some form and some language by most Christians. In the Anglican communion, for instance, it is used each Sunday in the service of Morning Prayer.

Through the years there has been a great deal of conjecture as to the authorship of this historic poem. One old legend maintained that it was improvised responsively by St. Ambrose and St. Augustine, when the latter was baptized. Others have credited it to Hilary of Gaul (the first known Latin hymnist) or to Charlemagne the Great. Scholars today believe that it is probably the work of a missionary-bishop, Niceta, whose field was Remesiana in Dacia, which is now part of Jugoslavia. In his writings, St. Jerome gives Niceta credit for spreading the gospel among the fourth century European barbarians, and refers to his method as by "sweet songs of the cross."

The entire *Te Deum* is a very long hymn of praise in three parts. The stanza-version, "Holy God, We Praise Thy Name," is taken from the first phrases, which appear this way in English prose:

We praise thee, O God; we acknowledge thee to be the Lord. All the earth doth worship thee, the Father everlasting. To thee all angels cry aloud; the heavens and all the powers therein; To thee cherubim and seraphim continually do cry, "Holy, holy, holy, Lord God of Sabaoth; heaven and earth are full of the majesty of thy glory."

The glorious company of the apostles praise thee. The goodly fellowship of the prophets praise thee. The noble army of martyrs praise thee. The holy church throughout all the world doth acknowledge thee; the Father of an infinite majesty; thine adorable, true and only Son; also the Holy Ghost, the Comforter.

The enduring quality and extensive use of this hymn must be representative of mankind's deepest need — to express a relationship with God. Otherwise, why should Christians speak or sing their worship of God at all? The response to this question as posed in a typical Sunday school class or in family devotions would be, "We praise God because of what He has done for us." Such a response to God's providence is certainly a good reason for worship, but is it the highest incentive?

The word "worship" is of Anglo-Saxon origin. It was once spelled "woerth-scipe" and meant "to ascribe worth." Here then is the purest and most basic motive for worship: of all the beings and objects in the universe, God alone is *worthy* of our praise. He is worthy, first of all, because of *what He is* — perfectly holy, all-knowing, all-powerful, never-changing and everywhere present.

It is not a sign of irreverence or unbelief to say that God is also inscrutable; we can never know or understand Him completely. He has said, "As the heavens are higher than the earth, so are my ways higher than your ways, and my thoughts than your thoughts" (Isaiah 55:9).

What God has done stems from *what He is;* to praise Him for His works as well as His character is certainly proper. He is the Creator, Sustainer and Redeemer of the universe. He is our Heavenly Father, and is concerned about our great need of salvation and our smaller needs of comfort, guidance, protection and material necessities.

The angels in heaven have never experienced God's love as we do, yet they worship Him continually. How much more praise we have to render to God in proportion, yet how inadequate our response may be! As you read or sing the stanzas of this hymn, and as you carry on your activities today, remember the attributes of the God who dwells about you and within you. Praise Him for what He has done for others and for you. Praise Him also just because He is worthy to be praised!

[Read or sing the entire hymn.]

104

WE LIFT OUR VOICE REJOICING

[*Crusader Hymns*, No. 14]

A Hymn Story by Cliff Barrows

[Read or sing stanza 1.]

"**O** sing unto the Lord a new song" is a challenge often repeated in the scriptures. This means that we should not be satisfied with yesterday's Christian experiences. Each new day should bring a better understanding of God and a growing relationship with Christ. And our daily spiritual victories should be expressed in fresh words of testimony and prayer, and also in new songs of faith and worship.

To encourage the writing and singing of new hymns, in 1961 the Billy Graham Evangelistic Association conducted a "new hymn contest" together with the National Church Music Fellowship. The winning title chosen from over 900 entries was "We Lift Our Voice Rejoicing" written by the Reverend Jack W. Hayford, a youth leader and later dean of students at L.I.F.E. Bible College in Los Angeles, California. The following is Mr. Hayford's own story of how his song was written:

> We had just concluded a conference held in the splendor of the autumn-spangled hills near Estes Park, Colorado, in 1960. The grand old hymn "To God Be the Glory" had themed the series there, and returning to Los Angeles I would hum that melody and nostalgically meditate on the beauty and blessing found during those days in the Rockies. Yet as excellent as that praiseful song is, something within me yearned to give vent to a *personal* expression of worship.

> One evening, as I left the office for home, the song came to me. Completely without labored premeditation, sparked by a glimpse of the clear, wind-driven sky which served as a backdrop to a single tree being stripped of its leaves, the words poured forth, together with the melody of the first two lines: "We lift our voice, rejoicing, because the Lord above hath sent His Son to save us and manifest His love." I turned the corner, and was confronted by the mountains north of the city. Walking briskly I added the next words: "Let every hill re-echo to this the song we raise;" then the words of the ransomed multitude in Revelation, chapter five, came to mind — "To Him whose blood hath brought us be glory, power and praise."

> It was as though the autumn atmosphere had served as a catalyst to unleash the joy of the Lord in my soul. God's own natural creation provided the setting, and His new creative work in me produced the song. Arriving home I went immediately to my study, and within minutes the hymn was completed. The overflow of my heart was on the paper before me.

A rich satisfaction came as I completed the song. It was the fulfillment sensed when you are able to express the emotion of a given moment; in this case, a moment when my heart thrilled at the wonder of God's creative power and the grandeur of His saving grace. For my part, at least, the hymn became a means by which I could sing to myself the praise of the living God.

Many Christians share in similar moments of spiritual exaltation when their whole being is in harmony with God the Creator. Few there are, however, that are able to capture the sensitivity of such an experience in song or the written word. Perhaps the expression of our own hymn of praise in a uniquely personal manner is limited to private devotions.

On the other hand, some Christians may develop their techniques in the use of language and melody to the point where God can use them extensively. Such a person is the author of this hymn, Jack Hayford. He recalls the time when he heard the late Phil Kerr tell the stories of famous hymns and their writers. Then fourteen years old, Hayford thought: "How wonderful! Though these men and women have long since died, their ministry still continues. How I would love to write something that would outlive me, that would be sung throughout the world by the people of God." Mr. Hayford's desire has been granted through the several fine songs that he has written.

Whether we write a hymn or simply join God's people in singing it, our lives and our lips should bring a new "offering of praise" to our Lord each day.

[Read or sing stanzas 2 and 3.]

We lift our voice rejoicing,
　　Because the Lord above
Hath sent His Son to save us,
　　And manifest His love.
Let every hill re-echo
　　With this the song we raise,
"To Him whose blood hath bought us
　　Be glory, pow'r and praise."

We lift our eyes in faith to
　　The cross whereon He died,
Redeemed at matchless price, now
　　In Christ we're justified.
His blood hath washed our garments,
　　His peace hath filled our souls,
The cross is now our glory
　　Since grace hath made us whole.

We lift our hearts to worship
　　The conquering Saviour's name,
Our tongues speak forth the praises
　　Of Him who is the same.
Christ Jesus reigns in power
　　Throughout eternity.
As yesterday, so now, and
　　Forever He shall be.

Refrain:

We praise Thee, O Father,
　　Unspeakable our joy,
In Christ our hearts find glory
　　Sin's pow'r can not destroy.

Jack W. Hayford (b. 1934)

Come, Thou Almighty King,
Help us Thy name to sing,
Help us to praise:
Father, all glorious,
O'er all victorious,
Come, and reign over us,
Ancient of Days.

Come, Thou Incarnate Word,
Gird on Thy mighty sword,
Our prayer attend:
Come, and Thy people bless,
And give Thy word success:
Spirit of holiness,
On us descend.

Come, Holy Comforter,
Thy sacred witness bear
In this glad hour:
Thou who almighty art,
Now rule in every heart,
And ne'er from us depart,
Spirit of power.

To the great One in Three
Eternal praises be
Hence, evermore!
His sovereign majesty
May we in glory see,
And to eternity
Love and adore!

Source Unknown

come, thou almighty king

[*Crusader Hymns*, No. 28]

"**C**ome, Thou Almighty King" is a hymn for which we have little or no background. Although it is one of the best known English hymns, we do not even know who wrote it. The text first appeared in a little pamphlet in 1757, together with a hymn by Charles Wesley. It too may be a Wesley hymn, but no hymnologist has ever claimed that it is.

The rhythm and meter of this hymn are most unusual; in fact, only one other hymn — "God save our gracious king," the British national anthem — uses it, and *that* melody was first used for *these* words. "God Save the King" had appeared about fifteen years earlier, and it seems as if "Come, Thou Almighty King" may have been conceived as a sequel to it. One hymn is a prayer for an earthly ruler; the other is a prayer to a heavenly King.

Some churchgoers who sing these words frequently may not have noticed that this is a Trinity hymn. Each of the first three stanzas is addressed to a different member of the God-head, and the last stanza to "the great One in Three." The first verse speaks to God the Father, our Almighty King, and is a prayer that He will help us to sing His praise. The last phrase mentions a name of God which is given in Daniel 7:22. "Ancient of Days" speaks of God's eternity, his timelessness. He has always existed and He will always exist.
[Read or sing stanza 1.]

The second stanza, addressed to God the Son, reminds us of the opening words of John's gospel: "In the beginning was the Word, and the Word was with God, and the Word was God." Here is a prayer to Jesus Christ who is God incarnate, God in the flesh. In Revelation 19, John's vision of Christ, we read that "his name is called The Word of God" (verse 13) and that "out of his mouth goeth a sharp sword, that with it he should smite the nations" (verse 15). Yes, Christ came the first time to be our Redeemer; He will come again to be our Judge.
[Read or sing stanza 2.]

If any songleader is tempted to omit the third stanza when singing this hymn, we would remind him not to slight the third person of the Trinity. For this is a prayer to God the Holy Spirit, the "Holy Comforter." The name here actually means "Paraclete" (Advocate or

Lawyer) because the Holy Spirit represents Jesus Christ, now that the Son has returned to His Father in heaven. One of these lines reminds us that it is the Holy Spirit who "beareth witness with our Spirit, that we are the children of God." Another phrase declares that, although God's Spirit is almighty, He can only rule our hearts when we allow Him to do so.

[Read or sing stanza 3.]

The truth of the Trinity, that God is One yet Three or "One in Three," cannot fully be understood. Many scholars have tried to probe its mystery and to express it in words. One of them, a certain Joseph Dare, has said: "Steam is water, and ice is water, and water is water; these three are one."

John Wesley once said: "Tell me how it is that in this room there are three candles and but one light, and I will explain to you the mode of the divine existence."

The late A. W. Tozer has written:

Some persons who reject all they cannot explain have denied that God is a Trinity. Subjecting the Most High to their cold, level-eyed scrutiny, they conclude that it is impossible that He could be both One and Three. These forget that their whole life is enshrouded in mystery. They fail to consider that any real explanation of even the simplest phenomenon in nature lies hidden in obscurity and can no more be explained than can the mystery of the Godhead . . .

The doctrine of the Trinity . . . is truth for the heart. The fact that it cannot be satisfactorily explained, instead of being against it, is in its favor. Such a truth had to be revealed; no one could have imagined it. (*The Knowledge of The Holy,* Harper and Row, 1961; pp. 25, 31. Used by permission.)

[Read or sing stanza 4.]

tRuSt anò OBEY

[*Crusader Hymns*, No. 181]

A Hymn Story by Cliff Barrows

I first learned to know the great songs of the church as a boy in Sunday school in Ceres, California. Sometime later I was drafted to be the third member of a family trio, singing with my two younger sisters. It seemed to me then that we were too often called upon to perform — at church services, youth rallies and camps, and even at weddings and funerals!

Consequently, as a growing boy, I must admit that hymn-singing was occasionally more pain than pleasure. But in later life, the hymnbook became one of my most important resources for personal worship. Today, I am thankful that I was required to memorize so many hymns at an early age. They will probably never leave my subconscious.

One of my longtime favorites, which is always included in crusade songbooks, is "Trust and Obey." The music for this song was composed by D. B. Towner, the first director of music at Moody Bible Institute in Chicago. The inspiration for the hymn's writing came in 1886 during an occasion when Towner was leading singing for D. L. Moody in Brockton, Massachusetts. In a testimony service which took place, he heard a young man say, "I am not quite sure — but I am going to trust, and I am going to obey."

Towner jotted down the words and sent them to his friend J. H. Sammis, a Presbyterian minister, who developed the idea into a full hymn. The refrain came first — it is a capsule version of the entire song — and the verses later.

[Read or sing stanzas 1 and 2.]

The song emphasizes the two aspects of being a Christian — faith and good works. And it places them in proper order! We come to Christ without any plea "but that He has shed His blood" for us. "For it is by His grace you are saved, through trusting Him; it is not your own doing" (Eph. 2:8, *New English Bible*).

But *after* we trust in Christ, our faith must be translated into action. Because God loves us and we love Him, we seek to obey Him, and to do His will in every realm of our lives. As James asks, "What use is it for a man to say he has faith when he does nothing to show it?" (James 2:14, *NEB*).

I am afraid that some Christians are tempted to think negatively about a commitment of obedience to God. To submit to the commands "to die to self" and "to present your body a living sacrifice" sounds like such a painful thing.

But the truth is clearly stated in this hymn. "We never can prove (experience) the delights of His love, until all on the altar we lay. There's no other way to be happy . . . but to trust and obey." Do we imagine that God who loves us so much would wish us anything less than that which brings us complete fulfillment in life? We can trust God to manage our affairs better than we can ourselves.

D. L. Moody said on one occasion: "The blood (of Christ) alone makes us safe. The Word (of God) alone makes us sure. Obedience (to God) makes us happy." What a formula for a poised and successful life! The death and resurrection of Christ provides a full and free salvation. God's Word assures us that it is settled for all eternity. And allowing God to order our lives each day insures complete serenity and happiness.

Somehow I always associate the message of "Trust and Obey" with Dawson Trotman of the *Navigators*, who worked with us for several years before his untimely death.

"Daws" often brought a message on the TNT of Christian service — "Trust 'n Tackle." The "trust" in this motto implies a complete, child-like confidence in our Heavenly Father, and an obedience to Him in all of life's activities. Then we can be assured of God's strength bolstering us to tackle any challenge that may appear. God will see us through!

[Read or sing stanzas 3 and 4.]

When we walk with the Lord
   In the light of His Word,
What a glory He sheds on our way,
   While we do His good will
He abides with us still,
   And with all who will trust and obey.

Not a shadow can rise,
   Not a cloud in the skies,
But His smile quickly drives it away;
   Not a doubt nor a fear,
Not a sigh nor a tear,
   Can abide while we trust and obey.

But we never can prove
   The delights of His love
Until all on the altar we lay;
   For the favor He shows,
And the joy He bestows,
   Are for them who will trust and obey.

Then in fellowship sweet
   We will sit at His feet,
Or we'll walk by His side in the way;
   What He says we will do,
Where He sends we will go —
   Never fear, only trust and obey.

Refrain:

Trust and obey,
   For there's no other way
To be happy in Jesus,
   But to trust and obey.

John H. Sammis (1846-1919)

Children of the heavenly Father
    Safely in His bosom gather;
Nestling bird nor star in heaven
    Such a refuge e'er was given.

God His own doth tend and nourish,
    In His holy courts they flourish;
Like a father kind He spares them,
    In His loving arms He bears them.

Neither life nor death can ever
    From the Lord His children sever;
For His love and deep compassion
    Comforts them in tribulation.

What He takes or what He gives us
    Shows the Father's love so precious;
We may trust His purpose wholly —
    'Tis His children's welfare solely.

Carolina V. (Sandell) Berg (1832-1903)

chilòRen of the heavenly father

[*Crusader Hymns*, No. 189]

A Hymn Story by Don Hustad

Throughout the history of the Christian church, most hymnwriters were men: pastors, theologians, monks, bishops and missionaries. But in the nineteenth century, women began to make important contributions to our hymnals. In Great Britain, there were Cecil Frances Alexander and Frances Ridley Havergal; in America, Harriet Beecher Stowe and Fanny J. Crosby; and in Sweden, Lina Sandell, the author of "Children of the Heavenly Father."

Her full name was actually Carolina Vilhelmina Sandell, and she was born in a Lutheran parsonage in 1832. In childhood she was probably known as "daddy's girl." She was not strong physically, and often stayed in her father's study while her classmates were playing outdoors.

Lina's poetic gift showed itself at a very early age. When she was just thirteen her first book of poems was published. This little volume contained some of her best-loved songs. During her lifetime she wrote 650 hymns in all, and 150 of these have been used by the church. "Children of the Heavenly Father" is perhaps the best known. When we took a choir on tour in Scandinavia a few years ago, our singers painstakingly learned the phonetic sounds so we could sing it in Swedish, "Tryggare kan ingen vara."

It does not take long to see that the hymn's basic message is about God's relationship as a Father to us, His children. Many of these phrases are taken almost word-for-word from the Bible. See if you can identify them as you sing the hymn or read the poem.
[Read or sing the entire hymn.]

The Bible tells us: "Not one sparrow (What do they cost? Two for a penny?) can fall to the ground without your Father knowing it" (Matt. 10:29, *Living Gospels*). Scientists tell us that it is impossible to see all the stars in our universe, even with their most powerful telescopes. Yet Psalm 147:4 says that our heavenly Father "telleth the number of the stars: he calleth them all by their names." And God cares more for us than he does for stars and sparrows!

Perhaps the hymn reminded you of these scripture passages as well:

> He shall feed his flock like a shepherd: he shall gather the lambs with his arm, and carry them in his bosom, and shall gently lead those that are with young (Isa. 40:11).
>
> For I am persuaded, that neither death, nor life, nor angels, nor principalities, nor powers, nor things present, nor things to come, nor height, nor depth, nor any other creature, shall be able to separate us from the love of God, which is in Christ Jesus our Lord (Rom. 8:38, 39).
>
> The Lord gave and the Lord hath taken away; blessed be the name of the Lord (Job 1:21).

These stanzas come directly out of the personal experience of Lina Sandell. When she was twenty-six, while taking a boat trip with her father, he fell overboard and she saw him drown. When she lost her earthly father, she learned even more personally the extent of the heavenly Father's love and care.

Recently some theologians have said that we should not think and talk so much of God as a father—that we should grow up and stand on our own two feet, instead of running to God every time we're in a little trouble.

Yet Jesus said in Luke 18:17, "Whosoever shall not receive the kingdom of God as a little child shall in no wise enter therein." And throughout life, as mature men and women, we should remain not childish, but child-like, in our faith and trust, as well as in our obedience to God.

If we do, we can say with confidence: "We know that all that happens to us is working for our good if we love God, and if we are fitting into His plans" (Rom. 8:28, *Living Letters*).

I SURRENDER ALL

[*Crusader Hymns*, No. 177]

A Hymn Story by Billy Graham

One of the evangelists who influenced my early preaching was also a hymnist who wrote "I Surrender All" — the Rev. Mr. J. W. Van De Venter. He was a regular visitor at the Florida Bible Institute (now Trinity Bible College) in the late 1930's. We students loved this kind, deeply spiritual gentleman and often gathered in his winter home at Tampa, Florida, for an evening of fellowship and singing.

Mr. Van De Venter was not always a minister. According to his own testimony, his first interest and passion was for art. Having finished college, he taught school for a while in order to finance his continued study of drawing and painting. Later he became supervisor of art in the public schools of Sharon, Pennsylvania.

At that time, evangelistic meetings were being held in his church and Van De Venter became involved in counseling and personal work. Since he had obvious ability in this direction, several of his friends urged him to give up teaching and become an evangelist. For five years he wavered between this challenge and his ambition to become a recognized artist.

As he told the story himself:

> At last the pivotal hour of my life came and I surrendered all. A new day was ushered into my life. I became an evangelist and discovered down deep in my soul a talent hitherto unknown to me. God had hidden a song in my heart, and touching a tender chord He caused me to sing songs I had never sung before.

The hymn "I Surrender All" was written some time later in his life, when J. W. Van De Venter recalled this long struggle and final yielding to God's will.

[Read or sing stanzas 1 and 2.]

We begin to surrender to God when we first accept Jesus Christ as Saviour and Lord. The word "Lord" means just that — "Master." At the close of a crusade meeting I ask those who come forward to pray, using these words: "I receive Christ as Saviour; I accept Him as Lord." It is a mistake to think that we can receive Christ's offer of forgiveness and then go out to live our lives as we please. From that moment of commitment, God has a claim on us and we must expect Him to tell us how we should live.

Often this truth comes to an individual in a more forceful way, a little later in his Christian life and walk. A young person may be considering whom he should marry, or what profession he should pursue. A man may be contemplating a new business relationship. A woman may be weighing her obligations to the church, to the community, to her home. Suddenly the true meaning of what the Bible says dawns on them: "Your body is the home of the Holy Spirit God gave you, and . . . He lives within you. Your own body does not belong to you, for God has bought you with a great price. So use every part of your body to give glory back to God, because He owns it" (I Cor. 6:19,20, *Living Letters*).

We should never fear to give God complete control over our lives. He loves us more than we love ourselves, and He will only plan what is best for us. It isn't always true, as it was with Reverend Van De Venter, that God takes us down a different path from that which we would naturally follow. But if He does, we may be sure that it will be a happier and more fruitful life than the one we would have planned for ourselves.

Nor is it true that a person who yields up his own will becomes a weakling — a "mamby-pamby Milquetoast." Just the opposite is true. When we surrender our all to God, we find that we live with a new confidence, a new strength of purpose. No longer do we worry about the decisions we make, for now God is making them; from here on, He is responsible for the outcome. Furthermore, we find that He gives us His own supernatural strength to meet the challenge of each day!

[Read or sing stanzas 3 and 4.]

All to Jesus I surrender,
    All to Him I freely give;
I will ever love and trust Him,
    In His presence daily live.

All to Jesus I surrender,
    Humbly at His feet I bow,
Worldly pleasures all forsaken,
    Take me, Jesus, take me now.

All to Jesus I surrender,
    Make me, Saviour, wholly Thine;
Let me feel the Holy Spirit,
    Truly know that Thou art mine.

All to Jesus I surrender,
    Lord, I give myself to Thee;
Fill me with Thy love and power,
    Let Thy blessing fall on me.

Refrain:

I surrender all,
    I surrender all.
All to Thee, my blessed Saviour,
    I surrender all.

Judson W. Van De Venter (1855-1939)

We praise Thee, O God,
  For the Son of Thy love,
For Jesus who died
  And is now gone above.

We praise Thee, O God,
  For Thy Spirit of light,
Who has shown us our Saviour
  And scattered our night.

All glory and praise
  To the Lamb that was slain,
Who has borne all our sins,
  And has cleansed every stain.

Revive us again,
  Fill each heart with Thy love;
May each soul be rekindled
  With fire from above.

Refrain:

Hallelujah! Thine the glory,
  Hallelujah! Amen;
Hallelujah! Thine the glory,
  Revive us again.

William P. Mackay (1839-1885)

REVIVE US AGAIN

[*Crusader Hymns*, No. 156]

A Hymn Story by Cliff Barrows

"**R**evive Us Again" is a gospel song that we have used in almost every evangelistic crusade since 1946. When we sing it, we often revert to the ancient practice of *antiphony* which was common in the performance of the Hebrew psalms. In the refrain, the audience on one side of the auditorium or stadium will sing "Hallelujah!" and those on the other side will echo "Thine the glory," and so on until the final phrase "Revive us again," which we sing in unison.

There are technical problems, of course! Because of the size of the congregations and the relatively slow speed at which sound travels, it is sometimes difficult to stay together. Nevertheless, even without the help of organ and piano, it is a thrilling experience of praise in song.

Sometimes we have sung the hymn responsively over long distances. In our final meeting in Sydney, Australia in 1959, the first phrase was sung by 80,000 people in the Royal Agriculture Society's Showground. They were answered by 70,000 people in the Cricket Ground, almost two blocks away. In 1955, by use of a telephone line relay, the folk in Bangor, North Wales responded to the audience in Glasgow, Scotland.

A critic of hymns might point out that the text of this poem is a bit incongruous. It first appeared in 1875 under the scripture verse, "O Lord, revive Thy work" (Hab. 3:2). The reader's initial reaction is that it is a prayer for spiritual revival among God's people. Nevertheless, the first three stanzas consist entirely of praising God. Only the last stanza seems to conform to the thought of the title, and is a prayer that the Church and each Christian in it might be renewed in faith and spiritual vigor. In the same way, the refrain echoes its paeans of praise over and over, and at the end — almost as an afterthought — there is the prayer "Revive us again."

We can be sure, however, that the author, William P. Mackay (a physician who became a Scottish Presbyterian minister), knew what he was doing. There is deep spiritual insight shown here, and we are reminded of the experience of the Israelites during the reign of Jehoshaphat (ca. 896 B.C.)

God's chosen people were being threatened by the Moabites and the Ammonites, and they were very much afraid. A word of encouragement was brought to King Jehoshaphat by Jahaziel, one of the musicians in the temple:

> Thus saith the Lord unto you, Be not afraid nor dismayed by reason of this great multitude; for this battle is not yours, but God's . . . Ye shall not need to fight in this battle: set yourselves, stand ye still, and see the salvation of the Lord with you (II Chron. 20:15), 17).

The story goes on:

> And when he (Jehoshaphat) had consulted with the people, he appointed singers unto the Lord, and that should praise the beauty of holiness, as they went out before the army, and to say, Praise the Lord; for his mercy endureth forever.
>
> And when they began to sing and to praise, the Lord set ambushments against the children of Ammon, Moab, and mount Seir, which were come against Judah; and they were smitten (II Chron. 20:21, 22).

The enemies of our souls are many, and we are often painfully aware of them — our own innate weaknesses, the world of allurements around us, and the Devil, who appears sometimes as a "roaring lion" and sometimes as an "angel of light." Our potential for victory against these foes will not be found within ourselves; it is not even the result of our own holy desires. The source of our victory is found in God, and our resources are His own divine holiness and power.

When we are properly conscious of God's attributes — as well as of our own weakness and vulnerability — and when we give Him glory, then His strength works through us. If you face a particularly heavy burden or a strong temptation today, lay it aside and sing a song of praise to God. "Revive Us Again" would be a good choice!

[Read or sing the entire hymn.]

now thank we all our god

[*Crusader Hymns*, No. 256]

[Read or sing stanza 1.]

Many of our Christian songs have been forged in the heat of dramatic and moving experience. One reason for publishing *Crusade Hymn Stories* is the conviction that, if we know the circumstances connected with a hymn's writing, we may better understand its message.

On the other hand, the text of a hymn itself may give us an inkling about the life and work of its writer. For instance, the chorale "A Mighty Fortress" reveals the cataclysmic struggle between God and satanic powers, which parallels Martin Luther's crusade against the entrenched and decadent ecclesiastics of the 16th century. Another hymn like Rinkart's "Now Thank We All Our God" may seem to have little connection with the period and the situation in which it was produced. Investigation into its history turns up amazing facts.

Martin Rinkart was a pastor at Eilenberg, Saxony during the Thirty Years' War (1618-1648). Because Eilenberg was a walled city, it became a severely overcrowded refuge for political and military fugitives from far and near. As a result, the entire city suffered from famine and disease. In 1637 a great pestilence swept through the area, resulting in the death of some eight thousand persons, including Rinkart's wife. At that time he was the only minister in Eilenberg because the others had either died or fled. Rinkart alone conducted the burial services for 4480 people, sometimes as many as 40 or 50 a day!

During the closing years of the war, Eilenberg was overrun or besieged three times, once by the Austrian army and twice by the Swedes. On one occasion, the Swedish general demanded that the townspeople make a payment of 30,000 thalers. Martin Rinkart served as intermediary, pleading that the impoverished city could not meet such a levy; however, his request was disregarded. Turning to his companions the pastor said, "Come, my children, we can find no mercy with man; let us take refuge with God." On his knees he led them in a fervent prayer and in the singing of a familiar hymn, "When in the hour of utmost need." The Swedish commander was so moved that he reduced the levy to 1350 thalers.

We may well ask why all this dramatic experience and difficulty is not reflected in Rinkart's hymn. Had the good pastor seen so much stark tragedy that he had become insensitive to human needs and problems? Of course not. He simply had come to believe that God's providence is always good, no matter how much we are tempted to doubt it.

One of the Christian's favorite, often-quoted Bible verses is Romans 8:28 *(Living Letters)*: "And we know that all that happens to us is working for our good if we love God, and if we are fitting into His plans." Do we really believe this assurance? In our testimonies and prayers, and even in some of the songs we sing, we seem to enjoy talking about our little troubles and difficulties, multiplying and magnifying them. We almost sound at times like "spiritual hypochondriacs!"

Actually, there is some hint of trouble in Rinkart's hymn. In the second stanza he asks that God will "guide us when perplexed, and free us from all ills." But the overwhelming atmosphere of the hymn breathes utter confidence in God, regardless of consequences. In fact, the last stanza is his own version of the *Gloria Patri* which many congregations sing every Sunday:

> Glory be to the Father,
> And to the Son, and to the Holy Ghost!
> As it was in the beginning, is now and ever shall be,
> World without end. Amen!

[Read or sing stanzas 2 and 3.]

In the nuclear world of tomorrow, it is entirely possible that we may experience great difficulty, persecution, and even war and death. Christians should prepare themselves and their families for this possibility, so that if and when it comes, we might face it in spiritual victory, giving testimony that ours is a faith that works. It may help us to know Martin Rinkart's experience and his hymn, which confirms these words of the Apostle Paul:

> What can separate us from the love of Christ? Can affliction or hardship? Can persecution, hunger, nakedness, peril, or the sword? "We are being done to death for thy sake all day long," as Scripture says; "we have been treated like sheep for slaughter" — and yet, in spite of all, overwhelming victory is ours through him who loved us. For I am convinced that there is nothing in death or life, in the realm of spirits or superhuman powers, in the world as it is or the world as it shall be, in the forces of the universe, in heights or depths — nothing in all creation that can separate us from the love of God in Christ Jesus our Lord (Rom. 8:35-39, *New English Bible*).

Now thank we all our God
With heart and hands and voices,
Who wondrous things hath done,
In whom His world rejoices;
Who, from our mother's arms,
Hath blessed us on our way
With countless gifts of love,
And still is ours today.

O may this bounteous God
Through all our life be near us,
With ever joyful hearts
And blessed peace to cheer us;
And keep us in His grace,
And guide us when perplexed,
And free us from all ills
In this world and the next.

All praise and thanks to God
The Father now be given,
The Son, and Him who reigns
With them in highest heaven,
The one eternal God,
Whom earth and heaven adore;
For thus it was, is now,
And shall be evermore.

Martin Rinkart (1586-1649)
Tr. by Catherine Winkworth (1827-1878)

I have a song that Jesus gave me,
 It was sent from heaven above;
There never was a sweeter melody,
 'Tis a melody of love.

I love the Christ who died on Calvary,
 For He washed my sins away;
He put within my heart a melody,
 And I know it's there to stay.

'Twill be my endless theme in glory,
 With the angels I will sing;
'Twill be a song with glorious harmony,
 When the courts of heaven ring.

Refrain:

In my heart there rings a melody,
 There rings a melody with heaven's harmony;
In my heart there rings a melody;
 There rings a melody of love.

Elton M. Roth (1891-1951)

In my heart there rings a melody

[*Crusader Hymns*, No. 105]

A Hymn Story by Tedd Smith

not many people are given a great singing voice, but everyone can have a song! The Psalmist explains the source of the music in a Christian's life:

> I waited patiently for the Lord: and he inclined unto me, and heard my cry. He brought me up also out of an horrible pit, out of the miry clay, and set my feet upon a rock, and established my goings. And he hath put a new song in my mouth, even praise unto our God: many shall see it, and fear, and shall trust in the Lord (Psalm 40:1-3).

This new song which God gives us may have no words whatever, no melody, no rhythm and no harmony! This is a "song in the heart." The hymn title says "In my heart there rings a melody;" it is based on the words of the apostle Paul in Ephesians 5:19: "singing and making melody *in your heart* to the Lord."
[Read or sing stanza 1.]

What is the heart singing? The final phrase of the refrain describes it: it is a "melody of love" — God's love to us, and our love to God and to other men. It is a song of joy — not merely happiness or pleasure, but an eternal joy that persists through all the sorrows and tragedies of life. It is also a song of peace and serenity that gives poise and maturity amid the pressures of our culture.

Someone has said, "If there were more singing Christians, there would be more Christians!" If this heart-song of love, joy and peace is evident in our daily lives, we will become very conspicuous in our communities and in our daily life-contacts. Others will want to know the secret of our victorious living. As the Psalmist declared in the passage quoted previously, "many shall see it, and fear, and shall trust in the Lord."

Elton Menno Roth, the hymn's writer, was for many years a distinguished church musician — singer, composer and conductor. In the 1930's, after serious study with several prominent teachers, he organized professional choirs which achieved national recognition in their concert tours.

Roth once said that this hymn was written while he was conducting an evangelistic meeting in Texas. As he recalls:

One hot summer afternoon I took a little walk to the cotton mill just outside of town. On my way back through the burning streets of this typical plantation village, I became weary with the oppressive heat, and paused at a church on the corner.

The door being open, I went in. There were no people in the pews, no minister in the pulpit. Everything was quiet, with a lingering sacred presence. I walked up and down the aisle and began singing, "In my heart there rings a melody," then hurried into the pastor's study to find some paper. I drew a staff and sketched the melody, remaining there for an hour or more to finish the song, both words and music.

That evening I introduced it by having over two hundred boys and girls sing it at the open air meeting; after which the audience joined in the singing. I was thrilled as it seemed my whole being was transformed into a song!

In my profession of church music, we hear a good deal of talk about the music which pleases God and which ministers to people. Like Roth, we must be concerned about the quality of our musical compositions, and our performance of them. But we dare not forget that God is more concerned about whether or not we have a song in our heart. It is this melody in a life which will convince other men and women that our Christian faith is vital and desirable.

[Read or sing stanzas 2 and 3.]

TRUSTING JESUS

[*Crusader Hymns*, No. 183]

A Hymn Story by Billy Graham

"**T**rusting Jesus" is a hymn that is completely American in background. Edgar Stites, author of the words, was a direct descendant of John Howland, one of the *Mayflower's* passengers. Active in the Civil War, he was later a riverboat pilot and then a missionary to the frontier churches in South Dakota.

The hymn poem first appeared in a newspaper, and was handed to the American evangelist D. L. Moody. In turn, Moody gave it to his soloist and songleader, Ira D. Sankey, asking him to set it to music. In his book, *Sankey's Story of the Gospel Hymns*, the singer says, "I assented, on condition that he should vouch for the doctrine taught in the verses, and he said he would."

This hymn was the favorite of my longtime friend, Dr. W. B. Riley, and it expresses well the motivating purpose of his life. During the more than forty years that Dr. Riley was the beloved pastor of the First Baptist Church in Minneapolis, Minnesota, he was a pillar of strength in the evangelical movement. He appeared many times at the Florida Bible Institute while I was a student there. He — and other men like Dr. H. H. Savage, Dr. William Evans and Dr. Vance Havner — instilled in me a love for the Word of God, and gave me my first doctrinal anchorage.

The frequent theme of Dr. Riley's preaching was the grace of God. He both taught and lived a practical Christianity that is proclaimed in this motto and title: "Trusting Jesus, That Is All."
[Read or sing stanzas 1 and 2.]

I have often emphasized that becoming a Christian is more than "making a decision" to live a better life or to attend church more regularly. When by faith we accept Christ as our Lord and Saviour, something supernatural takes place. He comes to dwell in our hearts, and gives us His own supernatural life — eternal life.

But it would be a mistake to imagine that from then on, we are automatically and almost magically victorious over sin and doubt. Not so! Each day we must have the same trust we experienced when we first came to know Christ. We all remember the words in Ephesians 2:8, "For by grace are ye saved through faith." But too many people forget Hebrews 10:38, "Now the just shall *live* by faith." This is the secret of *living* the Christian life — everyday faith — "simply trusting every day."

Each day we renew our faith in God's forgiveness. Sometimes after years of walking with God, the devil will tempt us to doubt our salvation. But on the strength of God's Word we can exercise faith and trust and drive the sin of doubt away.

We "simply trust" that God will keep us, guide us and protect us each day. It is probably a good thing that we know "not what a day may bring forth" (Prov. 27:1). For if we were to see the road ahead for the next month, or year, or ten years, we would probably not have the courage to face it.

The author Robert Louis Stevenson once said, "Every man can win through until nightfall." The Christian would agree, "Yes — with the consciousness that I am God's and He is mine!" God has not promised strength or grace or faith for tomorrow. He has said, "As thy days, so shall thy strength be" (Deut. 33:25).

If we use our resources of prayer, of God's Word, and of Christian fellowship — and if we exercise faith and trust for each day — we can live daily in glorious victory!

[Read or sing stanzas 3 and 4.]

Simply trusting every day,
    Trusting through a stormy way;
Even when my faith is small,
    Trusting Jesus, that is all.

Brightly doth His Spirit shine
    Into this poor heart of mine;
While He leads I cannot fall;
    Trusting Jesus, that is all.

Singing if my way is clear;
    Praying if the path be drear;
If in danger, for Him call;
    Trusting Jesus, that is all.

Trusting Him while life shall last,
    Trusting Him till earth be past;
Till within the jasper wall:
    Trusting Jesus, that is all.

Refrain:

Trusting as the moments fly,
    Trusting as the days go by;
Trusting Him whate'er befall,
    Trusting Jesus, that is all.

Edgar P. Stites (1836-1921)

Immortal, invisible, God only wise,
    In light inaccessible hid from our eyes,
Most blessed, most glorious, the Ancient of Days,
    Almighty, victorious, Thy great name we praise.

Unresting, unhasting, and silent as light,
    Nor wanting, nor wasting, Thou rulest in might;
Thy justice like mountains high soaring above
    Thy clouds, which are fountains of goodness and love.

To all, life Thou givest, to both great and small,
    In all life Thou livest, the true life of all,
We blossom and flourish as leaves on the tree,
    And wither and perish — but nought changeth Thee.

Great Father of glory, pure Father of light,
    Thine angels adore Thee, all veiling their sight;
All praise we would render; O help us to see
    Tis only the splendor of light hideth Thee!

Walter Chalmers Smith (1824-1908)

immoRtal, invisible, goö only wise

[*Crusader Hymns*, No. 43]

have you ever tried to look at the sun? "Of course not," you say. "If I tried it even for a few moments, it would damage my eyes. This is why, to view an eclipse of the sun, I must look through a very dark lens." Isn't it interesting that the sun is obscured by the very light which it produces? The hymn "Immortal, Invisible, God Only Wise" says that this is one of the reasons why it is difficult to "see God" — to understand Him.
[Read or sing stanza 1.]

The Bible often speaks of God as "light." David said, "The Lord is my light and my salvation" (Psalm 27:1). Jesus himself stated, "I am the light of the world" (John 8:12). One of Jesus' disciples wrote, "God is light, and in him is no darkness at all" (I John 1:5).

Notice, in this hymn of worship, the many ways in which God is compared to the light of the sun. In stanza two, we are reminded that God never rests, never hurries. Despite all His power, God acts so quietly in the universe that those who are "spiritually blind" never perceive him. This anonymity is why it is possible for some ecclesiastic leaders to propose that God may be dead.

Like the sun, God needs nothing for sustenance; all things depend upon Him. Like the sun, God's power never diminishes; He is immutable, never changing. In a world of turmoil and incessant change, we can count on His eternal "justice, goodness and love."

Just as physical life depends upon the sun, so all life — physical and spiritual — depends upon God. Through the chemical phenomenon we call photosynthesis, plants derive food from the energy of the sun. We in turn obtain our nourishment from plants and from animals which live on plants. Yes, God uses light — physical and spiritual light — to give physical and spiritual life "to both great and small." This is why Jesus said: "I am the light of the world: he that followeth me shall not walk in darkness, but shall have the light of life" (John 8:12).

Revelation 21:23 promises that heaven's inhabitants will need neither a sun nor a moon, "for the glory of God did lighten it, and the Lamb (Christ) is the light thereof." Another passage of scripture (Isaiah 6:2) suggests that the angels cover their eyes because they cannot stand the brightness of His glory. If, while we are still mortal, we fail to fully comprehend God, we must remember that the light of the sun is what makes it invisible. So we sing to Him in humble praise: "Only the splendor of light hideth Thee!"

It is foolish to think that we dare not believe in a God we cannot completely understand. We are confident that there is an earthly plane of existence although we don't entirely comprehend it. The real wonder for us to ponder is that this transcendent being comes to dwell in our hearts if we invite Him. Scripture verifies this truth:

> For thus saith the high and lofty One that inhabiteth eternity, whose name is Holy; I dwell in the high and holy place, with him also that is of a contrite and humble spirit (Isa. 57:15).

Frederick Faber expresses this paradox of man's finiteness indwelt by Divine infinity, in a hymn of his own:

> My God, how wonderful Thou art,
> Thy majesty how bright!
> How beautiful Thy mercy seat,
> In depths of burning light!
>
> O how I fear thee, living God,
> With deepest, tend'rest fears;
> And worship Thee with trembling hope,
> And penitential tears.
>
> Yet I may love Thee too, O Lord,
> Almighty as Thou art;
> For Thou hast stooped to ask of me
> The love of my poor heart.

"Immortal, Invisible, God Only Wise", was written by Walter Chalmers Smith (1824-1908) who was a pastor and once moderator of the Free Church of Scotland (Presbyterian).

As you sing or read this hymn, notice that its opening phrase is a paean of praise appropriated from I Timothy 1:17: "Now unto the King eternal, immortal, invisible, the only wise God, be honour and glory forever and ever."

[Read or sing stanzas 2-4.]

he the peaRly Gates will open

[*Crusader Hymns*, No. 250]

A Hymn Story by Cliff Barrows

In preparation for a series of crusade services in Scandinavia in 1955, we were looking for something in simple Swedish to sing. Someone suggested "Han skall öppna pärleporten," in translation, "He the Pearly Gates Will Open." Because the song is a "natural" duet, Bev Shea graciously asked me to sing it with him. It is one of the two or three songs we sing together on rare occasions, and we have repeated it for the Danes in Copenhagen and for the American Swedes in places like Rockford, Illinois and Minneapolis, Minnesota.

Elsie Ahlwen, composer of this lovely tune, came to America from Sweden and became a student at the Moody Bible Institute. After graduation she began to work among the Swedish immigrants in Chicago, and later became a full-time evangelist. The words of this refrain had been known to her for a long time, and she often sang it to her own melody in evangelistic services throughout the country. It came to be the theme song of Elsie Ahlwen's ministry.

During a meeting in Chicago, Miss Ahlwen was approached by an old man who gave her the words for the stanzas. They had been written by Fred Blom, a former Christian worker in Sweden. Blom had come to New York early in this century, and, through circumstances that are not quite clear, had fallen into sin and was sent to prison. It was there, sick in soul and in body, that he found Christ anew. The song was his expression of joy because God had "healed his backsliding" and forgiven all his sin.

In keeping with the immigrant background of the song, it must be noted that the original was in the Swedish tongue. Not until the time of a great revival in Duluth, Minnesota was this hymn first translated into English. "He the Pearly Gates Will Open" has now been rendered in more than a dozen languages.

Before hearing this hymn story, I had always wondered just what was behind the words of the second stanza:

> Like a dove when hunted, frightened,
> As a wounded fawn was I;
> Broken hearted, yet He healed me —
> He will heed the sinner's cry.

This was Fred Blom's experience. At one time he had known God's peace and victory over sin, but he had fallen victim to the temptations of this world. Yet the love of Christ would not let him go. It pursued him relentlessly — almost as a hunter stalks a deer — and finally the arrow of conviction brought him down. We are reminded of the words of David in Psalm 38:1,2: "O Lord, rebuke me not in thy wrath: neither chasten me in thy hot displeasure. For thine arrows stick fast in me, and thy hand presseth me sore."

It is always tragic when a Christian falls into sin because he loses his sweet fellowship with God and compromises his witness for Christ. Yet all of us have failed at one time or another. We may not have committed some grossly evil act, but we have "fallen short" in word or thought or deed. Perhaps we have failed to do some deed of kindness, or to show love and concern for others. How wonderful to know that God "is married to the backslider" (Jer. 3:14). He will not allow us to be comfortable in our failure. Still His love follows us — sometimes it is shown in trouble and affliction — until we come to our senses and return to Him.

The hymn's message is very simple. Because of the love of God expressed in Christ our sins are forgiven, our lives are changed, and we anticipate a joyful entrance into heaven. It is said that Fred Blom died in the custody of the law. While the gates of prison did not open for him, he knew that heaven's "pearly gates" would be swung wide by his Redeemer.

Elsie Ahlwen's personal testimony voices the same assurance. She had married Daniel A. Sundeen, a business man, and they had continued a ministry together while raising their family. In 1962, they visited Chicago once again and sang "Pearly Gates" for their many friends. Shortly thereafter, Mr. Sundeen took sick and died within a week. Mrs. Sundeen wrote these words: "It is difficult to see beyond the bend in the road where your loved one disappeared. But how good it is to know that, when my Lord calls me, the Pearl Gates will open — not because of my worthiness but because He purchased my salvation."
[Read or sing the entire hymn.]

Love divine, so great and wondrous,
  Deep and mighty, pure, sublime;
Coming from the heart of Jesus —
  Just the same through tests of time.

Like a dove when hunted, frightened,
  As a wounded fawn was I;
Broken hearted, yet He healed me —
  He will heed the sinner's cry.

Love divine, so great and wondrous —
  All my sins He then forgave,
I will sing His praise forever,
  For His blood, His pow'r to save.

In life's eventide, at twilight,
  At His door I'll knock and wait;
By the precious love of Jesus
  I shall enter heaven's gate.

Refrain:

He the pearly gates will open,
  So that I may enter in;
For He purchased my redemption,
  And forgave me all my sin.

Fred Blom (20th Century)
Trans. by N. Carlson (1879-1957)

When all my labors and trials are o'er,
    And I am safe on that beautiful shore,
Just to be near the dear Lord I adore,
    Will through the ages be glory for me.

When by the gift of His infinite grace,
    I am accorded in heaven a place,
Just to be there and to look on His face,
    Will through the ages be glory for me.

Friends will be there I have loved long ago;
    Joy like a river around me will flow;
Yet, just a smile from my Saviour, I know,
    Will through the ages be glory for me.

Refrain:

O that will be glory for me,
    Glory for me, glory for me;
When by His grace I shall look on His face,
    That will be glory, be glory for me.

Charles H. Gabriel (1856-1932)

o that will be glory

[*Crusader Hymns*, No. 252]

A Hymn Story by Cliff Barrows

It is often difficult to predict whether or not a new hymn will "catch on" with the public. Actually, only a small number of those that are published ever reach a second edition. Of the 6500 hymns written by Charles Wesley during the 18th century, probably no more than 200 are sung anywhere today. The new *Methodist Hymnal* (1964), compiled by Americans of the Wesleyan tradition, contains only 79 of Charles Wesley's hymns. Even so, this is a remarkable record of poetic longevity that is not equaled by any other hymnwriter.

When "O That Will Be Glory" first appeared in 1900, a musical expert predicted, "It will never go. It has too many quarter notes." In other words, "the rhythm is too monotonous." But in a few years, it was the most popular hymn Homer Rodeheaver led in the Billy Sunday campaigns. It was affectionately called the "Glory Song" and was inspired, not by an experience, but by a personality!

The author, C. H. Gabriel, was perhaps the best known and most prolific gospel song writer of the early twentieth century. One of his good friends was Ed Card, superintendent of the Sunshine Rescue Mission of St. Louis, Missouri. Ed was a radiant believer who always seemed to be "bubbling over" with Christian joy. During a sermon or a prayer he would often explode with "Glory!" just as some people say "Amen!" or "Hallelujah!" His beaming smile earned him the nickname "old glory face." It was his custom to close his fervent prayers with a reference to heaven, usually ending with the phrase "and that will be glory for me!"

[Read or sing stanza 1.]

No doubt many Christians have a false view of what heaven will be. Our critics often say that we yearn for "pie in the sky by and by," while failing to really confront the issues that face us here and now. It is true that heaven will be free of the sorrow and death, the pressures and conflicts which beset us on earth. But it is not a truly Christian motive to look for heaven simply because we will have no problems there.

Many folks have a similar misconception of what the Bible calls "eternal life," imagining that this is the life which begins when we die or when Christ returns to this earth. "Eternal" life means a new *quality* of life — a supernatural life which begins when we enter God's family. The Bible says it clearly: "And what is it God has said? That He has given us eternal life, and that this life is in His Son. So whoever has God's Son has life; whoever does not have His Son, does not have life" (I John 5:11,12, *Living Letters*). We believe that heaven is really a continuation of that eternal life which we may possess right now.

At the same time, one of the delightful prospects of eternity is that we will be able to accomplish the things which are, for one reason or another, impossible in this world. For one thing, we will have new bodies which will not be limited by time or space. We believe also that many of the "mysteries of our faith" — mysteries because of our mental limitations — will then be made clear. We expect that we will gain victory over all our doubts and over the sinful weaknesses which plague us now. Some people contend that it is possible that we will continue to grow mentally and spiritually through all eternity. Furthermore, it is reasonable to anticipate that in heaven God will have service for us to perform, although the Bible does not specifically list our responsibilities.

I have heard some people say that they expect to be musical experts in heaven, although they have little musical talent now. It is true that we will all be able to sing the anthem mentioned in Revelation 5:12: "Worthy is the Lamb that was slain to receive power, and riches, and wisdom, and strength, and honour, and glory, and blessing."

What this "Glory Song" really says is that the central attraction in heaven will be Jesus Christ. We will see Him then "in His completeness, face to face," not "as if we were peering at His reflection in a poor mirror" (I Cor. 13:12, *LL*). And all the changes that will take place in us will happen because "when He comes we will be like Him, as a result of seeing Him as He really is" (I John 3:2, *LL*).

I shall see Him, I shall be like Him,
By one glance of His face transformed;
And this body of sin and darkness
To the image of Christ conformed. (A. J. Gordon)

[Read or sing stanzas 2 and 3.]

for the Beauty of the earth

[*Crusader Hymns*, No. 18]

A Hymn Story by Don Hustad

Suppose you were to visit a great artist in his studio, and all around you the walls were covered by his paintings. Is it possible that you might ignore all the beauty that he had created, and never once mention it?

Some of us treat God's artistry this way! Our heavenly Father is the Creator and Giver of all that is beautiful in the universe. The first chapter of Genesis tells us that God approved of all His handiwork, repeating several times "and God saw that it was good." Undoubtedly He is pleased when we recognize the beauty of our world and thank Him for it. Yes, a Christian does have an obligation with regard to beauty. "Whatsoever things are true, whatsoever things are honest. . . just. . . pure. . . lovely. . . of good report. . . think on these things" (Phil. 4:8).

There are many other aspects of our world which we take for granted: health, homes, friends, our country, even life itself. The hymn "For the Beauty of the Earth" lists some of God's blessings for which we may seem to be ungrateful. Do we feel that these are "secular" aspects of life, and that we should limit our praying and singing to "spiritual" things? Yet all of these so-called "ordinary" things are the gifts of God. We should thank Him for them!
[Read or sing stanzas 1 and 2.]

The late Dr. A. W. Tozer once said that every artist's work is in a sense "praise of God." The painter, the sculptor, and the musician are simply imitating God's own magnificent creative acts, using the talents which God has given them. For this reason, the Christian also sees the hand of God in all good art.

Not only did God put beautiful sounds and sights in the world—He also gave us ears and eyes to take them in, and minds to interpret what we hear and see. It is proper to thank God for a clear mind and the joy we find in developing it through study or in research. This too is His great gift to us and our gratitude is expressed in a stanza which is not always included in hymnals:

For the joy of ear and eye,
    For the heart and mind's delight,
For the mystic harmony
    Linking sense to sound and sight:
Lord of all, to Thee we raise
    This our hymn of grateful praise.

In the remaining stanzas, author Folliott S. Pierpoint gives thanks for all human relationships, whether of family or of friends, and for the fellowship of the Christian church encircling the world. A final verse, omitted in most books, gives thanks for God Himself, who has given us all the joys and beauty of life — but more than all this, "His only begotten Son."

For Thyself, best Gift Divine!
    To our race so freely given;
For that great, great love of Thine,
    Peace on earth, and joy in heaven:
Lord of all, to Thee we raise
    This our hymn of grateful praise.

When this hymn was first sung, the final phrase was:

Christ, our God, to Thee we raise
    This our sacrifice of praise.

Perhaps the present version sings better but it omits an important truth about church music. Throughout the Bible, singing is often spoken of as a "sacrifice" — a "sacrifice of joy" or a "sacrifice of praise." Hebrews 13:15 states this challenge: "By him *(Jesus Christ)* therefore let us offer the sacrifice of praise to God continually, that is, the fruit of our lips giving thanks to his name."

God wants nothing more than our praise, our worship. A "sacrifice" is something which costs the giver a great deal. I have often encouraged songleaders and ministers of music to challenge Christian believers to really exert themselves, both physically and mentally, when they sing. One of Charles Wesley's hymns wishes for a "thousand tongues to sing my great Redeemer's praise." We should at least use the one we have, to full advantage!

What shall I render unto the Lord for all his benefits toward me?...I will offer...the sacrifice of thanksgiving, and will call upon the name of the Lord (Psalm 116:12, 17).

[Read or sing stanzas 3 and 4.]

For the beauty of the earth,
For the glory of the skies,
For the love which from our birth
Over and around us lies,
Lord of all, to Thee we raise
This our hymn of grateful praise.

For the beauty of each hour
Of the day and of the night,
Hill and vale, and tree, and flower,
Sun and moon, and stars of light,
Lord of all, to Thee we raise
This our hymn of grateful praise.

For the joy of human love,
Brother, sister, parent, child,
Friends on earth, and friends above,
For all gentle thoughts and mild,
Lord of all, to Thee we raise
This our hymn of grateful praise.

For Thy Church that evermore
Lifteth holy hands above,
Offering up on every shore
Her pure sacrifice of love,
Lord of all, to Thee we raise
This our hymn of grateful praise.

Folliott S. Pierpoint (1835-1917

O come, O come, Emmanuel,
    And ransom captive Israel,
That mourns in lonely exile here
    Until the Son of God appear.
Rejoice! rejoice! Emmanuel
    Shall come to thee, O Israel!

O come, Thou Rod of Jesse, free
    Thine own from Satan's tyranny;
From depths of hell Thy people save
    And give them victory o'er the grave.
Rejoice! rejoice! Emmanuel
    Shall come to thee, O Israel!

O come, Thou Day-spring, come and cheer
    Our spirits by Thine advent here;
And drive away the shades of night,
    And pierce the clouds and bring us light!
Rejoice! rejoice! Emmanuel
    Shall come to thee, O Israel!

O come, Thou Key of David, come,
    And open wide our heavenly home;
Make safe the way that leads on high,
    And close the path to misery.
Rejoice! Rejoice! Emmanuel
    Shall come to thee, O Israel!

Latin Hymn, ca. 9th Century
Tr. by John Mason Neale (1818-1866)

O COME, O COME, EMMANUEL

[*Crusader Hymns*, No. 262]

Like Topsy in the story *Uncle Tom's Cabin*, some of our hymns were not specifically composed; they "just growed." The song "O Come, O Come, Emmanuel" evolved in this way.

This Advent hymn began to take shape more than a thousand years ago. In a series of seven Vesper services preceding Christmas, church choirs traditionally sang each night a different verse (or Antiphon) addressed to Christ. Three hundred years later these separate verses were united, a refrain was added, and the result was a hymn. About one hundred years ago the hymn was translated from Latin into English, and it is just now becoming known to many Christian congregations.

"O Come, O Come, Emmanuel" is a prayer that anticipates the coming of Christ to this earth. His coming as the Messiah ("deliverer") was first prophesied in the sixth century B.C., when the Jews were captive in Babylon. For centuries thereafter, faithful Hebrews looked for their Messiah with great longing and expectation, echoing the prayer that he would "ransom captive Israel." Indeed, many Jews are still looking for a Messiah, because they have failed to recognize Jesus as the Promised One.

Jesus Christ the Redeemer, capstone of man's longing through the ages, is addressed in the first stanza of this hymn as "Emmanuel." The words of Matthew 1:23 corroborate the prophecy in Isaiah 7:14, "Behold a virgin shall be with child, and shall bring forth a son, and they shall call his name Emmanuel, which being interpreted is, God with us."
[Read or sing stanza 1.]

Another title used in the song to refer to Jesus is "Thou Rod of Jesse." The source of this symbolism is Isaiah 11:1, "And there shall come forth a rod out of the stem of Jesse, and a Branch shall grow out of his roots." This particular prophecy was fulfilled by the birth of Jesus, whose heritage stemmed from the kingly line of David, the son of Jesse. But, contrary to the Jews' expectation, the purpose of Christ's first coming was not to restore their kingdom or to bring them political freedom. He came rather to free "all who will believe" from the tyranny of Satan, from hell and the grave. Ultimately, when Christ comes again He will indeed rule as absolute King over the universe.

[Read or sing stanza 2.]

"The Dayspring" is the vivid image applied to Jesus in the third stanza; it means literally "sun rising." Jesus' birth had been prophesied shortly before the event by the priest Zacharias, in these words: "The dayspring from on high hath visited us, to give light to them that sit in darkness and in the shadow of death" (Luke 1:78b, 79a). Christ's coming into the world is thus likened to the sun breaking on the horizon after a long dark night.

[Read or sing stanza 3.]

The final stanza again mentions the prophetic aspect of Christ's advent; He is called "Thou Key of David." This reference is first recorded in Isaiah 22:22, "and the key of the house of David will I lay upon his shoulder." These words remind us that in Oriental countries, keys were a symbol of authority and were sometimes worn hanging from the shoulder. Another well-known passage confirms this royal authority of Christ, "and the government shall be upon his shoulder" (Isa. 9:6).

The spiritual significance of "Christ the Key" is vividly demonstrated to modern-day visitors to the Near East. In Nablus, Jordan there is an old Samaritan synagogue that welcomes tourists. A bearded priest takes out three brass keys and opens three locks to let the visitors into the "holy place." In the hymn, however, the "key" is Christ who opens the entrance to God; keys of brass are no longer needed. When Christ died and His deed of redemption was finished on Golgotha, the veil before the "holy place" in the temple was rent. He, "the key," opened up the way to God for all.

From beginning to end, all the stanzas of the hymn remind us of Christ's first advent and project our attention to His second coming. Expectation must necessarily be a part of the Christian's life. The real home of the believer is with Christ in heaven; here on earth he is, in a sense, an exile. One day, like a glorious sunrise, Christ will "pierce the clouds" and bring us final and total victory over death.

The hymn's title is similar to the words of the next-to-the-last verse of the Bible: "Even so, come, Lord Jesus." And we can joyfully echo the refrain: "Rejoice! rejoice! Emmanuel shall come!"

[Read or sing stanza 4.]

awake, my soul, and with the sun

[*Crusader Hymns*, No. 50]

A Hymn Story by Don Hustad

When Thomas Ken was a student in the cathedral school at Winchester, England in 1650, that institution was already nearly 300 years old! His day of classes, study and worship began at five o'clock in the morning; in the summer the sun was just breaking through, but in the winter it was still very dark. How hard it was to get out of their "truckle beds" in the cold dormitory, and then to participate in "morning prayers" and a hymn — all before breakfast. In those days, as had been the custom for those 300 years, the boys sang the Latin hymn *Jam lucis orto sidere*, "Now the daylight fills the sky."

A few years later, Ken returned to Winchester as a Fellow in the College and a member of the Cathedral staff. By this time English was largely replacing Latin for worship and the young teacher wrote a book of prayers and hymns for the boys to use. He added the recommendation that they "be sure to sing the morning and evening hymn in their chamber devoutly."

Ken's morning hymn began: "Awake, my soul, and with the sun thy daily stage of duty run." He must have remembered his own school days when he urged: "Shake off dull sloth, and joyful rise to pay thy morning sacrifice." All through the Old Testament, singing to God is called a "sacrifice of joy" or a "sacrifice of praise." This is one sacrifice which believers still offer to God. As we read in Hebrews 13:15, "By him (Jesus Christ) let us offer the sacrifice of praise to God continually, that is, the fruit of our lips giving thanks to his name."

Perhaps early morning is the very best time for us to worship God privately. Throughout the night, though we have been asleep, the angels have continued to praise God as the second stanza suggests. In Revelation 4:8, heavenly beings are spoken of who "rest not day and night, saying, Holy, holy, holy, Lord God Almighty, which was, and is, and is to come." Certainly it is appropriate that after we have rested through the night, we should join the angels in worship. Our first thoughts should be of our heavenly Father; our first conversation should be with Him.

We should also acknowledge, as does the third stanza, that God has cared for us through the night. The psalmist said of the Lord: "He that keepeth thee will not slumber." There are periods in the night and even through the day when our minds are not completely fixed on God. On my desk at home, I have a quotation Lord Astley made before the battle of Edgehill: "Lord, Thou knowest I shall be very busy this day. I may forget Thee. Do not Thou forget me." We may be assured that He never does forget us.

An early morning prayer, Bible reading and even a hymn can determine the quality of the entire day ahead. When we seek the face of God before we see other faces, even those of our own family, somehow the day is off to a better start.

As we pray, we should acknowledge that the new day is God's and that we are His *for this day*. We should echo Thomas Ken's petition made in the final stanza, that God shall "direct and control" all that we think or do or say, so that all our physical, mental and spiritual "powers might unite" — that is, might be focused and coordinated to the glory of God.

[Read or sing the entire hymn.]

My good friend, the Chinese evangelist Leland Wang, has long practiced the motto "No Bible, no breakfast." I am sure that he also meant "No prayer, no breakfast." May we be bold enough to add "No hymn of praise, no breakfast"? It may be difficult to really vocalize early in the morning without the lubrication of a cup of coffee. But we can at least repeat in our hearts the words of that other stanza given us by Thomas Ken. We call it the "Doxology:"

> Praise God, from whom all blessings flow;
> Praise Him, all creatures here below;
> Praise Him above, ye heavenly host;
> Praise Father, Son, and Holy Ghost.

Awake, my soul, and with the sun
    Thy daily stage of duty run;
Shake off dull sloth, and joyful rise
    To pay thy morning sacrifice.

Wake, and lift up thyself, my heart,
    And with the angels bear thy part,
Who all night long unwearied sing
    High praise to the Eternal King.

All praise to Thee, who safe hast kept,
    And hast refreshed me while I slept:
Grant, Lord, when I from death shall wake,
    I may of endless life partake.

Direct, control, suggest, this day,
    All I design, or do, or say;
That all my powers, with all their might,
    In Thy sole glory may unite.

Thomas Ken (1637-1711)

I will sing of my Redeemer
    And His wondrous love to me;
On the cruel cross He suffered,
    From the curse to set me free.

I will tell the wondrous story,
    How my lost estate to save,
In His boundless love and mercy,
    He the ransom freely gave.

I will praise my dear Redeemer,
    His triumphant power I'll tell,
How the victory He giveth
    Over sin, and death, and hell.

I will sing of my Redeemer
    And His heavenly love for me;
He from death to life hath brought me,
    Son of God, with Him to be.

Refrain:

Sing, oh, sing of my Redeemer,
    With His blood He purchased me,
On the cross He sealed my pardon,
    Paid the debt, and made me free.

Philip P. Bliss (1838-1876)

I WILL SING OF MY REDEEMER

[*Crusader Hymns*, No. 93]

A Hymn Story by Cliff Barrows

Ninety years of world-wide popularity have established the gospel song "I Will Sing of My Redeemer" as part of our musical heritage. Less well known, however, is the miraculous legend of how it was preserved for the future. The composition was found in a piece of baggage rescued from a fiery train wreck on the day of December 20, 1876. The poem's author, 38-year-old Philip P. Bliss, had been traveling with his wife to Chicago to fulfill an engagement at D. L. Moody's Tabernacle. Near Ashtabula, Ohio a bridge collapsed and the train plunged into an icy river bed. It is said that Bliss survived the fall and climbed out through a coach window only to return, looking for his wife. Reunited, they died together in the flaming wreckage.

These circumstances, to all appearances, cut a brilliant career short, very suddenly. It had only been two years that Bliss had served as soloist and songleader in the evangelistic campaigns of Major D. W. Whittle. All his life, it would seem, had been leading up toward this ministry. Born in a log cabin, young Philip had left home at the age of eleven to work on farms and in lumber camps. He had become a Christian at the age of twelve and soon afterward developed interest in the study of music.

In the early nineteenth century, popular music training in America was centered in "singing schools" — schools which were characterized by a strong spiritual emphasis, and which also provided social activity for the small towns and rural communities. The "singing school" was strictly a one-man operation; a musician of some degree of ability traveled from place to place, organizing the classes, teaching them and collecting his fees (which might be paid either in cash or in farm produce!)

Most of the classes in sight-reading and in conducting were held at night. In the country schoolhouses, churches or town halls, the students sang the syllables (do-re-mi) while seated on planks placed between two chairs. Each music student also "beat time" for himself by moving his hand and arm in a prescribed pattern. Many of our early gospel musicians started out as "singing school" teachers. This tradition lasted more than a hundred years, and had a profound effect on the quality of congregational singing and the development of church choirs.

Philip Bliss found himself strongly attracted to "singing school" life. At the age of 21, he was married and a year later began a career as an itinerant music teacher. Using a little twenty-dollar folding organ hauled from place to place by his faithful horse Fanny, he taught music during the winter seasons. During the summer he followed his own musical education and became a student himself at the Normal Academy of Music at Geneseo, New York.

Song-writing came naturally to Bliss; he composed equally well in both words and music. Even during his short lifetime he was recognized as the leading writer of simple sacred songs, many of which are still widely used today. The new *Baptist Hymnal*, published in 1956, includes twelve hymns for which Bliss wrote either the words or the music, or both. Our small volume, *Crusader Hymns*, has seven of his compositions.

Although Bliss's ministry was very brief, his influence has continued down through the years. It was D. L. Moody who challenged him to leave teaching and to give his time to evangelistic crusades. In turn, Bliss urged his close friend and fellow-musician James McGranahan to undertake a similar task in gospel work. It was McGranahan who took Bliss's place in that fateful weekend meeting at the Moody Tabernacle in Chicago, when Bliss died enroute. At a later date, McGranahan joined the evangelistic party of D. W. Whittle.

We team musicians have been greatly inspired by the lives and contributions of these early evangelistic song leaders. And today — almost a century later — God still uses their simple songs and hymns to touch men's hearts, and to challenge many to decide for Christ.

God may not give each of us a great talent to use for Him. We may not have many years of service. But what we have — in talent and in time — is enough for God to bless and to use in accomplishing His purposes.

This song of Philip Bliss is a very simple expression of the truth of the gospel — so obvious that it does not require elaboration. In fact, the title itself might be considered the motto of his short and brilliant life: "I Will Sing of My Redeemer."

[Read or sing the entire hymn.]

join all the glorious names

[*Crusader Hymns*, No. 17]

[Read or sing stanza 1]

the meaning of words may change drastically over a period of time. For this reason, it may take some effort to fully comprehend "Join All The Glorious Names," a 250-year-old hymn of Isaac Watts, even though some publishers have already made efforts to modernize it. For instance, the word "poor" in stanza 1 was originally "mean." (Try reading it that way.) The message of the hymn is basically this: all the names which have been given to Jesus Christ are altogether inadequate to express the glory of the character of this God-man.

Some of the most common names of Christ are mentioned in the five stanzas given here. The original hymn had seven more verses, but even these do not exhaust the titles given to our Lord. Jesus is often spoken of as "Prophet, Priest, and King." As prophet, He brought the good news of the gospel contained in such familiar passages as Luke 19:10, "The Son of man is come to seek and to save that which was lost;" and John 10:10, "I am come that they might have life, and that they might have it more abundantly."

A priest is one who represents the people before God. Hebrews 2:17 says of Christ, "Wherefore in all things it behooved him to be made like unto his brethren, that he might be a merciful and faithful high priest in things pertaining to God, to make reconciliation for the sins of the people." Jesus Himself *became* our "sacrifice for sin" when He died on the cross, and we believe that He continues to represent us at the throne of God. The third stanza suggests that it is Jesus' blood which pleads our cause. Another hymn (by Charles Wesley) speaks thus of the continuing priesthood of Christ:

> Five bleeding wounds He bears,
> Received on Calvary;
> They pour effectual prayers,
> They strongly plead for me;
> "Forgive him, O forgive," they cry,
> "Nor let that ransomed sinner die!"

[Read or sing stanzas 2 and 3.]

When the Jews looked for a "Messiah," they expected a powerful military and political figure. They rejected Jesus — and that name means "deliverer" — partly because they did not understand how this "lowly Nazarene" could liberate them from the power of Rome. We should not forget that Jesus came to be a "King." When Pilate asked Him, "Art thou a king then?" Jesus answered, "To this end was I born, and for this cause came I into the world" (John 18:37). Those of us who accept Christ as our Lord make him "King of our lives." Certainly, He is King of Heaven now, and there will come a day when He shall rule the earth as well, as an absolute Monarch. As we sing in Handel's *Messiah*, He shall be "King of Kings, and Lord of Lords, and shall reign forever and ever" (Rev. 19:16).

Some of the names of Christ were first spoken by prophets many years before Jesus' birth. Isaiah (9:6) says that "His name shall be called Wonderful, Counsellor, The mighty God, The everlasting Father, the Prince of Peace." Many of the poetic passages of the Old Testament psalms refer to the glory of Christ with such titles as "the Rose of Sharon" and the "lily of the valleys" (Song of Solomon 2:1). In the last book of the Bible, Jesus said, "I am the bright and morning star" (Rev. 22:16).

Other terms are used to speak of Christ's work in salvation. He is the "Lamb of God," "Saviour," "Redeemer," "Mediator" and "Emmanuel."

Of course, Jesus gave Himself many other descriptive names. He said: "I am the living bread which came down from heaven" (John 6:51). "I am the Good Shepherd" (John 10:14). "I am the Door" (John 10:9). "I am the light of the world" (John 8:12). "I am the true vine" (John 15:1). "I am the resurrection and the life" (John 11:25). These are just a few of the more than one hundred names of Christ which are found in the Bible.

Hymnwriters have also added new names to our Lord. Some of them are borrowed from scripture, with just a bit of poetic alteration: "The Son of Mary," "The Sun of Righteousness," "The Solid Rock," "Rock of Ages," "Blessed Redeemer," "Rod of Jesse," "Key of David," "Love Divine," "The Church's One Foundation," "Blessed Master," "High King of Heaven," "Heart of My Own Heart," "The Deep Sweet Well of Love," "Our Captain in the well-fought fight," "Risen, conquering Son," "Chief of ten thousand," "Fount of Every Blessing," "Friend for sinners," "Joy of Loving Hearts," "Prince of Glory," "Man of Sorrows," "Lover of my soul," and "My Guide and Keeper." (Suggestion: You might like to try to remember what hymns contain these phrases. They are all found in the book, *Crusader Hymns*.)

But we have not yet mentioned some of the most striking and significant names of Christ. He is the Son of God and the Son of Man. He said, "I am Alpha and Omega, the beginning and the end, the first and the last" (Rev. 22:13). He also said, "I am the Way, the Truth and the

Life" (John 14:6). No other sober and responsible person in the world's history ever uttered such audacious words!

It is obvious that all the names that might be invented would fail to adequately describe the character of our Lord. Yet writers and hymnists will no doubt continue to search for more. It is a good thing to express praise of Christ with such an expanded vocabulary. But more than this, we should praise Him with our daily lives and our willing service.

[Read or sing stanzas 4 and 5.]

Join all the glorious names
Of wisdom, love, and power,
That ever mortals knew,
That angels ever bore:
All are too poor to speak His worth,
Too poor to set my Saviour forth.

Great Prophet of my God,
My tongue would bless Thy name:
By Thee the joyful news
Of our salvation came,
The joyful news of sins forgiv'n,
Of hell subdued and peace with heav'n.

Jesus, my great High Priest,
Offered His blood, and died;
My guilty conscience seeks
No sacrifice beside:
His pow'rful blood did once atone
And now it pleads before the throne.

Thou art my Counsellor,
My Pattern, and my Guide,
And Thou my Shepherd art;
Oh, keep me near Thy side;
Nor let my feet e'er turn astray,
To wander in the crooked way.

My Saviour and my Lord,
My Conqueror and my King,
Thy sceptre and Thy sword,
Thy reigning grace I sing:
Thine is the pow'r; behold I sit
In willing bonds beneath Thy feet.

Isaac Watts (1674-1748)

Hark! the herald angels sing,
    "Glory to the new-born King:
Peace on earth, and mercy mild,
    God and sinners reconciled!"
Joyful, all ye nations, rise,
    Join the triumph of the skies;
With th'angelic host proclaim,
    "Christ is born in Bethlehem!"

Christ, by highest heaven adored;
    Christ, the Everlasting Lord!
Late in time behold Him come,
    Offspring of the Virgin's womb:
Veiled in flesh the Godhead see;
    Hail th'Incarnate Deity,
Pleased as man with men to dwell,
    Jesus, our Emmanuel.

Hail the heaven-born Prince of Peace!
    Hail the Sun of Righteousness!
Light and life to all He brings,
    Risen with healing in His wings.
Mild He lays His glory by,
    Born that man no more may die,
Born to raise the sons of earth,
    Born to give them second birth.

Refrain:

Hark! the herald angels sing,
    "Glory to the new-born King."

Charles Wesley, alt. (1707-1788)

hark, the heralo angels sing

[*Crusader Hymns*, No. 258]

A Hymn Story by Cliff Barrows

Some people become very disturbed when a publisher changes the words of an old hymn. Of course, this is not legally possible while a copyright is in force, and great caution must be exercised in "editing" a very old hymn that is now public property. A poet must be granted some rights with his own creation.

However, an author often makes alterations himself, even after his work has appeared in print. The first line of this Christmas hymn, as originally published in 1739, was "Hark, how all the welkin rings, Glory to the King of Kings!" Fourteen years later, author Charles Wesley changed those words to "Hark! the herald angels sing, Glory to the newborn King." During the ensuing decades there were many changes; some stanzas were dropped and others were rearranged. The hymn as we know it appeared in the *New Version* of the Tate and Brady Psalter in 1782, while Wesley was still living.
[Read or sing stanza 1.]

"Welkin" is an archaic word for "heavens" or "sky," and so we see that Wesley begins his hymn with the song of the angels on the first Christmas morning. "Glory to God in the highest heaven . . . and peace on earth, for all those pleasing Him" (Luke 2:14, *Living Gospels*). As we sing these deeply meaningful phrases, it soon becomes clear that this is something more than a simple Christmas carol. The phrase "God and sinners reconciled" reminds us that Christ came, not to enforce political amity, but to bring peace between God and man. The Christmas story is told concisely in II Corinthians 5:19 *(New English Bible)*: "God was in Christ reconciling the world to himself." Of course this involves a change in us. As Romans 5:1 *(Living Letters)* says, "Since we have been made right in God's sight by faith in His promises, we can have real peace with Him because of what Jesus Christ our Lord has done for us." This is the peace promised by the angels on Christmas morning!
[Read or sing stanza 2.]

Throughout the hymn Charles Wesley continues to probe the deep mystery of Christmas, the mystery we call the Incarnation. Christ — who is the eternal King of heaven, worshipped by angels and archangels — lays aside the glory which is properly His, and condescends to be born of a virgin in a dark, dirty stable. Philippians 2:6 *(Phillips)* puts it this way: "For He, who had always been God by nature, did not cling to his prerogatives as God's equal, but stripped himself of all privilege by consenting to be a slave by nature and being born as mortal man."

Of course, Jesus was still God, and He often displayed His divine power and personality. But most men did not recognize Him as God because His divinity was hidden (the hymn says "veiled") in human flesh. This is the Lord of heaven who was pleased to dwell as a man with ordinary men. This also explains one of His names, found in the Old Testament and quoted by the angel to Joseph, "Behold, a virgin shall be with child, and shall bring forth a son, and they shall call his name *Emmanuel,* which being interpreted is, *God with us"* (Matt. 1:23).
[Read or sing stanza 3.]

Finally, the hymn reminds us of two more of Christ's names, given by Hebrew prophets long before His birth. The great passage in Isaiah 9:6 foretells: "And his name shall be called Wonderful, Counsellor, The Mighty God, The everlasting Father, The *Prince of Peace."* Malachi 4:2 speaks also of the coming of Christ, "But unto you that fear my name shall the *Sun of righteousness* arise with healing in his wings." Wesley adds his own commentary about this figure of Christ the Sun. The physical sun is not only our source of light; it is the origin of life itself. Without the sun, all plant life would die. Without vegetation, animal life could not subsist. In the same way, Jesus Christ is the source of our spiritual light and our spiritual life.

Yes, Jesus' birth holds many mysteries. He who is immortal was born a mortal in order that man might live eternally with Him. He was born once in order that we might be born again.

Many folk who join in singing the carols, sharing all the happy festivities of Christmas, are unwilling to think of Christ in this way. It has been said that as long as we can keep Jesus as a charming baby in a manger, He makes no demands upon our lives. But Jesus was *born to die!* He grew to manhood, lived a perfect life, and then died on the cross, and rose again, for our eternal salvation. This is the true Christ of Christmas, and we must acknowledge Him our Lord, if we are to celebrate this season properly.

index

church calendar index

CRUSADER
hymns

Compiled and edited by
Cliff Barrows and Donald Hustad

contents

hymns of worship

The Anglo-Saxon predecessor of our word
"worship" was "woerthscipe" and meant "to ascribe
worth." Today's Christian sings his adoration
and his submission because God is worthy of it.
All-holy, all-knowing, all-powerful and everywhere
present, He is our Heavenly Father — the Creator,
Sustainer and Redeemer of the universe.

how great thou art
O STORE GUD. 11 10 11 10 Ref.

1

Carl Boberg
Trans. by Stuart K. Hine

Swedish Folk Melody
Arr. by Manna Music, Inc.

1. O Lord my God, when I in awe-some won-der Con-sid-er
2. When through the woods and for-est glades I wan-der And hear the
3. And when I think that God, His Son not spar-ing, Sent Him to
4. When Christ shall come with shout of ac-cla-ma-tion And take me

all the worlds Thy hands have made, I see the stars, I hear the roll-ing
birds sing sweet-ly in the trees, When I look down from loft-y moun-tain
die, I scarce can take it in, That on the cross, my bur-den glad-ly
home, what joy shall fill my heart! Then I shall bow in hum-ble ad-o-

REFRAIN

thun-der, Thy pow'r thro'-out the u-ni-verse dis-played.
gran-deur, And hear the brook and feel the gen-tle breeze. Then sings my
bear-ing, He bled and died to take a-way my sin.
ra-tion, And there pro-claim, my God, how great Thou art.

soul, my Sav-iour God, to Thee; How great Thou art, how great Thou art! Then sings my

soul, my Sav-iour God, to Thee: How great Thou art, how great Thou art!

hymns of worship

The story of this hymn is on page....9

come, thou fount

NETTLETON. 8 7 8 7 D.

Robert Robinson

John Wyeth

1. Come, Thou Fount of ev - ery bless - ing, Tune my heart to sing Thy grace;
2. Here I raise mine Eb - en - e - zer; Hith - er by Thy help I'm come;
3. O to grace how great a debt - or Dai - ly I'm con-strained to be!

Streams of mer - cy, nev - er ceas - ing, Call for songs of loud - est praise.
And I hope, by Thy good pleas - ure, Safe - ly to ar - rive at home.
Let Thy good - ness, like a fet - ter, Bind my wan-dering heart to Thee:

Teach me some me - lo - dious son - net, Sung by flam - ing tongues a-bove;
Je - sus sought me when a stran - ger, Wan-dering from the fold of God;
Prone to wan - der, Lord, I feel it, Prone to leave the God I love;

Praise the mount—I'm fixed up-on it—Mount of Thy re - deem-ing love.
He, to res - cue me from dan-ger, In - ter-posed His pre-cious blood.
Here's my heart, O take and seal it; Seal it for Thy courts a - bove. A - MEN.

TO GOD BE THE GLORY

TO GOD BE THE GLORY. 11 11 11 11 Ref.

Fanny J. Crosby

William H. Doane

1. To God be the glo-ry, great things He hath done, So loved He the world that He gave us His Son, Who yield-ed His life an a-tone-ment for sin, And o-pened the Life-gate that all may go in.

2. O per-fect redemption, the pur-chase of blood, To ev-'ry be-liev-er the prom-ise of God; The vil-est of-fen-der who tru-ly believes, That moment from Je-sus a par-don re-ceives.

3. Great things He hath taught us, great things He hath done, And great our re-joic-ing thro' Je-sus the Son; But pu-rer, and higher, and greater will be Our won-der, our transport, when Jesus we see.

REFRAIN

Praise the Lord, praise the Lord, Let the earth hear His voice! Praise the Lord, praise the Lord, Let the peo-ple re-joice! O come to the Fa-ther thro' Je-sus the Son, And give Him the glo-ry, great things He hath done.

The story of this hymn is on page...93

hymns of worship

4
OUR GREAT SAVIOUR

HYFRYDOL. 8 7 8 7 Ref.

J. Wilbur Chapman

Rowland H. Prichard
Arr. by Robert Harkness

1. Je - sus! what a Friend for sin - ners! Je - sus! Lov - er of my soul;
2. Je - sus! what a Strength in weakness! Let me hide my - self in Him;
3. Je - sus! what a Help in sor - row! While the bil - lows o'er me roll,
4. Je - sus! what a Guide and Keep - er! While the tem - pest still is high,
5. Je - sus! I do now re - ceive Him, More than all in Him I find,

Friends may fail me, foes as - sail me, He, my Sav - iour, makes me whole.
Tempt - ed, tried, and some-times fail - ing, He, my Strength, my vic - t'ry wins.
E - ven when my heart is breaking, He, my Com - fort, helps my soul.
Storms a - bout me, night o'er - takes me, He, my Pi - lot, hears my cry.
He hath grant - ed me for - give-ness, I am His, and He is mine.

REFRAIN

Hal - le - lu - jah! what a Sav - iour! Hal - le - lu - jah! what a Friend!

Sav - ing, help-ing, keep-ing, lov - ing, He is with me to the end.

hymns of worship

I SING THE MIGHTY POWER OF GOD

ELLACOMBE. C.M.D.

Isaac Watts

Gesangbuch der Herzogl. Württemberg, 1784

1. I sing the might-y power of God, That made the moun-tains rise;
2. I sing the good-ness of the Lord, That filled the earth with food;
3. There's not a plant or flower be-low, But makes Thy glo-ries known;

That spread the flow-ing seas a-broad, And build the loft-y skies.
He formed the crea-tures with His word, And then pro-nounced them good.
And clouds a-rise, and tem-pests blow, By or-der from Thy throne;

I sing the wis-dom that or-dained The sun to rule the day;
Lord, how Thy won-ders are dis-played, Wher-e'er I turn my eye:
While all that bor-rows life from Thee Is ev-er in Thy care,

The moon shines full at His com-mand, And all the stars o-bey.
If I sur-vey the ground I tread, Or gaze up-on the sky!
And ev-ery-where that man can be, Thou, God, art pres-ent there. A-MEN.

hymns of worship

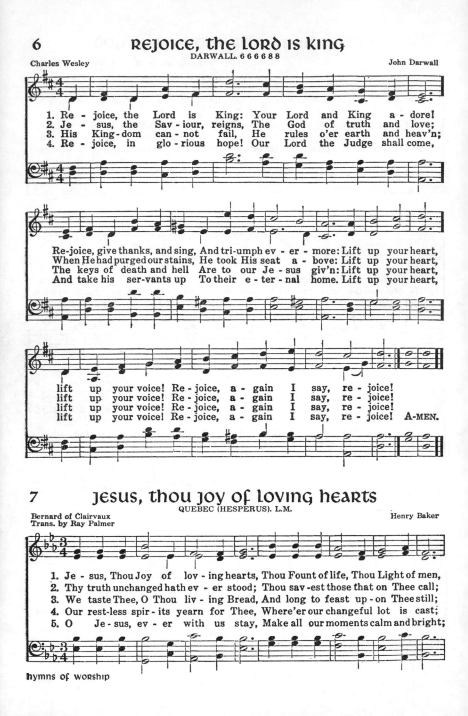

6

REJOICE, THE LORD IS KING
DARWALL. 6 6 6 6 8 8

Charles Wesley

John Darwall

1. Re - joice, the Lord is King: Your Lord and King a - dore!
2. Je - sus, the Sav - iour, reigns, The God of truth and love;
3. His King - dom can - not fail, He rules o'er earth and heav'n;
4. Re - joice, in glo - rious hope! Our Lord the Judge shall come,

Re-joice, give thanks, and sing, And tri-umph ev - er - more: Lift up your heart,
When He had purged our stains, He took His seat a - bove: Lift up your heart,
The keys of death and hell Are to our Je - sus giv'n: Lift up your heart,
And take his ser-vants up To their e - ter - nal home. Lift up your heart,

lift up your voice! Re - joice, a - gain I say, re - joice!
lift up your voice! Re - joice, a - gain I say, re - joice!
lift up your voice! Re - joice, a - gain I say, re - joice!
lift up your voice! Re - joice, a - gain I say, re - joice! A-MEN.

7

JESUS, THOU JOY OF LOVING HEARTS
QUEBEC (HESPERUS). L.M.

Bernard of Clairvaux
Trans. by Ray Palmer

Henry Baker

1. Je - sus, Thou Joy of lov - ing hearts, Thou Fount of life, Thou Light of men,
2. Thy truth unchanged hath ev - er stood; Thou sav - est those that on Thee call;
3. We taste Thee, O Thou liv - ing Bread, And long to feast up - on Thee still;
4. Our rest-less spir - its yearn for Thee, Where'er our changeful lot is cast;
5. O Je - sus, ev - er with us stay, Make all our moments calm and bright;

holy, holy, holy 8

The story of this hymn is on page...27

hymns of worship

9   SING PRAISE TO GOD WHO REIGNS ABOVE

MIT FREUDEN ZART. 8 7 8 7 8 8 7

Johann J. Schütz
Trans. by Frances E. Cox

Bohemian Brethren's *Kirchengesänge*, 1566

1. Sing praise to God who reigns a-bove, The God of all cre-
2. What God's al-might-y pow'r hath made, His gra-cious mer-cy
3. The Lord is nev-er far a-way, But, through all grief dis-
4. Thus, all my toil-some way a-long, I sing a-loud Thy

a-tion, The God of power, the God of love, The God of our sal-
keep-eth; By morn-ing glow or eve-ning shade His watch-ful eye ne'er
tress-ing, An ev-er-pres-ent help and stay, Our peace, and joy, and
prais-es, That men may hear the grate-ful song My voice un-wea-ried

va-tion; With heal-ing balm my soul He fills, And
sleep-eth; With-in the king-dom of His might, Lo!
bless-ing; As with a moth-er's ten-der hand, He
rais-es, Be joy-ful in the Lord, my heart, Both

ev-ery faith-less mur-mur stills: To God all praise and glo-ry.
all is just and all is right: To God all praise and glo-ry.
leads His own, His cho-sen band: To God all praise and glo-ry.
soul and bod-y bear your part: To God all praise and glo-ry. A-MEN.

LAUDA ANIMA. 8 7 8 7 8 7

Henry F. Lyte   John Goss

1. Praise, my soul, the King of heav - en, To His feet thy
2. Praise Him for His grace and fa - vor To our fa - thers
3. Fa - ther - like, He tends and spares us; Well our fee - ble
4. An - gels, help us to a - dore Him, Ye be - hold Him

trib - ute bring; Ran - somed, healed, re - stored, for - giv - en,
in dis - tress; Praise Him, still the same for - ev - er,
frame He knows, In His hands He gen - tly bears us,
face to face; Sun and moon, bow down be - fore Him;

Who, like me, His praise should sing? Al - le - lu - ia!
Slow to chide, and swift to bless. Al - le - lu - ia!
Res - cues us from all our foes. Al - le - lu - ia!
Dwell - ers all in time and space, Al - le - lu - ia!

Al - le - lu - ia! Praise the Ev - er - last - ing King!
Al - le - lu - ia! Glo - rious in His faith - ful - ness!
Al - le - lu - ia! Wide - ly as His mer - cy flows!
Al - le - lu - ia! Praise with us the God of grace! A - MEN.

11 holy God, we praise thy name

TE DEUM. 7 8 7 8 7 7

German, 18th Century
Trans. by Clarence Walworth

Katholisches Gesangbuch, 1774

1. Ho - ly God, we praise Thy name; Lord of all, we bow be - fore Thee;
2. Hark, the loud ce - les - tial hymn An - gel choirs a - bove are rais - ing;
3. Lo! the ap - os - tol - ic train Joins Thy sa - cred name to hal - low;
4. Ho - ly Fa - ther, Ho - ly Son, Ho - ly Spir - it, Three we name Thee;

All on earth Thy scep - ter claim, All in heav'n a - bove a - dore Thee.
Cher - u - bim and Ser - a - phim, In un - ceas - ing cho - rus prais - ing,
Proph-ets swell the glad re - frain, And the white-robed mar - tyrs fol - low;
While in es - sence on - ly One, Un - di - vid - ed God we claim Thee,

In - fi - nite Thy vast do - main, Ev - er - last - ing is Thy reign.
Fill the heav'ns with sweet ac-cord: Ho - ly, ho - ly, ho - ly Lord.
And, from morn to set of sun, Through the Church the song goes on.
And a - dor - ing bend the knee, While we sing our praise to Thee. A-MEN.

The story of this hymn is on page..103

12 O God, our help in ages past

ST. ANNE. C.M.

Isaac Watts
From Psalm 90

Ascribed to William Croft

1. O God, our help in a - ges past, Our hope for years to come,
2. Un - der the shad - ow of Thy throne Still may we dwell se - cure;
3. Be - fore the hills in or - der stood, Or earth re - ceived her frame,
4. A thou - sand a - ges, in Thy sight, Are like an eve - ning gone;
5. O God, our help in a - ges past, Our hope for years to come,

hymns of worship

Our shel-ter from the storm-y blast, And our e-ter-nal home!
Suf-fi-cient is Thine arm a-lone, And our de-fense is sure.
From ev-er-last-ing Thou art God, To end-less years the same.
Short as the watch that ends the night, Be-fore the ris-ing sun.
Be Thou our guide while life shall last, And our e-ter-nal home. A-MEN.

GIVE TO OUR GOD IMMORTAL PRAISE 13
WARRINGTON. L.M.

Isaac Watts
From Psalm 136

Ralph Harrison

1. Give to our God im-mor-tal praise; Mer-cy and
2. Give to the Lord of lords re-nown; The King of
3. He built the earth, He spread the sky, And fixed the
4. He fills the sun with morn-ing light; He bids the
5. He sent His Son with pow'r to save From guilt, and
6. Through this vain world He guides our feet, And leads us

truth are all His ways: Won-ders of grace to God be-
kings with glo-ry crown: His mer-cies ev-er shall en-
star-ry lights on high: Won-ders of grace to God be-
moon di-rect the night: His mer-cies ev-er shall en-
dark-ness, and the grave: Won-ders of grace to God be-
to His heav'n-ly seat: His mer-cies ev-er shall en-

long; Re-peat His mer-cies in your song.
dure, When lords and kings are known no more.
long; Re-peat His mer-cies in your song.
dure, When suns and moons shall shine no more.
long; Re-peat His mer-cies in your song.
dure, When this vain world shall be no more. A-MEN.

hymns of worship

14 WE LIFT OUR VOICE REJOICING

FOURSQUARE. 7 6 7 6 D. Ref.

Jack W. Hayford   Jack W. Hayford

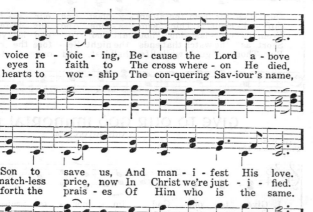

1. We lift our voice re - joic - ing, Be - cause the Lord a - bove
2. We lift our eyes in faith to The cross where - on He died,
3. We lift our hearts to wor - ship The con-quering Sav-iour's name,

Hath sent His Son to save us, And man - i - fest His love.
Re - deemed at match-less price, now In Christ we're just - i - fied.
Our tongues speak forth the prais - es Of Him who is the same.

Let ev - ery hill re - ech - o With this the song we raise,
His blood hath washed our gar-ments, His peace hath filled our souls,
Christ Je - sus reigns in pow - er Through-out e - ter - ni - ty.

"To Him whose blood hath bought us Be glo - ry, pow'r and praise."
The cross is now our glo - ry Since grace hath made us whole.
As yes - ter - day, so now, and For - ev - er He shall be.

REFRAIN

We praise Thee, O Fa - ther, Un - speak - a - ble our joy,

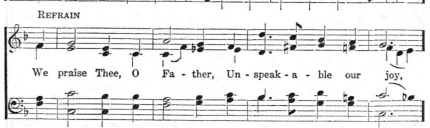

The story of this hymn is on page. 105

In Christ our hearts find glo-ry sin's pow'r can not de-stroy.

who is he in yonder stall? 15

HANBY. 7 7 7 7 Ref.

Benjamin R. Hanby

Benjamin R. Hanby

1. Who is He in yon-der stall, At whose feet the shep-herds fall?
2. Who is He the peo-ple bless For His words of gen-tle-ness?
3. Who is He that stands and weeps At the grave where Laz-arus sleeps?
4. Lo! at mid-night, who is He Prays in dark Geth-se-ma-ne?
5. Who is He who from the grave Comes to suc-cour, help, and save?

Who is He in deep dis-tress, Fast-ing in the wil-der-ness?
Who is He to whom they bring, All the sick and sor-row-ing?
Who is He the gathering throng Greet with loud tri-um phant song?
Who is He on yon-der tree Dies in grief and ag-o-ny?
Who is He who from His throne Rules through all the worlds a-lone?

REFRAIN

'Tis the Lord! oh won-drous sto-ry! 'Tis the Lord! the King of

glo-ry! At His feet we hum-bly fall, Crown Him! crown Him, Lord of all!

16 all cReatures of our god and king

LASST UNS ERFREUEN. 8 8 4 4 8 8 Alleluias.

St. Francis of Assisi
Trans. by William H. Draper

Geistliche Kirchengesänge, 1623
Harm. by Ralph Vaughan Williams

1. All crea-tures of our God and King, Lift up your voice and with us
2. Thou rush-ing wind that art so strong, Ye clouds that sail in heav'n a-
3. Dear moth-er earth, who day by day Un-fold-est bless-ings on our
4. And all ye men of ten-der heart, For-giv-ing oth-ers, take your
5. Let all things their Cre-a-tor bless, And wor-ship Him in hum-ble-
   Praise God from whom all bless-ings flow, Praise Him all crea-tures here be-

Harmony — *Unison*

sing, Al-le-lu-ia! Al-le-lu-ia! Thou burn-ing sun with gold-en
long, O praise Him! Al-le-lu-ia! Thou ris-ing morn, in praise re-
way, O praise Him! Al-le-lu-ia! The flow'rs and fruits that in thee
part, O sing ye! Al-le-lu-ia! Ye who long pain and sor-row
ness, O praise Him! Al-le-lu-ia! Praise, praise the Fa-ther, praise the
low, Al-le-lu-ia! Al-le-lu-ia! Praise Him a-bove, ye heav'n-ly

Harmony

beam, Thou sil-ver moon with soft-er gleam! O praise Him, O
joice, Ye lights of eve-ning, find a voice! O praise Him, O
grow, Let them His glo-ry al-so show! O praise Him, O
bear, Praise God and on Him cast your care! O praise Him, O
Son, And praise the Spir-it, Three in One! O praise Him, O
host, Praise Fa-ther, Son and Ho-ly Ghost, Al-le-lu-ia, Al-le-

Unison

praise Him, Al-le-lu-ia! Al-le-lu-ia! Al-le-lu-ia! A-MEN.
lu-ia!

hymns of worship

The story of this hymn is on page...13

JOIN ALL THE GLORIOUS NAMES

DARWALL. 6 6 6 6 8 8

Isaac Watts

John Darwall

1. Join all the glo-rious names Of wis-dom, love, and power,
2. Great Pro-phet of my God, My tongue would bless Thy name:
3. Je - sus, my great High Priest, Of-fered His blood, and died;
4. Thou art my Coun-sel-lor, My Pat-tern, and my Guide,
5. My Sav-iour and my Lord, My Con-quer'r and my King,

That ev - er mor - tals knew, That an - gels
By Thee the joy - ful news Of our sal-
My guilt - y con - science seeks No sac - ri-
And Thou my Shep - herd art; Oh, keep me
Thy scep - tre and Thy sword, Thy reign - ing

ev - er bore: All are too poor to speak His worth,
va - tion came, The joy - ful news of sins for - giv'n,
fice be - side: His pow'r - ful blood did once a - tone
near Thy side; Nor let my feet e'er turn a - stray,
grace I sing: Thine is the pow'r; be - hold I sit

Too poor to set my Sav - iour forth.
Of hell sub - dued and peace with heav'n.
And now it pleads be - fore the throne.
To wan - der in the crook - ed way.
In will - ing bonds be - neath Thy feet. A - MEN.

The story of this hymn is on page . . 153

hymns of worship

18 fOR the BEAUTY Of the EARTH

DIX. 7 7 7 7 7 7

Folliott S. Pierpoint

Conrad Kocher, adapted

1. For the beau - ty of the earth, For the glo - ry
2. For the beau - ty of each hour Of the day and
3. For the joy of hu - man love, Broth - er, sis - ter,
4. For Thy Church that ev - er - more Lift - eth ho - ly

of the skies, For the love which from our birth
of the night, Hill and vale, and tree, and flower,
par - ent, child, Friends on earth and friends a - bove,
hands a - bove, Of - fering up on ev - ery shore

O - ver and a - round us lies, Lord of all, to
Sun and moon, and stars of light, Lord of all, to
For all gen - tle thoughts and mild, Lord of all, to
Her pure sac - ri - fice of love, Lord of all, to

Thee we raise This our hymn of grate - ful praise.
Thee we raise This our hymn of grate - ful praise.
Thee we raise This our hymn of grate - ful praise.
Thee we raise This our hymn of grate - ful praise. A-MEN.

By permission of the Estate of the late F. S. Pierpoint and Oxford University Press.

hymns of worship

The story of this hymn is on page..141

PRAISE YE THE LORD, THE ALMIGHTY

LOBE DEN HERREN. 14 14 4 7 8

Joachim Neander
Trans. by Catherine Winkworth

Stralsund Gesangbuch, 1665

1. Praise ye the Lord, the Al-might-y, the King of cre-a-
   tion! O my soul, praise Him, for He is thy health and sal-
   va - - tion! All ye who hear, Now to His tem - ple draw
   near; Join me in glad ad - o - ra - - - tion!

2. Praise ye the Lord, who o'er all things so won-drous-ly reigneth, Shel - ters thee un - der His wings, yea, so gen - tly sustain - - eth! Hast thou not seen How thy de - sires e'er have
   been Grant-ed in what He or - dain - - - eth?

3. Praise ye the Lord, who with mar - vel - ous wis - dom hath made
   thee! Decked thee with health, and with lov - ing hand guid - ed and
   stayed thee; How oft in grief Hath not He brought thee relief, Spread-ing His wings for to shade . . . thee!

4. Praise ye the Lord! O let all that is in me a - dore
   Him! All that hath life and breath, come now with prais - es before Him! Let the A - men Sound from His peo - ple a-
   gain: Glad - ly for aye we a - dore . . . Him. A - MEN.

hymns of worship

20

REJOICE, MY SOUL!

HARVEY. L.M. Ref.

Avis B. Christiansen

Donald P. Hustad

1. Re - joice, my soul! re - joice and sing E - ter - nal praise to Christ thy King;
2. Re - joice, my soul! re - joice in Him Whose pow'r hath conquered death and sin;
3. Re - joice, my soul! re - joice and sing! Glad hom-age yield to Christ, thy King!

All glo - rious is His ho - ly name, Through ev-er-last-ing years the same.
Who rose in vic - t'ry from the grave, And lives, al-might-y now to save.
Whose name all men shall one day own Be - fore His ev - er - last-ing throne.

REFRAIN

Re - joice, my soul! re - joice and sing Glad songs of praise to Christ, thy King.

Let notes of ad - o - ra - tion rise And ech - o through the vault-ed skies.

Let heav'n and earth His pow'r pro-claim, And mag - ni - fy His ho - ly name!

hymns of worship

Re - joice, my soul! re - joice and sing! For Christ the Lord is King!

There is no name so sweet on earth   21

THE SWEETEST NAME. 8 7 8 7 D.

Source Unknown

William B. Bradbury

1. There is   no name so   sweet on earth, No   name so sweet in   heav - en,
2. And when He hung up - on   the tree, They wrote His name a - bove Him;
3. So   now, up - on   His   Fa-ther's throne, Al-might-y   to   re - lease us
4. O   Je - sus, by   that match-less name, Thy grace shall fail us   nev - er;

The   name be - fore   His   won-drous birth, To   Christ the Sav - iour   giv - en.
That   all might see   the   rea - son we   For   ev - er-more must   love Him.
From   sin and pains, He   glad - ly reigns, The Prince and Sav - iour,   Je - sus.
To - day as yes - ter - day the same, Thou art   the same for - ev - er.

REFRAIN

We love to sing   of Christ our King, And hail him bless - ed   Je - sus;

For there's no word ear   ev - er heard So dear, so sweet as "Je - sus."

FOREVER
PLAGAL. 8 7 8 7

Effie Smith Ely   Donald P. Hustad

1. We sigh for hu-man love, from which A whim or chance may sev-er,
2. We seek earth's peace in things that pass Like foam up-on the riv-er,
3. Man's help, for which we long, gives way, As trees in storm-winds quiv-er,
4. Turn un-to Thee our wav-'ring hearts, O Thou who fail-est nev-er;

And leave un-sought the love of God, Tho' God's love lasts for-ev-er.
While steadfast as the stars on high, God's peace a-bides for-ev-er.
But might-ier than all hu-man need God's help re-mains for-ev-er.
Give us Thy love and Thy great peace, And be our Help for-ev-er! A-MEN.

23 PRAISE THE SAVIOUR, YE WHO KNOW HIM!
ACCLAIM. 8 8 8 5

Thomas Kelly   Traditional German Melody

1. Praise the Sav-iour, ye who know Him! Who can tell how much we owe Him?
2. Je-sus is the name that charms us; He for con-flict fits and arms us;
3. Trust in Him, ye saints, for-ev-er; He is faith-ful, chang-ing nev-er;
4. Keep us, Lord, O keep us cleav-ing To Thy-self and still be-liev-ing,
5. Then we shall be where we would be, Then we shall be what we should be;

Glad-ly let us ren-der to Him All we are and have.
Noth-ing moves and noth-ing harms us While we trust in Him.
Nei-ther force nor guile can sev-er Those He loves from Him.
Till the hour of our re-ceiv-ing Prom-ised joys with Thee.
Things that are not now, nor could be, Soon shall be our own. A-MEN.

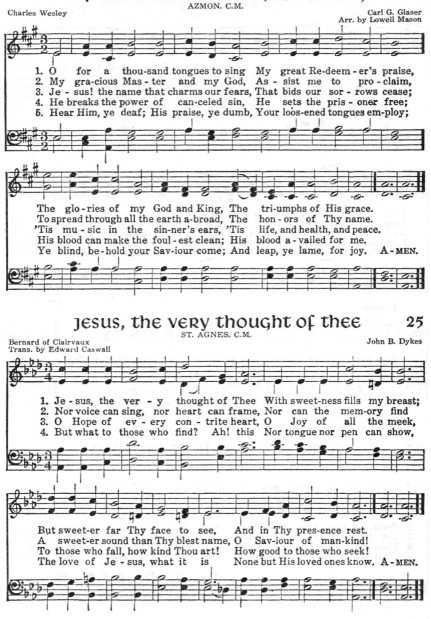

O for a thousand tongues to sing
AZMON. C.M.

24

Charles Wesley

Carl G. Glaser
Arr. by Lowell Mason

1. O for a thou-sand tongues to sing My great Re-deem-er's praise,
2. My gra-cious Mas-ter and my God, As-sist me to pro-claim,
3. Je-sus! the name that charms our fears, That bids our sor-rows cease;
4. He breaks the power of can-celed sin, He sets the pris-on-er free;
5. Hear Him, ye deaf; His praise, ye dumb, Your loos-ened tongues em-ploy;

The glo-ries of my God and King, The tri-umphs of His grace.
To spread through all the earth a-broad, The hon-ors of Thy name.
'Tis mu-sic in the sin-ner's ears, 'Tis life, and health, and peace.
His blood can make the foul-est clean; His blood a-vailed for me.
Ye blind, be-hold your Sav-iour come; And leap, ye lame, for joy. A-MEN.

Jesus, the very thought of thee
ST. AGNES. C.M.

25

Bernard of Clairvaux
Trans. by Edward Caswall

John B. Dykes

1. Je-sus, the ver-y thought of Thee With sweet-ness fills my breast;
2. Nor voice can sing, nor heart can frame, Nor can the mem-ory find
3. O Hope of ev-ery con-trite heart, O Joy of all the meek,
4. But what to those who find? Ah! this Nor tongue nor pen can show,

But sweet-er far Thy face to see, And in Thy pres-ence rest.
A sweet-er sound than Thy blest name, O Sav-iour of man-kind!
To those who fall, how kind Thou art! How good to those who seek!
The love of Je-sus, what it is None but His loved ones know. A-MEN.

26 REJOICE, YE PURE IN HEART

MARION. S.M. Ref.

Edward H. Plumptre

Arthur H. Messiter

1. Re - joice, ye pure in heart, Re - joice, give thanks, and sing;
2. With all the an - gel choirs, With all the saints on earth,
3. Still lift your stand - ard high, Still march in firm ar - ray;
4. Yes, on through life's long path, Still chant - ing as ye go;
5. Then on, ye pure in heart, Re - joice, give thanks, and sing;

Your fes - tal ban - ner wave on high, The cross of Christ your King.
Pour out the strains of joy and bliss, True rap - ture, no - blest mirth!
As war - riors through the dark - ness toil Till dawns the gold - en day.
From youth to age, by night and day, In glad - ness and in woe.
Your fes - tal ban - ner wave on high, The cross of Christ your King.

REFRAIN

Re - joice, re - joice, Re - joice, give thanks, and sing! A-MEN.

Re-joice, re-joice,

27 COME, WE THAT LOVE THE LORD

ST. THOMAS. S.M.

Isaac Watts

Aaron Williams

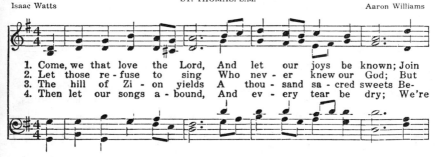

1. Come, we that love the Lord, And let our joys be known; Join
2. Let those re - fuse to sing Who nev - er knew our God; But
3. The hill of Zi - on yields A thou - sand sa - cred sweets Be -
4. Then let our songs a - bound, And ev - ery tear be dry; We're

hymns of worship

in a song with sweet ac - cord, And thus sur - round the throne.
chil - dren of the heaven - ly King May speak their joys a - broad.
fore we reach the heaven - ly fields, Or walk the gold - en streets.
march - ing thro' Em - man - uel's ground To fair - er worlds on high. A-MEN.

COME, THOU ALMIGHTY KING

MOSCOW (ITALIAN HYMN). 6 6 4 6 6 6 4

28

Source Unknown

Felice de Giardini

1. Come, Thou Al - might - y King, Help us Thy name to sing,
2. Come, Thou In - car - nate Word, Gird on Thy might - y sword,
3. Come, Ho - ly Com - fort - er, Thy sa - cred wit - ness bear
4. To the great One in Three E - ter - nal prais - es be

Help us to praise: Fa - ther, all - glo - ri - ous, O'er all vic -
Our prayer at - tend: Come, and Thy peo - ple bless, And give Thy
In this glad hour: Thou who al - might - y art, Now rule in
Hence, ev - er - more! His sov - ereign maj - es - ty May we in

to - ri - ous, Come, and reign o - ver us, An - cient of Days.
word suc - cess: Spir - it of ho - li - ness, On us de - scend.
ev - ery heart, And ne'er from us de - part, Spir - it of power.
glo - ry see, And to e - ter - ni - ty Love and a - dore! A-MEN.

hymns of worship

The story of this hymn is on page..109

29

PRAISE HIM! PRAISE HIM!

JOYFUL SONG. 12 10 12 10 D.

Fanny J. Crosby.

Chester G. Allen

1. Praise Him! praise Him! Je-sus, our bless-ed Re-deem-er! Sing, O Earth, His
2. Praise Him! praise Him! Je-sus, our bless-ed Re-deem-er! For our sins He
3. Praise Him! praise Him! Je-sus, our bless-ed Re-deem-er! Heavenly por-tals

won-der-ful love pro-claim! Hail Him! hail Him! highest archangels in glo-ry;
suffered, and bled and died; He our Rock, our hope of e-ter-nal sal-va-tion,
loud with ho-san-nas ring! Je-sus, Sav-iour, reigneth for-ev-er and ev-er;

Strength and hon-or give to His ho-ly name! Like a shep-herd Je-sus will
Hail Him! hail Him! Je-sus the Cru-ci-fied. Sound His prais-es! Je-sus who
Crown Him! crown Him! Prophet and Priest and King! Christ is com-ing! o-ver the

REFRAIN

guard His children, In His arms He carries them all day long:
bore our sor-rows; Love unbounded, wonderful, deep and strong: Praise Him! praise Him!
world vic-to-rious, Power and glo-ry un-to the Lord be-long:

tell of His ex-cel-lent greatness; Praise Him! praise Him! ever in joy-ful song!

hymns of worship

MADRID. 6 6 6 6 D.

Christian Henry Bateman

Traditional Melody
Harm. by David Evans

1. Come, Chris-tians, join to sing Al - le - lu - ia! A - men!
2. Come, lift your hearts on high, Al - le - lu - ia! A - men!
3. Praise yet our Christ a - gain, Al - le - lu - ia! A - men!

Loud praise to Christ our King; Al - le - lu - ia! A - men!
Let prais - es fill the sky; Al - le - lu - ia! A - men!
Life shall not end the strain; Al - le - lu - ia! A - men!

Let all, with heart and voice, Be - fore His throne re - joice;
He is our Guide and Friend; To us He'll con - de - scend;
On heav - en's bliss - ful shore His good - ness we'll a - dore,

Praise is His gra - cious choice: Al - le - lu - ia! A - men!
His love shall nev - er end: Al - le - lu - ia! A - men!
Sing - ing for - ev - er - more, "Al - le - lu - ia! A - men!" A-MEN.

CROWN hIm wITh many CROWns

DIADEMATA. S.M.D.

Matthew Bridges and
Godfrey Thring

George J. Elvey

1. Crown Him with man - y crowns, The Lamb up - on His throne;
2. Crown Him the Son of God Be - fore the worlds be - gan,
3. Crown Him the Lord of life, Who tri - umphed o'er the grave,
4. Crown Him the Lord of love! Be - hold His hands and side,

Hark! how the heaven-ly an - them drowns All mu - sic but its own!
And ye, who tread where He hath trod, Crown Him the Son of man;
And rose vic - to - rious in the strife For those He came to save;
Rich wounds, yet vis - i - ble a - bove, In beau - ty glo - ri - fied:

A - wake, my soul, and sing Of Him who died for thee,
Who ev - ery grief hath known That wrings the hu - man breast,
His glo - ries now we sing Who died, and rose on high,
All hail, Re - deem - er, hail! For Thou hast died for me:

And hail Him as thy matchless King Through all e - ter - ni - ty.
And takes and bears them for His own, That all in Him may rest.
Who died, e - ter - nal life to bring, And lives that death may die.
Thy praise shall nev-er, nev - er fail Throughout e - ter - ni - ty. A - MEN.

a mighty fortress is our god

EIN' FESTE BURG. 8 7 8 7 6 6 6 6 7

Martin Luther
Trans. by Frederick H. Hedge

Martin Luther

1. A might-y for-tress is our God, A bul-wark nev-er fail - ing;
2. Did we in our own strength confide, Our striv-ing would be los - ing,
3. And though this world, with dev-ils filled, Should threaten to un - do us,
4. That word a - bove all earth-ly powers—No thanks to them—a - bid - eth;

Our help - er He, a - mid the flood Of mor - tal ills pre - vail - ing.
Were not the right Man on our side, The Man of God's own choos - ing.
We will not fear, for God hath willed His truth to tri - umph through us.
The Spir - it and the gifts are ours Through Him who with us sid - eth.

For still our an - cient foe Doth seek to work us woe; His craft and power are
Dost ask who that may be? Christ Je-sus, it is He; Lord Sab - a - oth His
The prince of darkness grim—We trem-ble not for him; His rage we can en-
Let goods and kin-dred go, This mor-tal life al - so; The bod - y they may

great, And, armed with cru-el hate, On earth is not his e - qual.
name, From age to age the same, And He must win the bat - tle.
dure, For lo! his doom is sure, One lit - tle word shall fell him.
kill: God's truth a - bid - eth still, His King-dom is for - ev - er. A-MEN.

hymns of worship

33 GREAT IS THY FAITHFULNESS

FAITHFULNESS. 11 10 11 10 Ref.

Thomas O. Chisholm

William M. Runyan

1. "Great is Thy faith-ful-ness," O God my Fa-ther, There is no shad-ow of
2. Sum-mer and win-ter, and springtime and harvest, Sun, moon and stars in their
3. Par-don for sin and a peace that en-dur-eth, Thy own dear pres-ence to

turn-ing with Thee; Thou chang-est not, Thy com-pas-sions, they fail not;
cours-es a-bove, Join with all na-ture in man-i-fold wit-ness
cheer and to guide; Strength for to-day and bright hope for to-mor-row,

REFRAIN

As Thou hast been Thou for-ev-er wilt be.
To Thy great faith-ful-ness, mer-cy and love. "Great is Thy faith-ful-ness!
Bless-ings all mine, with ten thou-sand be-side!

Great is Thy faithfulness!" Morning by morning new mer-cies I see; All I have

need-ed Thy hand hath pro-vid-ed—"Great is Thy faithfulness," Lord, un-to me!

The story of this hymn is on page...31

O SACRED HEAD, NOW WOUNDED

PASSION CHORALE. 7 6 7 6 D.

Ascribed to Bernard of Clairvaux
Trans. by Paul Gerhardt
Trans. by James W. Alexander

Hans L. Hassler
Harm. by J. S. Bach

1. O sa-cred Head, now wound-ed, With grief and shame weighed down;
2. What Thou, my Lord, hast suf-fered Was all for sin-ners' gain:
3. What lan-guage shall I bor-row To thank Thee, dear-est Friend:

Now scorn-ful-ly sur-round-ed With thorns, Thine on-ly crown;
Mine, mine was the trans-gres-sion, But Thine the dead-ly pain.
For this Thy dy-ing sor-row, Thy pit-y with-out end?

O sa-cred Head, what glo - ry, What bliss till now was Thine!
Lo, here I fall, my Sav - iour! 'Tis I de-serve Thy place;
O make me Thine for-ev - - er; And should I faint-ing be,

Yet, though de-spised and go - ry, I joy to call Thee mine.
Look on me with Thy fa - vor, Vouch-safe to me Thy grace.
Lord, let me nev-er, nev - er Out-live my love to Thee. A-MEN.

hymns of worship

35

all hail the power

CORONATION. C.M.

Edward Perronet
Alt. by John Rippon

Oliver Holden

1. All hail the power of Je - sus' name! Let an - gels pros-trate fall;
2. Ye cho - sen seed of Is - rael's race, Ye ran-somed from the fall,
3. Let ev - ery kin - dred, ev - ery tribe, On this ter - res - trial ball,
4. O that with yon - der sa - cred throng We at His feet may fall!

Bring forth the roy - al di - a - dem, And crown Him Lord of all;
Hail Him who saves you by His grace, And crown Him Lord of all;
To Him all maj - es - ty as - cribe, And crown Him Lord of all;
We'll join the ev - er - last - ing song, And crown Him Lord of all;

Bring forth the roy - al di - a - dem, And crown Him Lord of all!
Hail Him who saves you by His grace, And crown Him Lord of all!
To Him all maj - es - ty as - cribe, And crown Him Lord of all!
We'll join the ev - er - last-ing song, And crown Him Lord of all! A-MEN.

(Second Tune)

MILES LANE. C.M.

William Shrubsole

1. All hail the power of Je-sus' name! Let angels prostrate fall; Bring forth the roy-al

di - a - dem, And crown Him, crown Him, crown Him, Crown Him Lord of all! A-MEN.

my God and King!

ALL THE WORLD. 14 12 12 14

George Herbert

Robert G. McCutchan

1. Let all the world in ev - ery cor - ner sing, "My God and
2. Let all the world in ev - ery cor - ner sing, "My God and

King!" The heavens are not too high, His praise may thith - er fly; The
King!" The Church with psalms must shout, No door can keep them out: But

earth is not too low, His prais - es there may grow. Let all the world in
more than all, the heart Must bear the lar - gest part. Let all the world in

ev - ery cor - ner sing, "My God and King!" God and King!"

37

I love thee

I LOVE THEE. 11 11 11 11

Source Unknown

Ingall's *Christian Harmony*, 1805

1. I love Thee, I love Thee, I love Thee, my Lord;
2. I'm hap - py, I'm hap - py, oh, won - drous ac - count!
3. O Je - sus, my Sav - iour, with Thee I am blest,
4. Oh, who's like my Sav - iour? He's Sa - lem's bright King;

I love Thee, my Sav - iour, I love Thee, my God;
My joys are im - mor - tal, I stand on the mount;
My life and sal - va - tion, my joy and my rest;
He smiles and He loves me and helps me to sing;

I love Thee, I love Thee, and that Thou dost know;
I gaze on my treas - ure and long to be there,
Thy name be my theme, and Thy love be my song;
I'll praise Him, I'll praise Him with notes loud and clear,

But how much I love Thee my ac - tions will show.
With Je - sus and an - gels and kin - dred so dear.
Thy grace shall in - spire both my heart and my tongue.
While riv - ers of pleas - ure my spir - it shall cheer. A - MEN.

hymns of worship

the God of abraham praise

LEONI. 6 6 8 4 D.

Thomas Olivers
Based on *The Yigdal*
by Daniel ben Judah

Hebrew Melody
Arr. by Meyer Lyon

1. The God of A-braham praise, Who reigns en-throned a - bove;
2. The God of A-braham praise, At whose su - preme com - mand
3. He by Him - self hath sworn, I on His oath de - pend;
4. The whole tri - um - phant host Give thanks to God on high;

An - cient of ev - er - last - ing days, And God of love.
From earth I rise, and seek the joys At His right hand.
I shall, on ea - gles' wings up - borne, To heaven as - cend;
"Hail, Fa - ther, Son and Ho - ly Ghost!" They ev - er cry.

Je - ho - vah, great I AM, By earth and heaven con - fessed;
I all on earth for - sake, Its wis - dom, fame, and power;
I shall be - hold His face, I shall His power a - dore,
Hail, A-braham's God and mine! I join the heaven - ly lays;

I. bow and bless the sa - cred Name, For - ev - er blest.
And Him my on - ly por - tion make, My shield and tower.
And sing the won - ders of His grace For - ev - er - more.
All might and maj - es - ty are Thine, And end - less praise. A-MEN.

hymns of worship

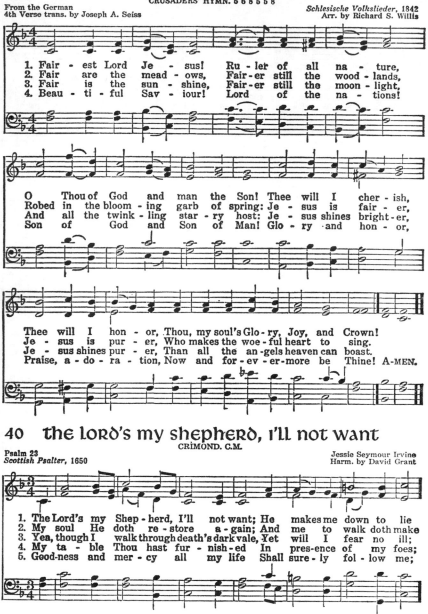

FAIREST LORD JESUS
CRUSADERS' HYMN. 5 6 8 5 5 8

From the German
4th Verse trans. by Joseph A. Seiss

Schlesische Volkslieder, 1842
Arr. by Richard S. Willis

1. Fair - est Lord Je - sus! Ru - ler of all na - ture,
2. Fair are the mead - ows, Fair - er still the wood - lands,
3. Fair is the sun - shine, Fair - er still the moon - light,
4. Beau - ti - ful Sav - iour! Lord of the na - tions!

O Thou of God and man the Son! Thee will I cher - ish,
Robed in the bloom - ing garb of spring: Je - sus is fair - er,
And all the twink - ling star - ry host: Je - sus shines bright - er,
Son of God and Son of Man! Glo - ry and hon - or,

Thee will I hon - or, Thou, my soul's Glo - ry, Joy, and Crown!
Je - sus is pur - er, Who makes the woe - ful heart to sing.
Je - sus shines pur - er, Than all the an - gels heaven can boast.
Praise, a - do - ra - tion, Now and for - ev - er - more be Thine! A-MEN.

40 THE LORD'S MY SHEPHERD, I'LL NOT WANT
CRIMOND. C.M.

Psalm 23
Scottish Psalter, 1650

Jessie Seymour Irvine
Harm. by David Grant

1. The Lord's my Shep - herd, I'll not want; He makes me down to lie
2. My soul He doth re - store a - gain; And me to walk doth make
3. Yea, though I walk through death's dark vale, Yet will I fear no ill;
4. My ta - ble Thou hast fur - nish - ed In pres - ence of my foes;
5. Good - ness and mer - cy all my life Shall sure - ly fol - low me;

hymns of worship

In pas-tures green; He lead - eth me The qui - et wa - ters by.
With-in the paths of right-eous-ness, E'en for His own name's sake.
For Thou art with me, and Thy rod And staff me com-fort still.
My head Thou dost with oil a-noint, And my cup o - ver-flows.
And in God's house for - ev - er-more My dwell-ing place shall be. A-MEN.

WHEN MORNING GILDS THE SKIES 41
LAUDES DOMINI. 6 6 6 6 6 6

From the German, c. 1800
Trans. by Edward Caswall

Joseph Barnby

1. When morn - ing gilds the skies, My heart a - wak - ing cries:
2. Does sad - ness fill my mind, A sol - ace here I find:
3. In heaven's e - ter - nal bliss The love - liest strain is this,
4. Be this, while life is mine, My can - ti - cle di - vine,

May Je - sus Christ be praised; A - like at work or prayer
May Je - sus Christ be praised; Or fades my earth - ly bliss,
May Je - sus Christ be praised; The powers of dark - ness fear,
May Je - sus Christ be praised; Be this th' e - ter - nal song,

To Je - sus I re - pair: May Je - sus Christ be praised.
My com - fort still is this: May Je - sus Christ be praised.
When this sweet chant they hear: May Je - sus Christ be praised.
Through all the a - ges long: May Je - sus Christ be praised. AMEN

HYMNS OF WORSHIP

42 WHAT A WONDERFUL SAVIOUR!

BENTON HARBOR. 8 7 8 7 Ref.

Elisha A. Hoffman   Elisha A. Hoffman

1. Christ has for sin a-tone-ment made, What a won-der-ful Sav-iour!
2. I praise Him for the cleans-ing blood, What a won-der-ful Sav-iour!
3. He cleansed my heart from all its sin, What a won-der-ful Sav-iour!
4. He gives me o-ver-com-ing pow'r, What a won-der-ful Sav-iour!
5. To Him I've giv-en all my heart, What a won-der-ful Sav-iour!

We are re-deemed! the price is paid! What a won-der-ful Sav-iour!
That rec-on-ciled my soul to God; What a won-der-ful Sav-iour!
And now He reigns and rules there-in; What a won-der-ful Sav-iour!
And tri-umph in each try-ing hour; What a won-der-ful Sav-iour!
The world shall nev-er share a part; What a won-der-ful Sav-iour!

REFRAIN

What a won-der-ful Sav-iour is Je-sus, my Je-sus!

What a won-der-ful Sav-iour is Je-sus, my Lord!

hymns of worship

JOANNA. 11 11 11 11

Walter Chalmers Smith   Welsh Hymn Melody

1. Im - mor - tal, in - vis - i - ble, God on - ly wise,
2. Un - rest - ing, un - hast - ing, and si - lent as light,
3. To all, life Thou giv - est, to both great and small,
4. Great Fa - ther of glo - ry, pure Fa - ther of light,

In light in - ac - ces - si - ble hid from our eyes,
Nor want - ing, nor wast - ing, Thou rul - est in might;
In all life Thou liv - est, the true life of all.
Thine an - gels a - dore Thee, all veil - ing their sight;

Most bless - ed, most glo - rious, the An - cient of Days,
Thy jus - tice like moun - tains high soar - ing a - bove
We blos - som and flour - ish as leaves on the tree,
All praise we would ren - der; O help us to see

Al - might - y, vic - to - rious, Thy great name we praise.
Thy clouds, which are foun - tains of good - ness and love.
And with - er and per - ish— but nought chang - eth Thee.
'Tis on - ly the splen - dor of light hid - eth Thee! A - MEN.

The story of this hymn is on page . .133

44 this is my father's world

TERRA BEATA. S.M.D.

Maltbie D. Babcock

Franklin L. Sheppard

1. This is my Fa-ther's world, And to my lis-tening ears All
2. This is my Fa-ther's world, The birds their car-ols raise, The
3. This is my Fa-ther's world, O let me ne'er for-get That

na - ture sings, and round me rings The mu - sic of the spheres.
morn-ing light, the lil - y white, De - clare their Mak - er's praise.
though the wrong seems oft so strong, God is the Rul - er yet.

This is my Fa-ther's world: I rest me in the thought Of
This is my Fa-ther's world: He shines in all that's fair; In the
This is my Fa-ther's world: The bat - tle is not done; Je-

rocks and trees, of skies and seas—His hand the won - ders wrought.
rus - tling grass I hear Him pass, He speaks to me ev-ery-where.
sus who died shall be sat - is - fied, And earth and heaven be one. A - MEN.

HERE, O MY LORD

LANGRAN. 10 10 10 10

Horatius Bonar

James Langran

1. Here, O my Lord, I see Thee face to face;
2. Here would I feed up - on the bread of God;
3. This is the hour of ban - quet and of song;
4. Too soon we rise; the sym - bols dis - ap - pear;
5. Feast af - ter feast thus comes and pass - es by,

Here would I touch and han - dle things un - seen,
Here drink with Thee the roy - al wine of heav'n;
This is the heav'n - ly ta - ble spread for me;
The feast, though not the love, is past and gone;
Yet, pass - ing, points to the glad feast a - bove,

Here grasp with firm - er hand th'e - ter - nal grace,
Here would I lay a - side each earth - ly load,
Here let me feast, and feast - ing, still pro - long
The bread and wine re - move, but Thou art here,
Giv - ing sweet fore - taste of the fes - tal joy,

And all my wea - ri - ness up - on Thee lean.
Here taste a - fresh the calm of sin for - giv'n.
The brief bright hour of fel - low - ship with Thee.
Near - er than ev - er; still my shield and sun.
The Lamb's great brid - al feast of bliss and love. A - MEN.

46

PRAISE YE THE TRIUNE GOD!

FLEMMING. 11 11 11 5

Source Unknown

Friedrich F. Flemming

1. Praise ye the Fa-ther! for His lov-ing kind-ness, Ten-der-ly
2. Praise ye the Sav-iour! great is His com-pas-sion, Gra-cious-ly
3. Praise ye the Spir-it! Com-fort-er of Is-rael, Sent of the

cares He for His err-ing chil-dren; Praise Him, ye an-gels,
cares He for His cho-sen peo-ple; Young men and maid-ens,
Fa-ther and the Son to bless us; Praise ye the Fa-ther,

praise Him in the heav-ens, Praise ye Je-ho-vah!
ye old men and chil-dren, Praise ye the Sav-iour!
Son and Ho-ly Spir-it, Praise ye the Tri-une God! A-MEN.

47

JESUS, GENTLEST SAVIOUR

EUDOXIA. 6 5 6 5

Frederick W. Faber

Sabine Baring-Gould

1. Je - sus, gen - tlest Sav - iour, God of might and power,
2. Na - ture can - not hold thee, Heav'n is all too strait
3. Out be - yond the shin - ing Of the far - thest star,
4. Yet the hearts of child - ren Hold what worlds can - not,
5. Je - sus, gent - lest Sav - iour, Thou art with us now;
6. Mul - ti - ply our gra - ces, Give us love and fear,

By permission of J. Curwen & Sons Ltd., 29 Maiden Lane, London, W. C. 2.

hymns of worship

Thou thy-self art dwell-ing With us at this hour.
For Thine end-less glo-ry And thy roy-al state.
Thou art ev-er stretch-ing In - fi - nite-ly far.
And the God of won-ders Loves the low-ly spot.
Fill us with thy good-ness Till our hearts o'er-flow.
And, dear Lord, the chief-est, Grace to per-se-vere. A-MEN.

O WORSHIP THE KING

LYONS. 10 10 11 11

48

Robert Grant
From Psalm 104

Adapted from J. Michael Haydn

1. O wor-ship the King, all - glo-rious a - bove, O grate-ful-ly
2. O tell of His might, O sing of His grace, Whose robe is the
3. Thy boun - ti - ful care what tongue can re - cite? It breathes in the
4. Frail chil-dren of dust, and fee-ble as frail, In Thee do we

sing His power and His love; Our Shield and De-fend-er, the An - cient of
light, whose can-o-py space. His char-iots of wrath the deep thun-der-clouds
air, it shines in the light, It streams from the hills, it de-scends to the
trust, nor find Thee to fail; Thy mer-cies how ten-der! how firm to the

Days, Pa - vil-ioned in splen-dor, and gird - ed with praise.
form, And dark is His path on the wings of the storm.
plain, And sweet-ly dis - tills in the dew and the rain.
end! Our Mak-er, De - fend-er, Re - deem-er and Friend. A - MEN.

49 O could I speak the matchless worth

ARIEL. 8 8 6 D.

Samuel Medley

Wolfgang A. Mozart
Arr. by Lowell Mason

1. O could I speak the match - less worth,
2. I'd sing the pre - cious blood He spilt,
3. I'd sing the char - ac - ters He bears,
4. Soon the de - light - ful day will come

O could I sound the glo - ries forth Which in my Sav - iour shine,
My ran - som from the dread - ful guilt Of sin and wrath di - vine!
And all the forms of love He wears, Ex - alt - ed on His throne:
When my dear Lord will bring me home, And I shall see His face;

I'd soar and touch the heav'nly strings, And vie with Ga-briel while he sings
I'd sing His glo - rious right-eous-ness, In which all-per - fect heavenly dress
In loft - iest songs of sweet-est praise, I would to ev - er - last - ing days
Then with my Sav - iour, Brother, Friend, A blest e - ter - ni - ty I'll spend,

In notes al - most di - vine, In notes al - most di - vine.
My soul shall ev - er shine, My soul shall ev - er shine.
Make all His glo - ries known, Make all His glo - ries known.
Tri - um - phant in His grace, Tri - um-phant in His grace. A-MEN.

awake, my soul, and with the sun

MORNING HYMN. L.M.

Thomas Ken

Francois H. Barthélémon

50

1. A - wake, my soul, and with the sun Thy dai - ly stage of du - ty run;
2. Wake, and lift up thy - self, my heart, And with the an - gels bear thy part,
3. All praise to Thee, who safe hast kept, And hast re-freshed me while I slept;
4. Di - rect, con-trol, sug-gest, this day, All I de - sign, or do, or say;

Shake off dull sloth, and joy - ful rise To pay thy morn-ing sac - ri - fice.
Who all night long un-wear-ied sing High praise to the E - ter - nal King.
Grant, Lord, when I from death shall wake, I may of end - less life par-take.
That all my powers, with all their might, In Thy sole glo - ry may u - nite. A-MEN.

The story of this hymn is on page . . 147

all people that on earth do dwell

OLD HUNDREDTH. L.M.

Psalm 100
Ascribed to William Kethe: alt.

Genevan Psalter. 1551
Louis Bourgeois

51

1. All peo-ple that on earth do dwell, Sing to the Lord with cheerful voice;
2. Know that the Lord is God in - deed; With-out our aid He did us make;
3. O en - ter then His gates with praise, Ap-proach with joy His courts un - to;
4. For why? the Lord our God is good, His mer - cy is for - ev - er sure;

Him serve with fear His praise forth tell, Come ye be-fore Him and re - joice.
We are His folk, He doth us feed, And for His sheep He doth us take.
Praise, laud, and bless His name al-ways, For it is seem-ly so to do.
His truth at all times firm-ly stood, And shall from age to age en - dure. A-MEN.

52 hOW GREAT thy lOVING kINDNESS IS

INFINITY. 8 6 8 6 8 8 8 6

E. Margaret Clarkson

E. Margaret Clarkson

1. How great Thy lov-ing kind-ness is, O God of grace, to me!
2. How great Thy lov-ing kind-ness is! Be-fore I sought Thy face,
3. How great Thy lov-ing kind-ness is! So in-fi-nite Thou art,
4. How great Thy lov-ing kind-ness is, To car-ry all my care,
5. How great Thy lov-ing kind-ness is! When pil-grim days are past,

How stead-fast is Thy faith-ful-ness, Thy mer-cies, O how free!
Lo, I was sought of Thee, and found By pure, re-sist-less grace,
So far tran-scend-ing high-est thought Of mor-tal mind or heart,
To walk be-side me day by day My joys and griefs to share!
In Je-sus' like-ness per-fect-ed I'll see Thy face at last,

I wor-ship Thee, my God and King, With burn-ing heart Thy prais-es sing:
Was lift-ed in its might-y flow And taught re-deem-ing love to know:
Yet Thou didst give Thy-self for me In ut-ter-most hu-mil-i-ty:
Thy way is per-fect:Thou wilt lead, Make plain my path, sup-ply my need:
Thru-out e-ter-nal years to sing Thy ho-ly praise, my God and King:

REFRAIN

How great Thy lov-ing kind-ness is, How vast, how rich, how free!

How great Thy lov-ing kind-ness is, O God of grace, to me!

hymns of worship

hymns of salvation

The word "crusader" is derived from the Latin "crux" — meaning "cross." In the age of chivalry knights decorated their shields and banners with the cross, to proclaim their faith in Jesus Christ.

In any age preaching and singing about the Cross is central, for it is through the death and resurrection of Christ that we have forgiveness of sins and the assurance of eternal life.

Songs of salvation express both the sorrow we feel over Christ's suffering on our behalf, and the joy we experience through our new and redeemed life in Him.

BRYN CALFARIA. 8 7 8 7 4 7

Joseph Hart

William Owen

1. Come, ye sin - ners, poor and wretch-ed, Weak and wound-ed, sick and sore;
2. Come, ye need - y, come, and wel-come; God's free boun-ty glo - ri - fy;
3. Come, ye wea - ry, heav - y la - den, Bruised and brok-en by the fall;
4. Lo! th'in-car-nate God, as-cend-ed, Pleads the mer - it of His blood;

Je - sus read - y stands to save you, Full of pit - y, joined with power:
True be - lief and true re - pent-ance, Ev - ery grace that brings us nigh,
If you tar - ry till you're bet-ter, You will nev - er come at all:
Ven - ture on Him, ven-ture whol - ly; Let no oth - er trust in-trude:

He is a - ble, He is a - ble, He is a - ble,
With-out mon - ey, with - out mon - ey, with - out mon - ey,
Not the right - eous, not the right - eous, not the right - eous,
None but Je - sus, none but Je - sus, none but Je - sus,

1. He is a - ble, He is a - ble, He is a - ble,

He is will-ing, doubt no more; He is will - ing, doubt no more.
Come to Je - sus Christ and buy; Come to Je - sus Christ and buy.
Sin - ners Je - sus came to call; Sin - ners Je - sus came to call.
Can do help-less sin - ners good; Can do help-less sin - ners good. A - MEN.

YE MUST BE BORN AGAIN

BORN AGAIN. Irregular. Ref.

William T. Sleeper

George C. Stebbins

1. A rul - er once came to Je - sus by night To ask Him the
2. Ye chil - dren of men, at - tend to the word So sol - emn - ly
3. O ye who would en - ter that glo - ri - ous rest, And sing with the
4. A dear one in heav-en thy heart yearns to see, At the beau - ti - ful

way of sal - va-tion and light; The Mas-ter made an-swer in words true and plain,
ut - tered by Je - sus the Lord; And let not this mes-sage to you be in vain,
ran-somed the song of the blest; The life ev - er - last-ing if ye would ob - tain,
gate may be watching for thee; Then list to the note of this sol - emn re - frain,

REFRAIN

"Ye must be born a - gain." "Ye must be born a-
a - gain.

gain, Ye must be born a - gain; I ver - i - ly
a - gain, a - gain;

ver - i - ly say un - to thee, Ye must be born a - gain."
a - gain.

The call of Christ

CHRIST RECEIVETH SINFUL MEN

NEUMEISTER. 7 7 7 7 Ref.

Erdmann Neumeister
Trans. by Emma F. Bevan

James McGranahan

1. Sin - ners Je - sus will re - ceive; Sound this word of grace to all
2. Come, and He will give you rest; Trust Him, for His word is plain;
3. Now my heart con-demns me not, Pure be - fore the law I stand;
4. Christ re - ceiv - eth sin - ful men, E - ven me with all my sin;

Who the heaven-ly path-way leave, All who lin - ger, all who fall.
He will take the sin - ful - est; Christ re - ceiv - eth sin - ful men.
He who cleansed me from all spot, Sat - is - fied its last de - mand.
Purged from ev - ery spot and stain, Heaven with Him I en - ter in.

REFRAIN

Sing it o'er and o'er a - gain; Christ re-
Sing it o'er a - gain, sing it o'er a - gain; Christ re-

ceiv - eth sin - ful men; Make the mes - sage
ceiv-eth sin-ful men, Christ re-ceiv-eth sin-ful men; Make the message plain,

clear and plain: Christ re - ceiv - eth sin - ful men.
make the message plain:

hymns of salvation

VOX DILECTI. C.M.D.

Horatius Bonar   John B. Dykes

1. I heard the voice of Je - sus say, "Come un - to Me and rest;
2. I heard the voice of Je - sus say, "Be - hold, I free - ly give
3. I heard the voice of Je - sus say, "I am this dark world's Light;

Lay down, thou wea - ry one, lay down Thy head up - on My breast."
The liv - ing wa - ter; thirst - y one, Stoop down, and drink, and live."
Look un - to Me, thy morn shall rise, And all thy day be bright."

I came to Je - sus as I was, Wea - ry, and worn, and sad;
I came to Je - sus, and I drank Of that life - giv - ing stream;
I looked to Je - sus, and I found In Him my Star, my Sun;

I found in Him a rest - ing - place, And He has made me glad.
My thirst was quenched, my soul revived, And now I live in Him.
And in that Light of life I'll walk, Till travel - ing days are done. A-MEN.

the call of christ

57 JUST AS I AM, WITHOUT ONE PLEA
WOODWORTH. L.M.

Charlotte Elliott

William B. Bradbury

1. Just as I am, with-out one plea, But that Thy blood was shed for me, And
2. Just as I am, and wait-ing not To rid my soul of one dark blot, To
3. Just as I am, though tossed about With many a con-flict, many a doubt, Fight-
4. Just as I am, poor, wretched, blind; Sight, rich-es, heal-ing of the mind, Yea,
5. Just as I am, Thou wilt re-ceive, Wilt welcome, pardon, cleanse, relieve; Be-

that Thou bidd'st me come to Thee, O Lamb of God, I come! I come!
Thee whose blood can cleanse each spot, O Lamb of God, I come! I come!
ings and fears with-in, with-out, O Lamb of God, I come! I come!
all I need, in Thee I find, O Lamb of God, I come! I come!
cause Thy prom-ise I be-lieve, O Lamb of God, I come! I come! A-MEN.

The story of this hymn is on page...33

58 ONLY TRUST HIM
MINERVA. C.M. Ref.

John H. Stockton

John H. Stockton

1. Come, ev - ery soul by sin op-pressed, There's mer-cy with the Lord,
2. For Je - sus shed His pre-cious blood, Rich bless-ings to be - stow;
3. Yes, Je - sus is the Truth, the Way, That leads you in - to rest:
4. Come, then, and join this ho - ly band, And on to glo - ry go,

And He will sure - ly give you rest By trust - ing in His word.
Plunge now in - to the crim - son flood That wash - es white as snow.
Be - lieve in Him with - out de - lay, And you are ful - ly blest.
To dwell in that ce - les - tial land, Where joys im - mor - tal flow.

hymns of salvation

On - ly trust Him, on - ly trust Him, On - ly trust Him now.
He will save you, He will save you, He will (*Omit* ....) save you now.

COME TO THE SAVIOUR NOW 59
INVITATION. 6 6 6 6 D.

John M. Wigner

Frederick C. Maker

1. Come to the Sav - iour now, He gen - tly call - eth thee;
2. Come to the Sav - iour now, Ye who have wan - dered far;
3. Come to the Sav - iour, all, What - e'er your bur - dens be;

In true re - pent - ance bow, Be - fore Him bend the knee;
Re - new your sol - emn vow, For His by right you are;
Hear now His lov - ing call, "Cast all your care on me."

He wait - eth to be - stow Sal - va - tion, peace, and love,
Come, like poor wan - d'ring sheep Re - turn - ing to His fold;
Come, and for ev - ery grief, In Je - sus you will find

True joy on earth be - low, A home in heav'n a - bove.
His arm will safe - ly keep, His love will ne'er grow cold.
A sure and safe re - lief, A lov - ing Friend and kind.

the call of christ

60 BELIEVE ON THE LORD JESUS CHRIST

BELIEVE. 10 7 10 7 Ref.

Avis B. Christiansen

Harry D. Clarke

1. "What must I do?" the trem-bling jail-or cried, When dazed by
2. What must I do! O wea-ry, trem-bling soul, Just turn to-
3. His blood is all thy plea for sav-ing grace, The pre-cious

fear and won-der; "Be-lieve on Christ!" was all that Paul re-plied,
day to Je-sus; He will re-ceive, for-give and make thee whole—
fount of cleans-ing! O come, ac-cept His love, be-hold His face,

REFRAIN

"And thou shalt be saved from sin." Be-lieve on the
Christ a-lone can set thee free. Be-lieve
And be saved for-ev-er-more.

Lord Je-sus Christ, Be-lieve on the Lord Je-sus Christ, Be-
Be-lieve

lieve on the Lord Je-sus Christ, And thou shalt be saved!
Be-lieve

hymns of salvation

GIVE ME THY HEART

ZERUIAH. 10 10 10 10 Ref.

61

Eliza E. Hewitt

William J. Kirkpatrick

1. "Give Me thy heart," says the Fa-ther a-bove, No gift so pre-cious to
2. "Give Me thy heart," says the Sav-iour of men, Call-ing in mer-cy a-
3. "Give Me thy heart," says the Spir-it di-vine, "All that thou hast, to My

Him as our love; Soft-ly He whis-pers, wher-ev-er thou art,
gain and a-gain; "Turn now from sin, and from e-vil de-part,
keep-ing re-sign; Grace more a-bound-ing is Mine to im-part,

REFRAIN

"Grate-ful-ly trust Me, and give Me thy heart."
Have I not died for thee? give Me thy heart." "Give Me thy heart,
Make full sur-ren-der and give Me thy heart."

give Me thy heart," Hear the soft whis-per, wher-ev-er thou art: From this dark

world He would draw thee a-part; Speak-ing so ten-der-ly, "Give Me thy heart."

THE CALL OF CHRIST

62

LOOK TO THE LAMB OF GOD

PINE STREET. 10 6 10 6 Ref.

H. G. Jackson

James M. Black

1. If you from sin are long-ing to be free, Look to the Lamb of God;
2. When Satan tempts, and doubts and fears assail, Look to the Lamb of God;
3. Are you a-wea-ry, does the way seem long? Look to the Lamb of God;
4. Fear not when shad-ows on your path-way fall, Look to the Lamb of God;

He, to re-deem you, died on Cal-va-ry, Look to the Lamb of God.
You in His strength shall o-ver all pre-vail, Look to the Lamb of God.
His love will cheer and fill your heart with song, Look to the Lamb of God.
In joy or sor-row Christ is all in all, Look to the Lamb of God.

REFRAIN

Look to the Lamb of God, Look to the Lamb of God,
the Lamb of God, the Lamb of God,

For He a-lone is a-ble to save you, Look to the Lamb of God.

63

ART THOU WEARY, HEAVY LADEN?

STEPHANOS. 8 5 8 3

John Mason Neale
Based on an ancient Greek Hymn

Henry W. Baker

1. Art thou wea-ry, heav-y lad-en, Art thou sore dis-trest?
2. Hath He marks to lead me to Him, If He be my Guide?
3. Is there di-a-dem, as Mon-arch, That His brow a-dorns?
4. If I still hold close-ly to Him, What hath He at last?
5. If I ask Him to re-ceive me, Will He say me nay?
6. Find-ing, follow-ing, keep-ing, strug-gling, Is He sure to bless?

O JESUS, THOU ART STANDING

ST. HILDA. 7 6 7 6 D.

William W. How

Justin H. Knecht and
Edward Husband

1. O Je-sus, Thou art standing Out-side the fast-closed door, In low-ly pa-tience
2. O Je-sus, Thou art knocking; And lo! that hand is scarred, And thorns Thy brow en-
3. O Je-sus, Thou art pleading In ac-cents meek and low, "I died for you, My

wait-ing To pass the thresh-old o'er: Shame on us, Christian brothers, His Name and
cir - cle, And tears Thy face have marred: O love that passeth knowledge, So pa-tient-
chil-dren, And will ye treat Me so?" O Lord, with shame and sorrow We o - pen

sign who bear, O shame, thrice shame up-on us, To keep Him standing there!
ly to wait! O sin that hath no e-qual, So fast to bar the gate!
now the door; Dear Saviour, en-ter, en - ter, And leave us nev-er-more! A-MEN.

66

JUST AS I AM, THINE OWN TO BE

JUST AS I AM. 8 8 8 6

Marianne Hearn

Joseph Barnby

1. Just as I am, Thine own to be, Friend of the young, who lov-est me,
2. In the glad morn-ing of my day, My life to give, my vows to pay,
3. I would live ev-er in the light, I would work ev-er for the right,
4. Just as I am, young, strong, and free, To be the best that I can be

To con-se-crate my-self to Thee, O Je-sus Christ, I come.
With no re-serve and no de-lay, With all my heart I come.
I would serve Thee with all my might; Therefore to Thee I come.
For truth, and righteousness and Thee, Lord of my life, I come. A-MEN.

lead me to calvary
DUNCANNON. C.M. Ref.

Jennie Evelyn Hussey

William J. Kirkpatrick

1. King of my life, I crown Thee now, Thine shall the glo - ry be;
2. Show me the tomb where Thou wast laid, Ten - der - ly mourned and wept;
3. Let me like Ma-ry, through the gloom, Come with a gift to Thee;
4. May I be will-ing, Lord, to bear Dai - ly my cross for Thee;

Lest I for-get Thy thorn-crowned brow, Lead me to Cal - va - ry.
An - gels in robes of light ar - rayed Guard-ed Thee whilst Thou slept.
Show to me now the emp - ty tomb, Lead me to Cal - va - ry.
E - ven Thy cup of grief to share, Thou hast borne all for me.

REFRAIN

Lest I for-get Geth-sem - a - ne; Lest I for-get Thine ag - o - ny;

Lest I for-get Thy love for me, Lead me to Cal - va - ry.

the call of christ

JESUS, I COME

JESUS, I COME. Irregular.

William T. Sleeper

George C. Stebbins

1. Out of my bond-age, sor-row, and night, Je-sus, I come, Je-sus, I come;
2. Out of my shame-ful fail - ure and loss, Je-sus, I come, Je-sus, I come;
3. Out of un - rest and ar - ro-gant pride, Je-sus, I come, Je-sus, I come;
4. Out of the fear and dread of the tomb, Je-sus, I come, Je-sus, I come;

In - to Thy free-dom, gladness, and light, Je-sus, I come to Thee; Out of my
In - to the glo-rious gain of Thy cross, Je-sus, I come to Thee; Out of earth's
In - to Thy bless-ed will to a - bide, Je-sus, I come to Thee; Out of my-
In - to the joy and light of Thy home, Je-sus, I come to Thee; Out of the

sick - ness in - to Thy health, Out of my want and in - to Thy wealth,
sor - rows in - to Thy balm, Out of life's storms and in - to Thy calm,
self to dwell in Thy love, Out of de-spair in - to rap-tures a - bove,
depths of ru - in un-told, 'In - to the peace of Thy shel-ter-ing fold,

Out of my sin and in - to Thy-self, Je-sus, I come to Thee.
Out of dis-tress to ju - bi-lant psalm, Je-sus, I come to Thee.
Up-ward for aye on wings like a dove, Je-sus, I come to Thee.
Ev - er Thy glo-rious face to be-hold, Je-sus, I come to Thee. A-MEN.

hymns of salvation

IS MY NAME WRITTEN THERE?

KIDDER. 7 6 7 6 D. Ref.

Mary A. Kidder

Frank M. Davis

69

1. Lord, I care not for rich-es, Nei-ther sil-ver nor gold; I would
2. Lord, my sins they are man-y, Like the sands of the sea, But Thy
3. Oh! that beau-ti-ful cit-y, With its man-sions of light, With its

make sure of heav-en, I would en-ter the fold. In the book of Thy
blood, O my Sav-iour, Is suf-fi-cient for me; For Thy prom-ise is
glo-ri-fied be-ings, In pure gar-ments of white; Where no e-vil thing

king-dom, With its pa-ges so fair, Tell me, Je-sus, my Sav-iour, Is my
writ-ten, In bright let-ters that glow, "Tho' your sins be as scar-let, I will
com-eth To de-spoil what is fair; Where the an-gels are watch-ing, Yes, my

REFRAIN

name writ-ten there?
make them like snow." Is my name writ-ten there, On the page white and fair?
name's writ-ten there. (3) Yes, my name's, etc.

In the book of Thy king-dom, Is my name writ-ten there?
(3) Yes, my name's writ-ten there.

the call of christ

70 WHEN I SURVEY THE WONDROUS CROSS
ROCKINGHAM OLD. L.M.

Isaac Watts

Source Unknown
Adapted by Edward Miller

1. When I sur-vey the wondrous cross, On which the Prince of glo - ry died,
2. For - bid it, Lord, that I should boast, Save in the death of Christ, my God;
3. See, from His head, His hands, His feet, Sor-row and love flow min - gled down;
4. Were the whole realm of na-ture mine, That were a pres - ent far too small;

My rich-est gain I count but loss, And pour contempt on all my pride.
All the vain things that charm me most I sac - ri - fice them to His blood.
Did e'er such love and sor-row meet, Or thorns compose so rich a crown?
Love so a-maz-ing, so di-vine, De-mands my soul, my life, my all. A-MEN.

See alternate tune below   The story of this hymn is on page...45

71 O THOU THAT HEAR'ST WHEN SINNERS CRY
HAMBURG. L.M.

Isaac Watts
From Psalm 51

Gregorian Melody
Arr. by Lowell Mason

1. O Thou that hear'st when sin-ners cry, Though all my crimes be - fore Thee lie,
2. I can - not live with - out Thy light, Cast out and ban - ished from Thy sight;
3. A bro-ken heart, my God, my King, Is all the sac - ri - fice I bring;
4. Then will I teach the world Thy ways; Sin - ners shall learn Thy sov-ereign grace;

Be-hold them not with an - gry look, But blot their mem-'ry from Thy book.
Thy ho-ly joys, my God, re - store, And guard me, that I fall no more.
The God of grace will ne'er de - spise A bro-ken heart for sac - ri - fice.
I'll lead them to my Sav-iour's blood, And they shall praise a pard'ning God. A-MEN.

hymns of salvation

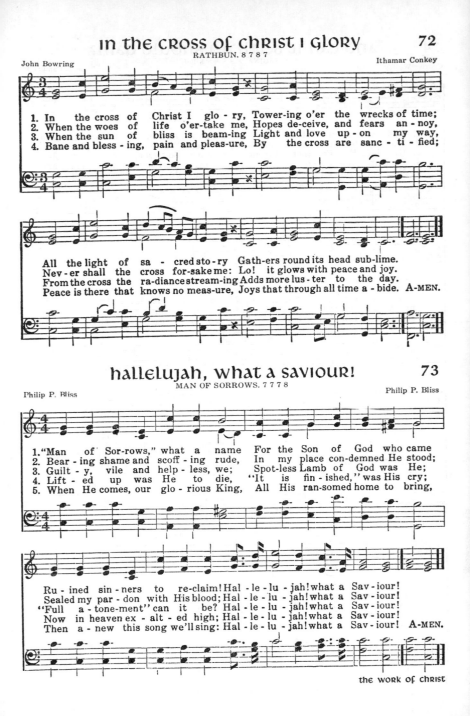

In the Cross of Christ I Glory 72

RATHBUN. 8 7 8 7

John Bowring

Ithamar Conkey

1. In the cross of Christ I glo - ry, Tower-ing o'er the wrecks of time;
2. When the woes of life o'er-take me, Hopes de-ceive, and fears an - noy,
3. When the sun of bliss is beam-ing Light and love up - on my way,
4. Bane and bless - ing, pain and pleas-ure, By the cross are sanc - ti - fied;

All the light of sa - cred sto - ry Gath-ers round its head sub-lime.
Nev - er shall the cross for-sake me: Lo! it glows with peace and joy.
From the cross the ra-diance stream-ing Adds more lus - ter to the day.
Peace is there that knows no meas-ure, Joys that through all time a - bide. A-MEN.

Hallelujah, What a Saviour! 73

MAN OF SORROWS. 7 7 7 8

Philip P. Bliss

Philip P. Bliss

1. "Man of Sor-rows," what a name For the Son of God who came
2. Bear - ing shame and scoff - ing rude, In my place con-demned He stood;
3. Guilt - y, vile and help - less, we; Spot-less Lamb of God was He;
4. Lift - ed up was He to die, "It is fin - ished," was His cry;
5. When He comes, our glo - rious King, All His ran-somed home to bring,

Ru - ined sin - ners to re-claim! Hal - le - lu - jah! what a Sav - iour!
Sealed my par - don with His blood; Hal - le - lu - jah! what a Sav - iour!
"Full a - tone-ment" can it be? Hal - le - lu - jah! what a Sav - iour!
Now in heaven ex - alt - ed high; Hal - le - lu - jah! what a Sav - iour!
Then a - new this song we'll sing: Hal - le - lu - jah! what a Sav - iour! A-MEN.

the work of Christ

74 And Can It Be That I Should Gain?

SAGINA. 8 8 8 8 8 8 Ref.

Charles Wesley

Thomas Campbell

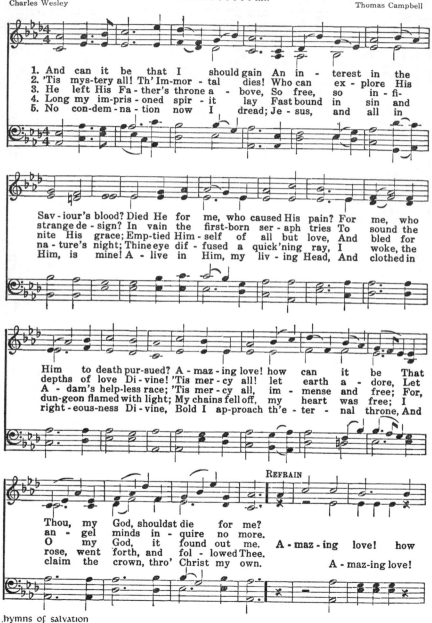

1. And can it be that I should gain An in - terest in the
2. 'Tis mys-tery all! Th' Im-mor - tal dies! Who can ex - plore His
3. He left His Fa - ther's throne a - bove, So free, so in - fi -
4. Long my im-pris - oned spir - it lay Fast bound in sin and
5. No con-dem - na - tion now I dread; Je - sus, and all in

Sav - iour's blood? Died He for me, who caused His pain? For me, who
strange de - sign? In vain the first-born ser - aph tries To sound the
nite His grace; Emp-tied Him - self of all but love, And bled for
na - ture's night; Thine eye dif - fused a quick'ning ray, I woke, the
Him, is mine! A - live in Him, my liv - ing Head, And clothed in

Him to death pur-sued? A - maz - ing love! how can it be That
depths of love Di - vine! 'Tis mer - cy all! let earth a - dore, Let
A - dam's help-less race; 'Tis mer - cy all, im - mense and free; For,
dun-geon flamed with light; My chains fell off, my heart was free; I
right - eous-ness Di - vine, Bold I ap-proach th'e - ter - nal throne, And

REFRAIN

Thou, my God, shouldst die for me?
an - gel minds in - quire no more.
O my God, it found out me.   A - maz - ing love! how
rose, went forth, and fol - lowed Thee.
claim the crown, thro' Christ my own.   A - maz-ing love!

hymns of salvation

The story of this hymn is on page...61

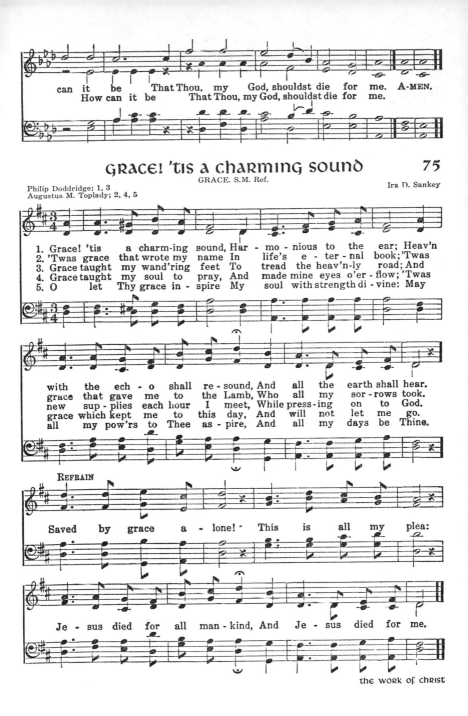

can it be   That Thou, my   God, shouldst die   for   me.   A-MEN.
How can it be   That Thou, my God, shouldst die   for   me.

GRACE! 'TIS A CHARMING SOUND

GRACE. S.M. Ref.

75

Philip Doddridge; 1, 3
Augustus M. Toplady; 2, 4, 5

Ira D. Sankey

1. Grace! 'tis   a charm-ing   sound, Har - mo - nious to the   ear; Heav'n
2. 'Twas grace   that wrote my   name In   life's   e - ter - nal book;'Twas
3. Grace taught   my wand'ring   feet To   tread the heav'n-ly   road; And
4. Grace taught   my soul to   pray, And   made mine eyes o'er - flow; 'Twas
5. O   let   Thy grace in - spire My   soul with strength di - vine: May

with   the ech - o   shall re - sound, And   all   the   earth shall hear.
grace   that gave   me to   the Lamb, Who   all   my   sor - rows took.
new   sup - plies each hour   I   meet, While press-ing   on   to   God.
grace which kept   me to   this day, And   will   not   let   me   go.
all   my pow'rs to   Thee as - pire, And   all   my   days be   Thine.

REFRAIN

Saved   by   grace   a - lone!   This   is   all   my   plea:

Je - sus died for   all   man - kind, And   Je - sus died   for   me.

the work of christ

76 GRACE GREATER THAN OUR SIN

MOODY. 9 9 9 9 Ref.

Julia H. Johnston

Daniel B. Towner

1. Mar - vel - ous grace of our lov - ing Lord, Grace that ex - ceeds our
2. Sin and de - spair like the sea waves cold, Threat-en the soul with
3. Dark is the stain that we can - not hide, What can a - vail to
4. Mar - vel - ous, in - fi - nite, match-less grace, Free - ly be-stowed on

sin and our guilt, Yon - der on Cal - va - ry's mount out-poured,
in - fi - nite loss; Grace that is great - er, yes, grace un - told,
wash it a - way? Look! there is flow - ing a crim - son tide;
all who be - lieve; You that are long - ing to see His face,

REFRAIN

There where the blood of the Lamb was spilt.
Points to the Ref - uge, the might - y Cross. Grace, grace,
Whit - er than snow you may be to - day.
Will you this mo - ment His grace re - ceive? Mar - vel - ous grace,

God's grace, Grace that will par - don and cleanse with-in; Grace,
in - fi - nite grace, Mar - vel - ous

grace, God's grace, Grace that is great - er than all our sin.
grace, in - fi - nite grace.

hymns of salvation

the OLD RUGGED CROSS

OLD RUGGED CROSS. Irregular. Ref.

77

George Bennard   George Bennard

1. On a hill far a-way stood an old rug-ged cross, The em-blem of
2. Oh, that old rug-ged cross, so de-spised by the world, Has a won-drous at-
3. In the old rug-ged cross, stained with blood so di-vine, A won-drous
4. To the old rug-ged cross I will ev-er be true, Its shame and re-

suf-fering and shame; And I love that old cross where the dear-est and best
trac-tion for me; For the dear Lamb of God left His glo-ry a-bove
beau-ty I see; For 'twas on that old cross Je-sus suf-fered and died
proach glad-ly bear; Then He'll call me some day to my home far a-way,

For a world of lost sin-ners was slain.
To bear it to dark Cal-va-ry.
To par-don and sanc-ti-fy me.
Where His glo-ry for-ev-er I'll share.

REFRAIN

So I'll cher-ish the old rug-ged
cross, the

cross,........ Till my tro-phies at last I lay down; I will cling to the
old rug-ged cross,

old rug-ged cross,......... And ex-change it some day for a crown.
cross, the old rug-ged cross,

the WORK of CHRIST

nailed upon golgotha's tree

MARTYN. 7 7 7 7 D.

Source Unknown
Alfred P. Gibbs, stanza 4

Simeon B. Marsh

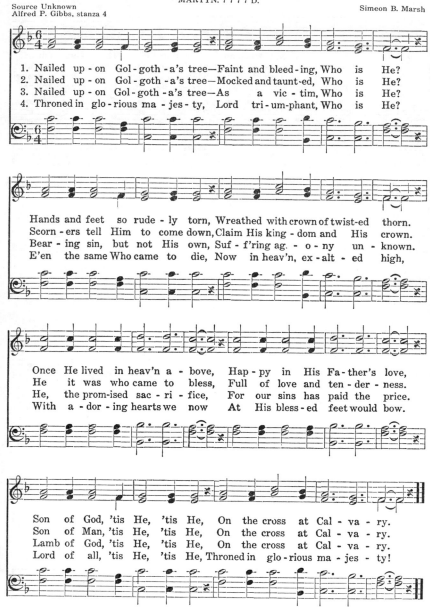

1. Nailed up - on Gol - goth - a's tree—Faint and bleed - ing, Who is He?
2. Nailed up - on Gol - goth - a's tree—Mocked and taunt-ed, Who is He?
3. Nailed up - on Gol - goth - a's tree—As a vic - tim, Who is He?
4. Throned in glo - rious ma - jes - ty, Lord tri - um-phant, Who is He?

Hands and feet so rude - ly torn, Wreathed with crown of twist-ed thorn.
Scorn - ers tell Him to come down, Claim His king - dom and His crown.
Bear - ing sin, but not His own, Suf - f'ring ag. - o - ny un - known.
E'en the same Who came to die, Now in heav'n, ex - alt - ed high,

Once He lived in heav'n a - bove, Hap - py in His Fa - ther's love,
He it was who came to bless, Full of love and ten - der - ness.
He, the prom-ised sac - ri - fice, For our sins has paid the price.
With a - dor - ing hearts we now At His bless - ed feet would bow.

Son of God, 'tis He, 'tis He, On the cross at Cal - va - ry.
Son of Man, 'tis He, 'tis He, On the cross at Cal - va - ry.
Lamb of God, 'tis He, 'tis He, On the cross at Cal - va - ry.
Lord of all, 'tis He, 'tis He, Throned in glo - rious ma - jes - ty!

hymns of salvation

Jesus, Lover of my soul

ABERYSTWYTH. 7 7 7 7 D.

Charles Wesley

Joseph Parry

1. Je - sus, Lov - er of my soul, Let me to Thy bos - om fly,
2. Oth - er ref - uge have I none; Hangs my help - less soul on Thee;
3. Thou, O Christ, art all I want; More than all in Thee I find;
4. Plen - teous grace with Thee is found, Grace to cov - er all my sin;

While the near - er wa - ters roll, While the tem - pest still is high:
Leave, ah! leave me not a - lone, Still sup - port and com - fort me.
Raise the fall - en, cheer the faint, Heal the sick, and lead the blind.
Let the heal - ing streams a - bound; Make and keep me pure with - in.

Hide me, O my Sav - iour, hide, Till the storm of life is past;
All my trust on Thee is stayed, All my help from Thee I bring;
Just and ho - ly is Thy name, I am all un - right - eous - ness;
Thou of life the Foun - tain art, Free - ly let me take of Thee;

Safe in - to the ha - ven guide; O re - ceive my soul at last!
Cov - er my de - fense - less head With the shad - ow of Thy wing.
False and full of sin I am, Thou art full of truth and grace.
Spring Thou up with - in my heart, Rise to all e - ter - ni - ty. A - MEN.

See alternate tune on opposite page

THE WORK OF CHRIST

80 BY FAITH IN CHRIST WE LIVE

BAUHOFER. Irregular. Ref.

Audrey B. Schultz

Audrey B. Schultz

1. By faith in Christ we live, Not trust-ing in our deeds:
2. By faith in Christ we live, We claim His right-eous-ness;
3. Of this we are a-ssured—Je-sus, our great High Priest,
4. By faith in Christ we live, Our plea is grace a-lone;

Our con-fi-dence and hope is in the Christ of Cal-va-ry.
Un-wor-thy in our-selves, but trust-ing Him who died for us.
Doth in-ter-cede in heav'n for all who come to God by Him.
O match-less gift of God's great love — we claim it for our own!

REFRAIN

O won-drous grace of God! (of God!) By faith we have re-ceived

The gift of our sal-va-tion Through the cross of Cal-va-ry.

hymns of salvation

there is a fountain

CLEANSING FOUNTAIN. 8 6 8 6 6 6 8 6

William Cowper

Early American Melody
Arr. by Lowell Mason

1. There is a foun-tain filled with blood Drawn from Im - man-uel's veins;
2. The dy - ing thief re - joiced to see That foun-tain in his day;
3. Dear dy - ing Lamb, Thy pre-cious blood Shall nev - er lose its power,
4. E'er since by faith I saw the stream Thy flow - ing wounds sup-ply,
5. When this poor lisp-ing, stammering tongue Lies si - lent in the grave,

And sin-ners, plunged be-neath that flood, Lose all their guilt - y stains:
And there may I, though vile as he, Wash all my sins a - way:
Till all the ran-somed Church of God Be saved, to sin no more:
Re - deem-ing love has been my theme, And shall be till I die:
Then in a no - bler, sweet-er song, I'll sing Thy power to save:

Lose all their guilt - y stains, Lose all their guilt-y stains; And
Wash all my sins a - way, Wash all my sins a - way; And
Be saved, to sin no more, Be saved, to sin no more; Till
And shall be till I die, And shall be till I die; Re-
I'll sing Thy power to save, I'll sing Thy power to save; Then

sin - ners, plunged be-neath that flood, Lose all their guilt - y stains.
there may I, though vile as he, Wash all my sins a - way.
all the ran-somed Church of God Be saved, to sin no more.
deem-ing love has been my theme, And shall be till I die.
in a no - bler, sweet - er song I'll sing Thy power to save. A-MEN.

the work of christ

82 JESUS, THY BLOOD AND RIGHTEOUSNESS

GERMANY. L.M.

Nicolaus L. von Zinzendorf
Trans. by John Wesley; alt.

William Gardiner's *Sacred Melodies*, 1815

1. Je - sus, Thy blood and right-eous-ness My beau-ty are, my glo - rious dress;
2. Bold shall I stand in Thy great day, For who aught to my charge shall lay?
3. Lord, I be-lieve Thy precious blood, Which, at the mer-cy seat of God,
4. Lord, I be-lieve were sin-ners more Than sands up-on the o - cean shore,

'Midst flaming worlds, in these arrayed, With joy shall I lift up my head.
Ful - ly ab-solved through these I am, From sin and fear, from guilt and shame.
For - ev - er doth for sin-ners plead, For me, e'en for my soul, was shed.
Thou hast for all a ran-som paid, For all a full a-tone-ment made. A-MEN.

83 I AM NOT SKILLED TO UNDERSTAND

GREENWELL. 8 8 8 7

Dora Greenwell

William J. Kirkpatrick

1. I am not skilled to un-der-stand What God hath willed, what God hath planned;
2. I take Him at His word indeed: "Christ died for sin - ners," this I read;
3. That He should leave His place on high And come for sin - ful man to die,
4. And oh, that He ful - filled may see The tra-vail of His soul in me,
5. Yes, liv - ing, dy - ing, let me bring My strength, my sol - ace from this Spring;

I on - ly know at His right hand Is One who is my Sav - iour!
For in my heart I find a need Of Him to be my Sav - iour!
You count it strange? so once did I, Be - fore I knew my Sav - iour!
And with His work con - tent-ed be, As I with my dear Sav - iour!
That He who lives to be my King Once died to be my Sav - iour! A-MEN.

I SAW THE CROSS OF JESUS

WHITFIELD. 7 6 7 6 D.

Frederick Whitfield

Source Unknown

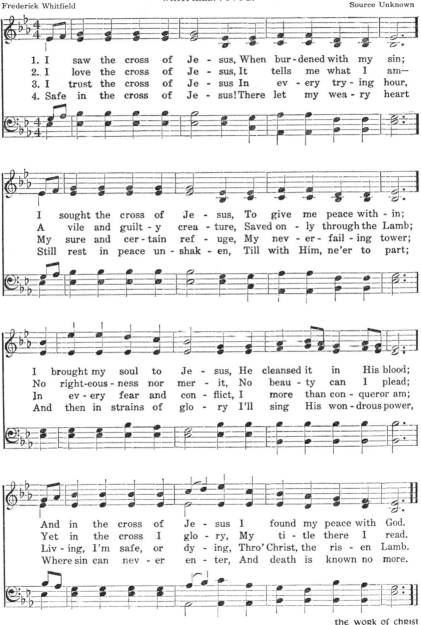

1. I saw the cross of Je - sus, When bur - dened with my sin;
2. I love the cross of Je - sus, It tells me what I am—
3. I trust the cross of Je - sus In ev - er - y try - ing hour,
4. Safe in the cross of Je - sus! There let my wea - ry heart

I sought the cross of Je - sus, To give me peace with - in;
A vile and guilt - y crea - ture, Saved on - ly through the Lamb;
My sure and cer - tain ref - uge, My nev - er - fail - ing tower;
Still rest in peace un - shak - en, Till with Him, ne'er to part;

I brought my soul to Je - sus, He cleansed it in His blood;
No right-eous - ness nor mer - it, No beau - ty can I plead;
In ev - er - y fear and con - flict, I more than con - queror am;
And then in strains of glo - ry I'll sing His won - drous power,

And in the cross of Je - sus I found my peace with God.
Yet in the cross I glo - ry, My ti - tle there I read.
Liv - ing, I'm safe, or dy - ing, Thro' Christ, the ris - en Lamb.
Where sin can nev - er en - ter, And death is known no more.

THE WORK OF CHRIST

85   O the deep, deep love of Jesus

TON-Y-BOTEL. 8 7 8 7 D.

S. Trevor Francis

Thomas J. Williams

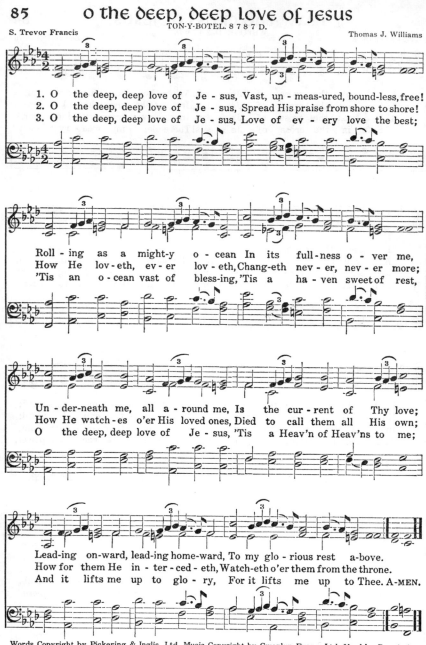

1. O the deep, deep love of Je - sus, Vast, un - meas-ured, bound-less, free!
2. O the deep, deep love of Je - sus, Spread His praise from shore to shore!
3. O the deep, deep love of Je - sus, Love of ev - ery love the best;

Roll - ing as a might-y o - cean In its full-ness o - ver me,
How He lov - eth, ev - er lov - eth, Chang-eth nev - er, nev - er more;
'Tis an o - cean vast of bless-ing, 'Tis a ha - ven sweet of rest,

Un - der-neath me, all a - round me, Is the cur - rent of Thy love;
How He watch - es o'er His loved ones, Died to call them all His own;
O the deep, deep love of Je - sus, 'Tis a Heav'n of Heav'ns to me;

Lead-ing on-ward, lead-ing home-ward, To my glo - rious rest a-bove.
How for them He in - ter - ced - eth, Watch-eth o'er them from the throne.
And it lifts me up to glo - ry, For it lifts me up to Thee. A-MEN.

Words Copyright by Pickering & Inglis, Ltd. Music Copyright by Gwenlyn Evans, Ltd. Used by Permission.

hymns of salvation

IVORY PALACES

MONTREAT. 9 6 9 6 Ref.

86

Henry Barraclough

Henry Barraclough
Arr. by Donald P. Hustad

1. My Lord has gar-ments so won-drous fine, And myrrh their tex-ture fills;
2. His life had al-so its sor-rows sore, For al-oes had a part;
3. His gar-ments too were in cas-sia dipped, With heal-ing in a touch;
4. In gar-ments glo-ri-ous He will come, To o-pen wide the door;

Its fra-grance reached to this heart of mine, With joy my be-ing thrills.
And when I think of the cross He bore, My eyes with tear-drops start.
Each time my feet in some sin have slipped, He took me from its clutch.
And I shall en-ter my heaven-ly home, To dwell for-ev-er-more.

mf REFRAIN

Out of the i-vo-ry pal-a-ces, In-to a world of woe,

p

On-ly His great, e-ter-nal love Made my Sav-iour go.

the WORK of CHRIST

The story of this hymn is on page...25

JESUS SAVES

JESUS SAVES. 7 6 7 6 7 7 7 6

Priscilla J. Owens

William J. Kirkpatrick

1. We have heard the joy - ful sound: Je - sus saves! Je - sus saves!
2. Waft it on the roll - ing tide; Je - sus saves! Je - sus saves!
3. Sing a - bove the bat - tle strife, Je - sus saves! Je - sus saves!
4. Give the winds a might - y voice, Je - sus saves! Je - sus saves!

Spread the ti - dings all a - round: Je - sus saves! Je - sus saves!
Tell to sin - ners far and wide: Je - sus saves! Je - sus saves!
By His death and end - less life, Je - sus saves! Je - sus saves!
Let the na - tions now re - joice— Je - sus saves! Je - sus saves!

Bear the news to ev - ery land, Climb the steeps and cross the waves;
Sing, ye is - lands of the sea; Ech - o back, ye o - cean caves;
Sing it soft - ly through the gloom, When the heart for mer - cy craves;
Shout sal - va - tion full and free, High - est hills and deep - est caves;

On - ward!—'tis our Lord's com - mand; Je - sus saves! Je - sus saves!
Earth shall keep her ju - bi - lee: Je - sus saves! Je - sus saves!
Sing in tri - umph o'er the tomb— Je - sus saves! Je -. sus saves!
This our song of vic - to - ry— Je - sus saves! Je - sus saves!

hymns of salvation

At the Cross

HUDSON. C.M. Ref.

Isaac Watts
Ralph E. Hudson, refrain

Ralph E. Hudson

88

1. A - las, and did my Sav - iour bleed? And did my Sov-'reign die?
2. Was it for crimes that I have done, He groaned up - on the tree?
3. Well might the sun in dark-ness hide, And shut his glo - ries in,
4. But drops of grief can ne'er re - pay The debt of love I owe:

Would He de-vote that sa - cred head For such a worm as I?
A - maz - ing pit - y! grace un-known! And love be - yond de - gree!
When Christ, the might-y Mak - er, died For man the crea-ture's sin.
Here, Lord, I give my - self a - way, 'Tis all that I can do!

REFRAIN

At the cross, at the cross where I first saw the light, And the bur-den of my heart rolled a - way, (rolled a-way,) It was there by faith I re - ceived my sight, And now I am hap-py all the day!

89 he lives

ACKLEY. Irregular. Ref.

Alfred H. Ackley

Alfred H. Ackley

1. I serve a ris-en Sav-iour, He's in the world to-day; I know that He is
2. In all the world a-round me I see His lov-ing care, And tho' my heart grows
3. Rejoice, rejoice, O Christian, lift up your voice and sing E - ter-nal hal-le-

liv-ing, what-ev-er men may say; I see His hand of mer-cy, I
wea-ry, I nev-er will de-spair; I know that He is lead-ing thro'
lu-jahs to Je-sus Christ the King! The Hope of all who seek Him, the

hear His voice of cheer, And just the time I need Him He's al-ways near.
all the storm-y blast, The day of His ap-pear-ing will come at last.
Help of all who find, None oth-er is so lov-ing, so good and kind.

REFRAIN

He lives, He lives, Christ Je-sus lives to-day! He walks with me and
He lives, He lives,

talks with me a-long life's nar-row way. He lives, He lives, sal-
He lives, He lives,

hymns of salvation

va-tion to im - part! You ask me how I know He lives? He lives within my heart.

oh, how i love jesus

90

OH, HOW I LOVE JESUS. C.M. Ref.

Frederick Whitfield

Source Unknown

1. There is a name I love to hear, I love to sing its worth; It sounds like
2. It tells me of a Sav-iour's love, Who died to set me free; It tells me
3. It tells me what my Fa - ther hath In store for ev - ery day, And though I
4. It tells of One whose lov-ing heart Can feel my deep-est woe, Who in each

mu-sic in mine ear, The sweetest name on earth.
of His pre-cious blood, The sin-ner's per-fect plea. Oh, how I love Je - sus,
tread a darksome path, Yields sunshine all the way.
sor-row bears a part, That none can bear be - low.

REFRAIN

Oh, how I love Je - sus, Oh, how I love Je - sus, Be-cause He first loved me!

the believer's experience

tell me the story of Jesus

STORY OF JESUS. 8 7 8 7 Ref.

Fanny J. Crosby

John R. Sweney

1. Tell me the sto - ry of Je - sus, Write on my heart ev - ery word;
2. Fast - ing a - lone in the des - ert, Tell of the days that are past,
3. Tell of the cross where they nailed Him, Writh - ing in an - guish and pain;

REF. — *Tell me the sto - ry of Je - sus, Write on my heart ev - ery word;*

FINE.

Tell me the sto - ry most pre - cious, Sweet-est that ev - er was heard.
How for our sins He was tempt - ed, Yet was tri - um - phant at last.
Tell of the grave where they laid Him, Tell how He liv - eth a - gain.

Tell me the sto - ry most pre - cious, Sweet-est that ev - er was heard.

Tell how the an - gels, in cho - rus, Sang as they wel - comed His birth,
Tell of the years of His la - bor, Tell of the sor - row He bore,
Love in that sto - ry so ten - der, Clear - er than ev - er I see:

D. C. for Refrain

"Glo - ry to God in the high - est! Peace and good ti - dings to earth."
He was de - spised and af - flict - ed, Home - less, re - ject - ed and poor.
Stay, let me weep while you whis - per, Love paid the ran - som for me.

hymns of salvation

the solid rock

SOLID ROCK. L.M. Ref.

Edward Mote

William B. Bradbury

1. My hope is built on noth-ing less Than Je-sus' blood and right-eous-ness;
2. When dark-ness veils His love-ly face, I rest on His un-chang-ing grace;
3. His oath, His cov-e-nant, His blood, Sup-port me in the whelm-ing flood;
4. When He shall come with trumpet sound, Oh, may I then in Him be found;

I dare not trust the sweet-est frame, But whol-ly lean on Je-sus' name.
In ev-ery high and storm-y gale, My an-chor holds with-in the veil.
When all a-round my soul gives way, He then is all my hope and stay.
Dressed in His right-eous-ness a-lone, Fault-less to stand be-fore the throne.

REFRAIN

On Christ, the sol-id Rock, I stand; All oth-er ground

is sink-ing sand, All oth-er ground is sink-ing sand.

the believer's experience

93 I WILL SING OF MY REDEEMER

HYFRYDOL. 8 7 8 7 D.

Philip P Bliss

Rowland H. Prichard

1. I will sing of my Re-deem-er And His won-drous love to me;
2. I will tell the won-drous sto-ry, How my lost es-tate to save,
3. I will praise my dear Re-deem-er, His tri-umph-ant power I'll tell,
4. I will sing of my Re-deem-er And His heaven-ly love for me;

On the cru-el cross He suf-fered, From the curse to set me free.
In His bound-less love and mer-cy, He the ran-som free-ly gave.
How the vic-to-ry He giv-eth O-ver sin, and death, and hell.
He from death to life hath brought me, Son of God, with Him to be.

REFRAIN

Sing, oh, sing of my Re-deem-er, With His blood He pur-chased me,

On the cross He sealed my par-don, Paid the debt, and made me free.

hymns of salvation

The story of this hymn is on page ..151

I WILL SING THE WONDROUS STORY

WONDROUS STORY. 8 7 8 7 Ref.

Francis H. Rowley

Peter P. Bilhorn

1. I will sing the won-drous sto - ry Of the Christ who died for me,
2. I was lost, but Je - sus found me, Found the sheep that went a - stray,
3. I was bruised, but Je - sus healed me; Faint was I from man-y a fall;
4. Days of dark - ness still come o'er me, Sor-row's paths I oft - en tread,
5. He will keep me till the riv - er Rolls its wa - ters at my feet;

How He left His home in glo - ry For the cross of Cal - va - ry.
Threw His lov - ing arms a - round me, Drew me back in - to His way.
Sight was gone, and fears pos-sessed me, But He freed me from them all.
But the Sav - iour still is with me; By His hand I'm safe - ly led.
Then He'll bear me safe - ly o - ver, Where the loved ones I shall meet.

REFRAIN

Yes, I'll sing the won-drous sto - ry Of the
Yes, I'll sing the won-drous sto - ry

Christ who died for me Sing it with the saints in
Of the Christ who died for me, Sing it with

glo - ry, Gath-ered by the crys-tal sea
the saints in glo - ry, Gath-ered by the crys-tal sea.

the believer's experience

95   I love to tell the story

HANKEY. 7 6 7 6 D. Ref.

A. Catherine Hankey

William G. Fischer

1. I love to tell the sto - ry Of un - seen things a - bove, Of
2. I love to tell the sto - ry, More won-der - ful it seems Than
3. I love to tell the sto - ry, 'Tis pleas - ant to re - peat What
4. I love to tell the sto - ry, For those who know it best Seem

Je - sus and His glo - ry, Of Je - sus and His love. I love to
all the gold - en fan - cies Of all our gold - en dreams. I love to
seems, each time I tell it, More won - der - ful - ly sweet. I love to
hun - ger - ing and thirst - ing To hear it like the rest. And when, in

tell the sto - ry, Be - cause I know 'tis true; It sat - is - fies my
tell the sto - ry, It did so much for me; And that is just the
tell the sto - ry, For some have nev - er heard The mes - sage of sal -
scenes of glo - ry, I sing the new, new song, 'Twill be the old, old

REFRAIN

long-ings As noth-ing else can do.
rea - son I tell it now to thee. I love to tell the sto - ry, 'Twill
va - tion From God's own Ho-ly Word.
sto - ry That I have loved so long.

be my theme in glo - ry To tell the old, old sto - ry Of Je-sus and His love.

hymns of salvation

tell me the old, old story

OLD, OLD STORY. 7 6 7 6 D. Ref.

A. Catherine Hankey

William H. Doane

1. Tell me the old, old sto - ry Of un-seen things a - bove, Of Je - sus
2. Tell me the sto - ry slow - ly, That I may take it in— That won-der-
3. Tell me the sto - ry soft - ly, With ear-nest tones and grave; Re - mem-ber,
4. Tell me the same old sto - ry When you have cause to fear That this world's

and His glo - ry, Of Je - sus and His love. Tell me the sto - ry
ful re - demp-tion, God's rem - e - dy for sin. Tell me the sto - ry
I'm the sin - ner Whom Je - sus came to save. Tell me the sto - ry
emp - ty glo - ry Is cost - ing me too dear. Yes, and when that world's

sim - ply, As to a lit - tle child, For I am weak and wea - ry,
oft - en, For I for - get so soon; The "ear - ly dew" of morn - ing
al - ways, If you would real - ly be, In an - y time of troub - le,
glo - ry Is dawn-ing on my soul, Tell me the old, old sto - ry:

REFRAIN

And help - less and de - filed.
Has passed a - way at noon. Tell me the old, old sto - ry, Tell me the
A com - fort - er to me.
"Christ Je - sus makes thee whole."

old, old sto - ry, Tell me the old, old sto - ry Of Je - sus and His love.

the believer's experience

BLESSED ASSURANCE

ASSURANCE. 9 10 9 9 Ref.

Fanny J. Crosby

Phoebe P. Knapp

1. Bless-ed as - sur - ance, Je - sus is mine! Oh, what a fore - taste of
2. Per - fect sub - mis - sion, per - fect de - light, Vi - sions of rap - ture now
3. Per - fect sub - mis - sion, all is at rest, I in my Sav - iour am

glo - ry di - vine! Heir of sal - va - tion, pur-chase of God,
burst on my sight; An - gels de - scend - ing, bring from a - bove
hap - py and blest; Watch-ing and wait - ing, look - ing a - bove,

REFRAIN

Born of His Spir - it, washed in His blood.
Ech - oes of mer - cy, whis-pers of love. This is my sto - ry, this is my
Filled with His goodness, lost in His love.

song, Prais-ing my Sav-iour all the day long; This is my sto - ry,

this is my song, Prais-ing my Sav - iour all the day long.

hymns of salvation

The story of this hymn is on page...51

oh, It is wonderful!

HOMER. 13 13 13 13 Ref.

Charles H. Gabriel

Charles H. Gabriel
Arr. by Donald P. Hustad

1. I stand all a-mazed at the love Je-sus of-fers me, Con-fused at the
2. I mar-vel that He would de-scend from His throne di-vine, To res-cue a
3. I think of His hands pierced and bleeding to pay the debt! Such mer-cy, such

grace that so ful-ly He prof-fers me; I trem-ble to know that for me He was
soul so re-bel-lious and proud as mine; That He should ex-tend His great love un-to
love and de-vo-tion can I for-get? No, no! I will praise and a-dore at the

cru-ci-fied—That for me, a sin-ner, He suf-fered, He bled, and died.
such as I; Suf-fi-cient to own, to re-deem, and to jus-ti-fy.
mer-cy-seat, Un-til at the glo-ri-fied throne I kneel at His feet.

REFRAIN

Oh, it is won-der-ful that He should care for me, E-nough to

die for me! Oh, it is won-der-ful, won-der-ful to me!

the believer's experience

99

REDEEMED

REDEEMED. 9 8 9 8 Ref.

Fanny J. Crosby

William J. Kirkpatrick

1. Redeemed—how I love to pro-claim it! Re-deemed by the blood of the Lamb;
2. Redeemed and so hap-py in Je - sus, No lan-guage my rapture can tell;
3. I think of my bless-ed Re-deem-er, I think of Him all the day long;
4. I know I shall see in His beau-ty The King in whose law I de-light;

Redeemed through His in-fi-nite mer - cy, His child, and for-ev - er, I am.
I know that the light of His pres-ence With me doth con-tin - ual - ly dwell.
I sing, for I can-not be si - lent; His love is the theme of my song.
Who lov-ing - ly guard-eth my foot-steps, And giv-eth me songs in the night.

REFRAIN

Re - deemed, re - deemed, Re-deemed by the blood of the Lamb;
re-deemed, re-deemed,

Re - deemed, re - deemed, His child, and for-ev - er, I am.
re-deemed, re-deemed,

hymns of salvation

JESUS IS ALL THE WORLD TO ME

ELIZABETH. Irregular.

100

Will L. Thompson

Will L. Thompson

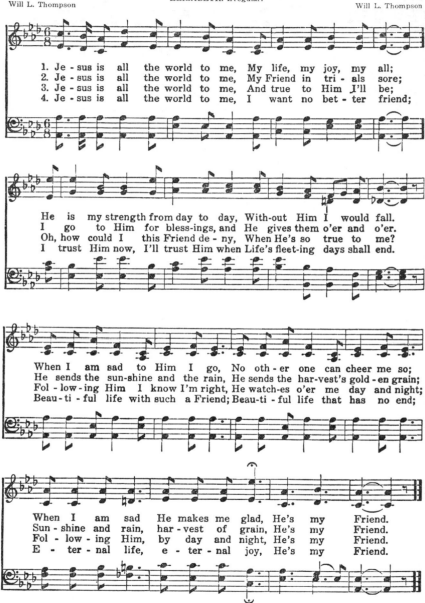

1. Je - sus is all the world to me, My life, my joy, my all;
2. Je - sus is all the world to me, My Friend in tri - als sore;
3. Je - sus is all the world to me, And true to Him I'll be;
4. Je - sus is all the world to me, I want no bet - ter friend;

He is my strength from day to day, With-out Him I would fall.
I go to Him for bless-ings, and He gives them o'er and o'er.
Oh, how could I this Friend de - ny, When He's so true to me?
I trust Him now, I'll trust Him when Life's fleet-ing days shall end.

When I am sad to Him I go, No oth - er one can cheer me so;
He sends the sun-shine and the rain, He sends the har-vest's gold - en grain;
Fol - low-ing Him I know I'm right, He watch-es o'er me day and night;
Beau-ti - ful life with such a Friend; Beau-ti - ful life that has no end;

When I am sad He makes me glad, He's my Friend.
Sun - shine and rain, har - vest of grain, He's my Friend.
Fol - low - ing Him, by day and night, He's my Friend.
E - ter - nal life, e - ter - nal joy, He's my Friend.

WONDERFUL WORDS OF LIFE

WORDS OF LIFE. 8 6 8 6 6 6 Ref.

Philip P. Bliss

Philip P. Bliss

1. Sing them o - ver a - gain to me, Won-der - ful words of Life;
2. Christ, the bless - ed One, gives to all Won-der - ful words of Life;
3. Sweet - ly ech - o the gos - pel call, Won-der - ful words of Life;

Let me more of their beau - ty see, Won-der - ful words of Life.
Sin - ner, list to the lov - ing call, Won-der - ful words of Life.
Of - fer par - don and peace to all, Won-der - ful words of Life.

Words of life and beau - ty, Teach me faith and du - ty:
All so free - ly giv - en, Woo - ing us to Heav - en:
Je - sus, on - ly Sav - iour, Sanc - ti - fy for - ev - er:

REFRAIN

Beau-ti-ful words, won-der-ful words, Wonderful words of Life. Life.

I AM TRUSTING THEE, LORD JESUS

BULLINGER. 8 5 8 3

Frances R. Havergal

Ethelbert W. Bullinger

1. I am trust - ing Thee, Lord Je - sus, Trust - ing on - ly Thee;
2. I am trust - ing Thee to guide me; Thou a - lone shalt lead,
3. I am trust - ing Thee for pow - er: Thine can nev - er fail;
4. I am trust - ing Thee, Lord Je - sus; Nev - er let me fall;

hymns of salvation

Trust - ing Thee for full sal - va - tion, Great and free.
Ev - ery day and hour sup - ply - ing All my need.
Words which Thou Thy - self shalt give me Must pre - vail.
I am trust - ing Thee for - ev - er, And for all. A - MEN.

now I Belong to Jesus

ELLSWORTH. 10 10 9 6 Ref.

Norman J. Clayton

Norman J. Clayton

103

1. Je - sus my Lord will love me for-ev - er, From Him no pow'r of e - vil can
2. Once I was lost in sin's deg-ra-da-tion, Je - sus came down to bring me sal -
3. Joy floods my soul for Jesus has saved me, Freed me from sin that long had en-

sev - er, He gave His life to ran - som my soul, Now I be-long to Him;
va - tion, Lift - ed me up from sor-row and shame, Now I be-long to Him;
slaved me, His pre-cious blood He gave to re-deem, Now I be-long to Him;

REFRAIN

Now I be - long to Je - sus, Je - sus be - longs to me,

Not for the years of time a - lone, But for e - ter - ni - ty.

the Believer's experience

I am his, and he is mine

EVERLASTING LOVE. 7 7 7 7 D.

George Wade Robinson   James Mountain

1. Loved with ev - er - last - ing love, Led by grace that love to know;
2. Heav'n a - bove is soft - er blue, Earth a - round is sweet-er green!
3. Things that once were wild a - larms Can - not now dis - turb my rest;
4. His for - ev - er, on - ly His; Who the Lord and me shall part?

Spir - it, breath-ing from a - bove, Thou hast taught me it is so!
Some-thing lives in ev - ery hue Christ-less eyes have nev - er seen:
Closed in ev - er - last - ing arms, Pil - lowed on the lov - ing breast.
Ah, with what a rest of bliss Christ can fill the lov - ing heart!

Oh, this full and per - fect peace! Oh, this trans - port all di - vine!
Birds with glad - der songs o'er - flow, Flow'rs with deep - er beau-ties shine,
Oh, to lie for - ev - er here, Doubt, and care, and self re - sign,
Heav'n and earth may fade and flee, First-born light in gloom de - cline;

In a love which can - not cease, I am His, and He is mine.
Since I know, as now I know, I am His, and He is mine.
While He whis - pers in my ear, I am His, and He is mine.
But while God and I shall be, I am His, and He is mine.

hymns of salvation

In My Heart There Rings a Melody 105

HEART MELODY. Irregular. Ref.

Elton M. Roth

Elton M. Roth

1. I have a song that Je-sus gave me, It was sent from
2. I love the Christ who died on Cal-vary, For He washed my
3. 'Twill be my end-less theme in glo-ry, With the an-gels

heaven a-bove; There nev-er was a sweet-er mel-o-dy, 'Tis a
sins a-way; He put with-in my heart a mel-o-dy, And I
I will sing; 'Twill be a song with glo-rious har-mo-ny, When the

REFRAIN

mel-o-dy of love.
know it's there to stay. In my heart there rings a mel-o-dy, There
courts of heav-en ring.

rings a mel-o-dy with heav-en's har-mo-ny; In my heart there

rings a mel-o-dy; There rings a mel-o-dy of love.

the believer's experience

The story of this hymn is on page..127

106 WONDERFUL GRACE OF JESUS

WONDERFUL GRACE. Irregular. Ref.

Haldor Lillenas   Haldor Lillenas

1. Won - der - ful grace of Je - sus, Great - er than all my sin;
2. Won - der - ful grace of Je - sus, Reach-ing to all the lost,
3. Won - der - ful grace of Je - sus, Reach-ing the most de - filed,

How shall my tongue de - scribe it, Where shall its praise be - gin?
By it I have been par - doned, Saved to the ut - ter - most;
By its trans-form - ing pow - er, Mak - ing him God's dear child,

Tak - ing a - way my bur - den, Set - ting my spir - it free;
Chains have been torn a - sun - der, Giv - ing me lib - er - ty;
Pur - chas-ing peace and heav - en, For all e - ter - ni - ty;

For the won - der - ful grace of Je - sus reach - es me.
For the won - der - ful grace of Je - sus reach - es me.
And the won - der - ful grace of Je - sus reach - es me.

REFRAIN

the match-less grace of Je - sus,

Won - der-ful the matchless grace of Je - - - sus,   Deep - er than the

hymns of salvation

all my life long

SATISFIED. 8 7 8 7 Ref.

Clara Tear Williams

Ralph E. Hudson

1. All my life-long I had pant-ed For a drink from some cool spring
2. Feed-ing on the husks a-round me Till my strength was al-most gone,
3. Poor I was, and sought for rich - es, Some-thing that would sat - is - fy;
4. Well of wa - ter, ev - er spring-ing, Bread of life, so rich and free,

That I hoped would quench the burn-ing Of the thirst I felt with-in.
Longed my soul for some-thing bet - ter, On - ly still to hun-ger on.
But the dust I gath-ered round me On - ly mocked my soul's sad cry.
Un - told wealth that nev - er fail - eth, My Re-deem - er is to me.

REFRAIN

Hal - le - lu - jah! I have found Him—Whom my soul so long has craved!

Je - sus sat - is - fies my long - ings; Thro' His blood I now am saved.

The story of this hymn is on page...75

108 amazing grace! how sweet the sound

AMAZING GRACE. C.M.

John Newton, 1-3
John P. Rees, 4 (ascribed)

Early American Melody
Arr. by Edwin O. Excell

1. A - maz - ing grace! how sweet the sound, That saved a wretch like me! I
2. 'Twas grace that taught my heart to fear, And grace my fears re-lieved; How
3. Through man-y dan - gers, toils and snares, I have al - read - y come; 'Tis
4. When we've been there ten thou-sand years, Bright shin-ing as the sun, We've

hymns of salvation

once was lost, but now am found, Was blind, but now I see.
pre - cious did that grace ap - pear The hour I first be-lieved!
grace hath brought me safe thus far, And grace will lead me home.
no less days to sing God's praise Than when we first be - gun. A - MEN.

The story of this hymn is on page....7

'tis so sweet to trust in Jesus

TRUST IN JESUS. 7 7 8 7 Ref.

109

Louisa M. R. Stead

William J. Kirkpatrick

1. 'Tis so sweet to trust in Je - sus, Just to take Him at His word;
2. O how sweet to trust in Je - sus, Just to trust His cleans-ing blood;
3. Yes, 'tis sweet to trust in Je - sus, Just from sin and self to cease;
4. I'm so glad I learned to trust Thee, Pre-cious Je - sus, Sav-iour, Friend;

Just to rest up - on His prom-ise; Just to know, "Thus saith the Lord."
Just in sim - ple faith to plunge me 'Neath the heal - ing, cleans-ing flood!
Just from Je - sus sim - ply tak - ing Life and rest, and joy and peace.
And I know that Thou art with me, Wilt be with me to the end.

REFRAIN

Je - sus, Je - sus, how I trust Him! How I've proved Him o'er and o'er!

Je - sus, Je - sus, pre - cious Je - sus! O for grace to trust Him more!

the believer's experience

110

SAVED!

Oswald J. Smith

PEOPLES CHURCH. 9 9 9 9 Ref.

Roger M. Hickman

1. Saved! saved! saved! my sins are all for - giv'n; Christ is
2. Saved! saved! saved! by grace and grace a - lone; Oh, what
3. Saved! saved! saved! oh, joy be - yond com - pare! Christ my

mine! I'm on my way to heav'n; Once a guilt - y
won - drous love to me was shown, In my stead Christ
life, and I His con - stant care; Yield - ing all and

sin - ner, lost, un - done, Now a child of God, saved thro' His Son.
Je - sus bled and died, Bore my sins, for me was cru - ci - fied.
trust-ing Him a - lone, Liv - ing now each mo - ment as His own.

REFRAIN

Saved! I'm saved thro' Christ, my all in all; Saved! I'm saved, what-
my all in all;

ev - er may be - fall; He died up - on the cross for me, He bore the aw - ful

hymns of salvation

The story of this hymn is on page...57

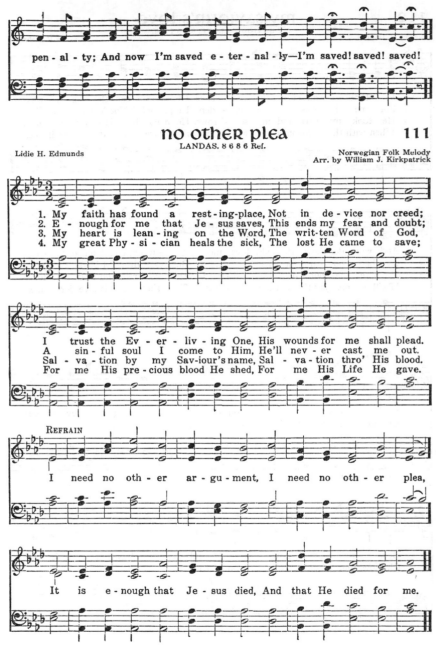

pen - al - ty; And now I'm saved e - ter - nal - ly—I'm saved! saved! saved!

no other plea
LANDAS. 8 6 8 6 Ref.

111

Lidie H. Edmunds

Norwegian Folk Melody
Arr. by William J. Kirkpatrick

1. My faith has found a rest-ing-place, Not in de - vice nor creed;
2. E - nough for me that Je - sus saves, This ends my fear and doubt;
3. My heart is lean - ing on the Word, The writ-ten Word of God,
4. My great Phy - si - cian heals the sick, The lost He came to save;

I trust the Ev - er - liv - ing One, His wounds for me shall plead.
A sin - ful soul I come to Him, He'll nev - er cast me out.
Sal - va - tion by my Sav-iour's name, Sal - va - tion thro' His blood.
For me His pre-cious blood He shed, For me His Life He gave.

REFRAIN

I need no oth - er ar - gu - ment, I need no oth - er plea,

It is e - nough that Je - sus died, And that He died for me.

the believer's experience

my saviour's love

MY SAVIOUR'S LOVE. 8 7 8 7 Ref.

Charles H. Gabriel

Charles H. Gabriel

1. I stand a-mazed in the pres-ence Of Je-sus the Naz-a-rene,
2. For me it was in the gar-den He prayed: "Not My will, but Thine;"
3. He took my sins and my sor-rows, He made them His ver-y own;
4. When with the ran-somed in glo-ry His face I at last shall see,

And won-der how He could love me, A sin-ner, con-demned, un-clean.
He had no tears for His own griefs, But sweat-drops of blood for mine.
He bore the bur-den to Cal-vary, And suf-fered, and died a-lone.
'Twill be my joy through the a-ges To sing of His love for me.

REFRAIN

How mar-vel-ous! how won-der-ful! And my song shall ev-er be:
Oh, how mar-vel-ous! oh, how won-der-ful!

How mar-vel-ous! how won-der-ful Is my Sav-iour's love for me!
Oh, how mar-vel-ous! oh, how won-der-ful

hymns of salvation

all things in jesus

OKMULGEE. 10 10 10 10 Ref.

Harry Dixon Loes

Harry Dixon Loes

113

1. Friends all a-round us are try-ing to find What the heart yearns for, by
2. Some car-ry bur-dens whose weight has for years Crushed them with sorrow and
3. No oth-er name stirs the joy-chords with-in, And thro' none else is re-
4. Je - sus is all this sad world needs to-day; Blind-ly men strive, for sin

sin un-der-mined; I have the se-cret, I know where 'tis found:
blind - ed with tears; Yet One stands read - y to help them just now,
mis - sion of sin; He knows the pain of the heart sore - ly tried,
dark - ens the way. O to draw back the grim cur-tains of night—

REFRAIN

On - ly in Je - sus true pleas-ures a - bound.
If they with faith and in pen - i - tence bow. All that I want is in
All of its needs will in Him be sup - plied.
One glimpse of Je - sus, and all will be bright!

Je - sus; He sat-is-fies, with the joy He sup-plies;
Je-sus, in Je-sus, free - ly;

Life would be worthless without Him, All things in Je - sus I find.
without Him, without Him,

the believer's experience

114

complete in thee
TALMADGE. L.M. Ref.

Aaron R. Wolfe and
James M. Gray

Talmadge J. Bittikofer

1. Com-plete in Thee! no work of mine May take, dear Lord, the place of Thine;
2. Com-plete in Thee! no more shall sin, Thy grace hath conquered, reign within;
3. Com-plete in Thee—each want supplied, And no good thing to me de-nied;
4. Dear Sav-iour! when be-fore Thy bar All tribes and tongues as-sem-bled are,

Thy blood hath par - don bought for me, And I am now com-plete in Thee.
Thy voice shall bid the tempt-er flee, And I shall stand com-plete in Thee.
Since Thou my por - tion, Lord, wilt be, I ask no more, com-plete in Thee.
A - mong Thy cho - sen will I be, At Thy right hand, com-plete in Thee.

REFRAIN

Yea, jus - ti - fied! O bless-ed thought! And sanc-ti - fied! Sal-va-tion wrought!

Thy blood hath par - don bought for me, And glo - ri - fied, I too, shall be!

I've heard the King

HIGHLANDS. 9 12 9 12 Ref.

115

Grant C. Tullar

Donald P. Hustad

1. I've heard the King! The King of heav-en! Nor can I e'er for-get the
2. I've heard the King! The King of glo-ry; For whom my heart's door o-pened
3. I've heard the King! Oh, had I missed Him, My life for-ev-er-more could
4. I've heard the King! and now I'm tell-ing To all the world the gos-pel

mu-sic of His voice. I've heard the King! His call I've answered. I've made the
wide and He came in. I've heard the King! Oh, bless-ed hear-ing, His voice spoke
not re-gain the loss. From heav'n He came, the world to ran-som, And this He
of un-dy-ing love, That oth-ers too may catch the mu-sic His voice can

Refrain

King of heav'n my ev-er-last-ing choice.
peace and par-don for my guilt and sin.   He came to me, and with Him came a
did one day on Calv'ry's cru-el cross.
bring, and find their way to heav'n a-bove.

mp

bless-ing. He spoke to me, and glo-ry filled my soul; His voice I heard, so

f

charm-ing and so won-drous. I've heard the King, and hear-ing am made whole.

the believer's experience

116 One Day!

CHAPMAN. 11 10 11 10 Ref.

J. Wilbur Chapman

Charles H. Marsh

1. One day when heav - en was filled with His prais - es, One day when
2. One day they led Him up Cal - va - ry's moun - tain, One day they
3. One day they left Him a - lone in the gar - den, One day He
4. One day the grave could con - ceal Him no lon - ger, One day the
5. One day the trum - pet will sound for His com - ing, One day the

sin was as black as could be, Je - sus came forth to be
nailed Him to die on the tree; Suf - fer - ing an - guish, de -
rest - ed, from suf - fer - ing free; An - gels came down o'er His
stone rolled a - way from the door; Then He a - rose, o - ver
skies with His glo - ry will shine; Won - der - ful day, my be -

born of a vir - gin, Dwelt a - mong men, my ex - am - ple is He!
spised and re - ject - ed, Bear - ing our sins, my Re - deem - er is He!
tomb to keep vig - il; Hope of the hope-less, my Sav - iour is He!
death He has con-quered; Now is as - cend - ed, my Lord ev - er - more!
lov - ed ones bring-ing; Glo - ri - ous Sav - iour, this Je - sus is mine!

REFRAIN

Liv - ing, He loved me; dy - ing, He saved me; Bur - ied, He

car - ried my sins far a - way; Ris - ing, He jus - ti - fied

hymns of salvation

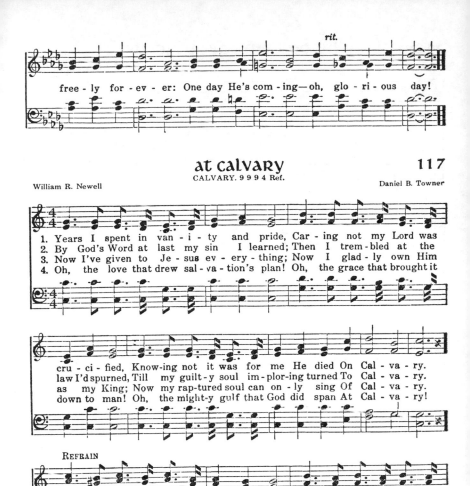

free - ly for - ev - er: One day He's com -ing—oh, glo - ri - ous day!

at calvary

CALVARY. 9 9 9 4 Ref.

117

William R. Newell

Daniel B. Towner

1. Years I spent in van - i - ty and pride, Car - ing not my Lord was
2. By God's Word at last my sin I learned; Then I trem - bled at the
3. Now I've given to Je - sus ev - ery - thing; Now I glad - ly own Him
4. Oh, the love that drew sal - va - tion's plan! Oh, the grace that brought it

cru - ci - fied, Know-ing not it was for me He died On Cal - va - ry.
law I'd spurned, Till my guilt - y soul im - plor - ing turned To Cal - va - ry.
as my King; Now my rap-tured soul can on - ly sing Of Cal - va - ry.
down to man! Oh, the might-y gulf that God did span At Cal - va - ry!

REFRAIN

Mer - cy there was great, and grace was free; Par - don there was mul - ti-

plied to me; There my burdened soul found lib - er - ty, At Cal - va - ry.

the believer's experience

WHY DO I SING ABOUT JESUS?

KETCHUM. 8 7 8 7 Ref.

Albert A. Ketchum

Albert A. Ketchum

1. Deep in my heart there's a glad-ness, Je - sus has saved me from sin!
2. On - ly a glimpse of His good-ness, That was suf - fi - cient for me;
3. He is the fair - est of fair ones, He is the Lil - y, the Rose;

Praise to His name—what a Sav - iour! Cleans-ing with-out and with - in.
On - ly one look at the Sav - iour, Then was my spir - it set free.
Riv - ers of mer - cy sur-round Him, Grace, love and pit - y He shows.

REFRAIN
Unison or Two Parts

Why do I sing a - bout Je - sus? Why is He pre - cious to me? . . . . He is my Lord and my Sav - iour, Dy - ing! He set me free. . . . . .
(set me free!)

hymns of salvation

ONCE FOR ALL

ONCE FOR ALL. 10 10 9 8 Ref.

Philip P. Bliss

Philip P. Bliss

1. Free from the law, O hap-py con - di - tion, Je - sus hath
2. Now are we free—there's no con-dem - na - tion, Je - sus pro-
3. "Chil - dren of God," O glo - ri - ous call - ing, Sure - ly His

bled, and there is re - mis - sion; Cursed by the law and bruised by the
vides a per-fect sal - va - tion; "Come un - to Me," O hear His sweet
grace will keep us from fall - ing; Pass - ing from death to life at His

REFRAIN

fall, Grace hath redeemed us once for all.
call, Come, and He saves us once for all.   Once for all, O sin-ner, re-
call, Bless-ed sal - va - tion once for all.

ceive it;   Once for all, O broth-er, be - lieve it; Cling to the

cross, the bur - den will fall, Christ hath re-deemed us once for all.

the believer's experience

The story of this hymn is on page...67

120 SINCE JESUS CAME INTO MY HEART

McDANIEL. 12 8 12 8 Ref.

Rufus H. McDaniel

Charles H. Gabriel

1. What a won-der-ful change in my life has been wrought Since Je-sus came
2. I have ceased from my wandering and go - ing a - stray, Since Je-sus came
3. There's a light in the val - ley of death now for me, Since Je-sus came
4. I shall go there to dwell in that Cit - y, I know, Since Je-sus came

in - to my heart! I have light in my soul for which long I have sought,
in - to my heart! And my sins, which were man-y, are all washed a - way,
in - to my heart! And the gates of the Cit - y be - yond I can see,
in - to my heart! And I'm hap - py, so hap - py, as on - ward I go,

REFRAIN

Since Je - sus came in - to my heart! Since Je - sus came in - to my
Since Je - sus came in, came

heart, Since Je-sus came in-to my heart, Floods of joy o'er my
in - to my heart, Since Je-sus came in, came in - to my heart,

soul like the sea bil-lows roll, Since Je - sus came in - to my heart.

hymns of salvation

In tenderness he sought me

CLARENDON. 7 6 7 6 8 8 Ref.

W. Spencer Walton

Adoniram J. Gordon

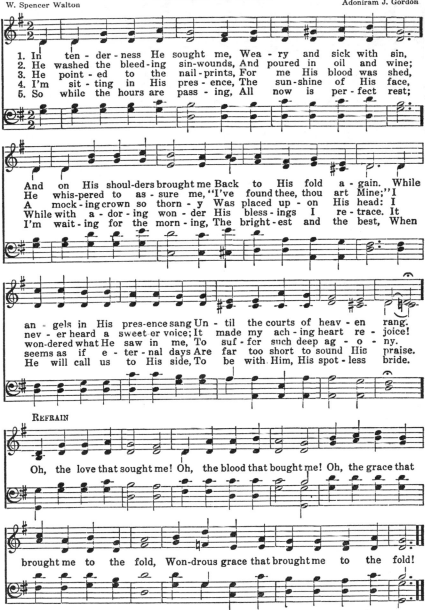

1. In ten - der - ness He sought me, Wea - ry and sick with sin,
2. He washed the bleed-ing sin-wounds, And poured in oil and wine;
3. He point - ed to the nail - prints, For me His blood was shed,
4. I'm sit - ting in His pres - ence, The sun - shine of His face,
5. So while the hours are pass - ing, All now is per - fect rest;

And on His shoul-ders brought me Back to His fold a - gain. While
He whis-pered to as - sure me, "I've found thee, thou art Mine;" I
A mock - ing crown so thorn - y Was placed up - on His head: I
While with a - dor - ing won - der His bless - ings I re - trace. It
I'm wait - ing for the morn - ing, The bright - est and the best, When

an - gels in His pres-ence sang Un - til the courts of heav - en rang.
nev - er heard a sweet-er voice; It made my ach - ing heart re - joice!
won-dered what He saw in me, To suf - fer such deep ag - o - ny.
seems as if e - ter - nal days Are far too short to sound His praise.
He will call us to His side, To be with Him, His spot - less bride.

REFRAIN

Oh, the love that sought me! Oh, the blood that bought me! Oh, the grace that

brought me to the fold, Won-drous grace that brought me to the fold!

the believer's experience

I've found a friend

FRIEND. 8 7 8 7 D.

James G. Small

George C. Stebbins

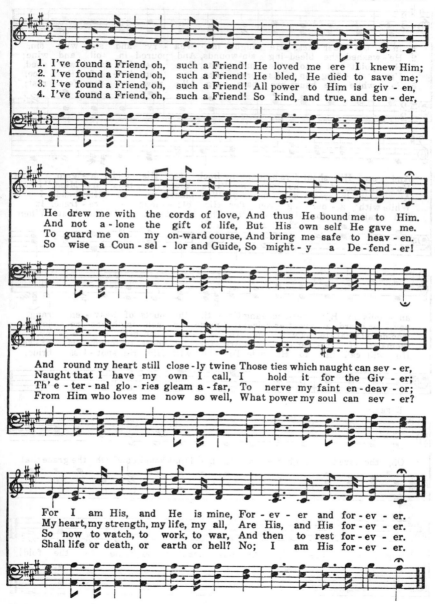

1. I've found a Friend, oh, such a Friend! He loved me ere I knew Him;
2. I've found a Friend, oh, such a Friend! He bled, He died to save me;
3. I've found a Friend, oh, such a Friend! All power to Him is giv-en,
4. I've found a Friend, oh, such a Friend! So kind, and true, and ten-der,

He drew me with the cords of love, And thus He bound me to Him.
And not a-lone the gift of life, But His own self He gave me.
To guard me on my on-ward course, And bring me safe to heav-en.
So wise a Coun-sel-lor and Guide, So might-y a De-fend-er!

And round my heart still close-ly twine Those ties which naught can sev-er,
Naught that I have my own I call, I hold it for the Giv-er;
Th' e-ter-nal glo-ries gleam a-far, To nerve my faint en-deav-or;
From Him who loves me now so well, What power my soul can sev-er?

For I am His, and He is mine, For-ev-er and for-ev-er.
My heart, my strength, my life, my all, Are His, and His for-ev-er.
So now to watch, to work, to war, And then to rest for-ev-er.
Shall life or death, or earth or hell? No; I am His for-ev-er.

hymns of salvation

I Know Whom I Have Believed

EL NATHAN. C.M. Ref.

Daniel W. Whittle

James McGranahan

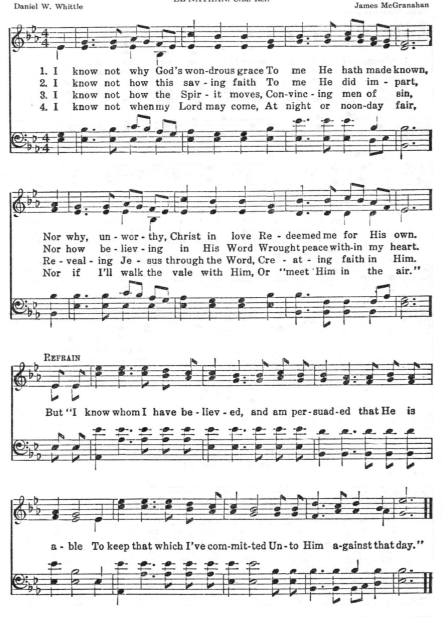

1. I know not why God's won-drous grace To me He hath made known,
2. I know not how this sav-ing faith To me He did im-part,
3. I know not how the Spir-it moves, Con-vinc-ing men of sin,
4. I know not when my Lord may come, At night or noon-day fair,

Nor why, un-wor-thy, Christ in love Re-deemed me for His own.
Nor how be-liev-ing in His Word Wrought peace with-in my heart.
Re-veal-ing Je-sus through the Word, Cre-at-ing faith in Him.
Nor if I'll walk the vale with Him, Or "meet Him in the air."

REFRAIN

But "I know whom I have be-liev-ed, and am per-suad-ed that He is

a-ble To keep that which I've com-mit-ted Un-to Him a-gainst that day."

the believer's experience

124

WOUNÒEÒ fOR ME

FOR ME. 8 10 10 10

W. G. Ovens and
Gladys Watkin-Roberts

W. G. Ovens

1. Wound-ed for me, wound-ed for me, There on the cross
2. Dy-ing for me, dy-ing for me, There on the cross
3. Ris-en for me, ris-en for me, Up from the grave
4. Liv-ing for me, liv-ing for me, Up in the skies
5. Com-ing for me, com-ing for me, One day to earth

He was wound-ed for me; Gone my trans-gres-sions, and
He was dy-ing for me; Now in His death my re-
He has ris-en for me; Now ev-er-more from death's
He is liv-ing for me; Dai-ly He's plead-ing and
He is com-ing for me; Then with what joy His dear

now I am free, All be-cause Je-sus was wound-ed for me.
demp-tion I see, All be-cause Je-sus was dy-ing for me.
sting I am free, All be-cause Je-sus has ris-en for me.
pray-ing for me, All be-cause Je-sus is liv-ing for me.
face I shall see, Oh, how I praise Him, He's com-ing for me.

125 ## not what these hands have done

ST. ANDREW. 6 6 8 6

Horatius Bonar

Joseph Barnby

1. Not what these hands have done Can save this guilt-y soul; Not
2. Not what I feel or do Can give me peace with God; Not
3. Thy work a-lone, O Christ, Can ease this weight of sin; Thy
4. Thy love to me, O God, Not mine, O Lord, to Thee, Can
5. Thy grace a-lone, O God, To me can par-don speak; Thy
6. I bless the Christ of God; I rest on love di-vine; And,

hymns of salvation

what this toil-ing flesh has borne Can make my spir-it whole.
all my prayers and sighs and tears Can bear my aw-ful load.
blood a-lone, O Lamb of God, Can give me peace with-in.
rid me of this dark un-rest, And set my spir-it free.
with un-fal-tering lip and heart, I call this Sav-iour mine. A-MEN.

christ liveth in me

126

CHRIST LIVETH. C.M. Ref.

Daniel W. Whittle

James McGranahan

1. Once far from God and dead in sin, No light my heart could see;
2. As rays of light from yon-der sun, The flow'rs of earth set free,
3. As lives the flow'r with-in the seed, As in the cone the tree,
4. With long-ing all my heart is filled, That like Him I may be,

But in God's Word the light I found, Now Christ liv-eth in me.
So life and light and love came forth From Christ liv-ing in me.
So, praise the God of truth and grace, His Spir-it dwell-eth in me.
As on the won-drous thought I dwell That Christ liv-eth in me.

REFRAIN

Christ liv-eth in me, Christ liv-eth in me,
Christ liv-eth in me, Christ liv-eth in

Oh! what a sal-va-tion this, That Christ liv-eth in me.
me, Oh,

the believer's experience

near the cross

NEAR THE CROSS. 7 6 7 6 Ref.

Fanny J. Crosby

William H. Doane

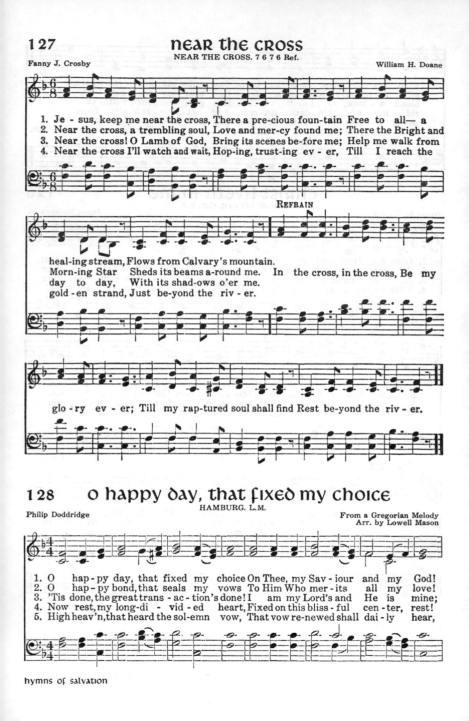

1. Je - sus, keep me near the cross, There a pre-cious foun-tain Free to all— a
2. Near the cross, a trembling soul, Love and mer-cy found me; There the Bright and
3. Near the cross! O Lamb of God, Bring its scenes be-fore me; Help me walk from
4. Near the cross I'll watch and wait, Hop-ing, trust-ing ev - er, Till   I reach the

REFRAIN

heal-ing stream, Flows from Calvary's mountain.
Morn-ing Star   Sheds its beams a-round me.   In   the cross, in the cross, Be   my
day to day, With its shad-ows o'er me.
gold - en strand, Just be-yond the riv - er.

glo - ry   ev - er; Till my rap-tured soul shall find Rest be-yond the riv - er.

128   o happy day, that fixed my choice

HAMBURG. L.M.

Philip Doddridge

From a Gregorian Melody
Arr. by Lowell Mason

1. O   hap - py day, that fixed my   choice On Thee, my Sav - iour   and   my   God!
2. O   hap - py bond, that seals   my   vows To Him Who mer - its   all   my   love!
3. 'Tis done, the great trans - ac - tion's done! I   am my Lord's and   He   is   mine;
4. Now rest, my long - di - vid - ed   heart, Fixed on this bliss - ful   cen - ter,   rest!
5. High heav'n, that heard the sol-emn   vow, That vow re-newed shall dai - ly   hear,

Well may this glow-ing heart re-joice And tell its rap-tures all a-broad.
Let cheer-ful an-thems fill His house, While to that sa-cred shrine I move.
He drew me, and I fol-lowed on, Charmed to confess the voice di-vine.
With ash-es who would grudge to part, When called on an-gels' bread to feast?
Till in life's lat-est hour I bow, And bless in death a bond so dear.

my hope is in the Lord

WAKEFIELD. 6 6 8 4 Ref.

129

Norman J. Clayton

Norman J. Clayton

1. My hope is in the Lord Who gave Him-self for me, And
2. No mer-it of my own His an-ger to sup-press. My
3. And now for me He stands Be-fore the Fa-ther's throne. He
4. His grace has planned it all, 'Tis mine but to be-lieve, And

REFRAIN

paid the price of all my sin at Cal-va-ry.
on-ly hope is found in Je-sus' right-eous-ness. For me He died, For
shows His wounded hands, and names me as His own. For me He died,
rec-og-nize His work of love and Christ re-ceive.

me He lives, And ev-er-last-ing life and light He free-ly gives.
For me He lives,

the believer's experience

JESUS, I WILL TRUST THEE

GOSHEN. 6 5 6 5 D.

Mary Jane Walker

Bible Class Magazine, 1860

1. Je - sus, I will trust Thee, Trust Thee with my soul; Guilt - y, lost, and
2. Je - sus, I must trust Thee, Pon - der - ing Thy ways, Full of love and
3. Je - sus, I can trust Thee, Trust Thy writ-ten Word, Though Thy voice of
4. Je - sus, I do trust Thee, Trust with-out a doubt; Who - so - ev - er

help-less, Thou canst make me whole. There is none in heav - en Or on earth like
mer - cy All Thine earth-ly days; Sinners gathered round Thee, Lep-ers sought Thy
pit - y I have nev - er heard. When Thy Spir-it teach-eth, To my taste how
com - eth Thou wilt not cast out. Faith-ful is Thy prom-ise, Pre-cious is Thy

Thee; Thou hast died for sin - ners—There-fore, Lord, for me.
face; None too vile or loath-some For a Sav-iour's grace.
sweet! On - ly may I heark - en Sit - ting at Thy feet.
blood; These my soul's sal - va - tion, Thou my Sav - iour God. A-MEN.

I BELONG TO JESUS

DEDICATION. 6 5 7 5

M. Fraser

M. A. Sea

1. I be - long to Je - sus; I am not my own;
2. I be - long to Je - sus; He is Lord and King,
3. I be - long to Je - sus; Bless - ed, bless - ed thought!
4. I be - long to Je - sus; He has died for me;
5. I be - long to Je - sus; He will keep my soul,
6. I be - long to Je - sus; And ere long I'll stand

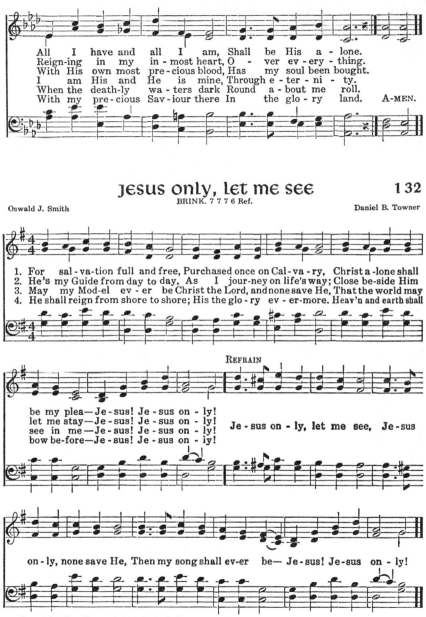

All I have and all I am, Shall be His a - lone.
Reign-ing in my in - most heart, O - ver ev - ery - thing.
With His own most pre - cious blood, Has my soul been bought.
I am His and He is mine, Through e - ter - ni - ty.
When the death-ly wa - ters dark Round a - bout me roll.
With my pre - cious Sav - iour there In the glo - ry land. A-MEN.

JESUS ONLY, LET ME SEE 132

BRINK. 7 7 7 6 Ref.

Oswald J. Smith

Daniel B. Towner

1. For sal - va-tion full and free, Purchased once on Cal - va - ry, Christ a - lone shall
2. He's my Guide from day to day, As I jour-ney on life's way; Close be-side Him
3. May my Mod-el ev - er be Christ the Lord, and none save He, That the world may
4. He shall reign from shore to shore; His the glo - ry ev - er-more. Heav'n and earth shall

REFRAIN

be my plea— Je - sus! Je - sus on - ly!
let me stay— Je - sus! Je - sus on - ly!
see in me— Je - sus! Je - sus on - ly!
bow be-fore— Je - sus! Je - sus on - ly!

Je - sus on - ly, let me see, Je - sus

on - ly, none save He, Then my song shall ev - er be— Je - sus! Je - sus on - ly!

the BeLiever's experience

133 I WAS A WANDERING SHEEP

LEBANON. S.M.D.

Horatius Bonar

John Zundel

1. I was a wan-d'ring sheep, I did not love the fold;
2. The Shep-herd sought His sheep, The Fa - ther sought His child;
3. Je - sus my Shep-herd is; T'was He that loved my soul,
4. I was a wan-d'ring sheep, I would not be con - trolled;

I did not love my Shep-herd's voice, I would not be con - trolled.
They fol - lowed me o'er vale and hill, O'er des - erts waste and wild;
'Twas He that washed me in His blood, 'Twas He that made me whole;
But now I love my Shep-herd's voice, I love, I love the fold.

I was a way - ward child, I did not love my home;
They found me nigh to death, Fam - ished and faint and lone;
'Twas He that sought the lost, That found the wan-d'ring sheep,
I was a way - ward child, I once pre - ferred to roam;

I did not love my Fa - ther's voice, I loved a - far to roam.
They bound me with the bands of love, They saved the wan-d'ring one.
'Twas He that brought me to the fold, 'Tis He that still doth keep.
But now I love my Fa - ther's voice, I love, I love His home.

hymns of salvation

hymns of the christian life

Poets and musicians have given us music that speaks to and interprets the whole range of the Christian life.

Here are words that lead us to a more complete consecration of ourselves to Jesus Christ — hymns that encourage us to trust the faithfulness of God's Word — and songs that reflect the serenity of a life of faith and commitment.

Both in public worship and in private prayer, these pages reflect today's Christian experience and speak our deepest hopes and highest aspirations for tomorrow.

fully surrendered

SNEAD. 9 9 6 6 6 4

Alfred C. Snead

George C. Stebbins

1. Ful - ly sur - ren - dered, Lord, I would be, Ful - ly sur - ren - dered,
2. Ful - ly sur - ren - dered—life, time, and all, All Thou hast giv'n me
3. Ful - ly sur - ren - dered—sil - ver and gold, His, who hath giv'n me
4. Ful - ly sur - ren - dered—Lord, I am Thine; Ful - ly sur - ren - dered,

dear Lord, to Thee. All on the al - tar laid, Sur - ren - der
held at Thy call. Speak but the word to me, Glad - ly I'll
rich - es un - told. All, all be - long to Thee, For Thou didst
Sav - iour di - vine! Live Thou Thy life in me, All full - ness

ful - ly made, Thou hast my ran - som paid; I yield to Thee.
fol - low Thee, Now and e - ter - nal - ly O - bey my Lord.
pur - chase me, Thine ev - er - more to be, Je - sus, my Lord.
dwells in Thee; Not I, but Christ in me, Christ all in all.

135 may the mind of christ, my saviour

ST. LEONARDS. 8 7 8 5

Kate B. Wilkinson

A. Cyril Barham-Gould

1. May the mind of Christ, my Sav - iour, Live in me from day to day,
2. May the Word of God dwell rich - ly In my heart from hour to hour,
3. May the peace of God, my Fa - ther, Rule my life in ev - ery-thing,
4. May the love of Je - sus fill me, As the wa - ters fill the sea;
5. May I run the race be - fore me, Strong and brave to face the foe,
6. May His beau - ty rest up - on me As I seek the lost to win,

hymns of the christian life

By His love and pow'r con-trol-ling All I do and say.
So that all may see I tri-umph On - ly through His pow'r.
That I may be calm to com-fort Sick and sor - row - ing.
Him ex - alt - ing, self a - bas - ing, This is vic - to - ry.
Look-ing on - ly un - to Je - sus As I on - ward go.
And may they for - get the chan-nel, See - ing on - ly Him. A-MEN.

take time to be holy

LONGSTAFF. 6 5 6 5 D.

136

William D. Longstaff

George C. Stebbins

1. Take time to be ho - ly, Speak oft with thy Lord; A - bide in Him
2. Take time to be ho - ly, The world rush-es on; Much time spend in
3. Take time to be ho - ly, Let Him be thy Guide, And run not be-
4. Take time to be ho - ly, Be calm in thy soul; Each thought and each

al - ways, And feed on His Word. Make friends of God's children; Help those who are
se - cret With Je - sus a - lone; By look-ing to Je - sus, Like Him thou shalt
fore Him, What-ev-er be - tide; In joy or in sor - row, Still fol - low thy
mo - tive Be-neath His con-trol; Thus led by His Spir - it To foun-tains of

weak; For - get-ting in noth - ing His bless-ing to seek.
be; Thy friends in thy con - duct His like-ness shall see.
Lord, And, look-ing to Je - sus, Still trust in His Word.
love, Thou soon shalt be fit - ted For serv-ice a - bove. A-MEN.

137
teach me thy will, o lord
TEACH ME. 10 10 12 10

Katherine A. Grimes

William M. Runyan

1. Teach me Thy will, O Lord, Teach me Thy way; Teach me to
2. Teach me Thy won-drous grace, Bound-less and free; Lord, let Thy
3. Teach me by pain Thy power, Teach me by love; Teach me to
4. Teach Thou my lips to sing, My heart to praise; Be Thou my

know Thy word, Teach me to pray. What-e'er seems best to Thee, That be my
bless - ed face Shine up - on me. Heal Thou sin's ev-ery smart, Dwell Thou with-
know, each hour, Thou art a - bove. Teach me as seem-eth best In Thee to
Lord and King Through all my days. Teach Thou my soul to cry, "Be Thou, dear

ear - nest plea, So that Thou draw-est me Clos - er each day.
in my heart; Grant that I nev - er part, Sav - iour, from Thee.
find sweet rest; Lean-ing up - on Thy breast, All doubt re - move.
Sav - iour, nigh, Teach me to live, to die, Saved by Thy grace." A - MEN.

138   let me come closer to thee, jesus
LLANTHONY ABBEY. 9 6 9 6

J. L. Lyne

John H. Lester

1. Let me come clos - er to Thee, Je - sus, Oh, clos - er day by day;
2. Let me show forth Thy beau-ty, Je - sus, Like sun-shine on the hills!
3. Yes, like a foun-tain, pre-cious Je - sus, Make me and let me be;
4. In all my heart and will, O Je - sus, Be al - to - geth - er King!
5. Thirsting and hung-'ring for Thee, Je - sus, With bless-ed hun - ger here,

Let me lean hard-er on Thee, Je - sus, Yes, hard - er all the way.
Oh, let my lips pour forth Thy sweetness In joy - ous, spark-ling rills!
Keep me and use me dai - ly, Je - sus, For Thee, for on - ly Thee.
Make me a loy - al sub - ject, Je - sus, To Thee in ev - ery-thing.
Looking for home on Zi - on's moun-tain, No thirst, no hun - ger there. A - MEN.

O Love that Wilt Not Let Me Go   139

ST. MARGARET. 8 8 8 8 6

George Matheson

Albert L. Peace

1. O Love that wilt not let me go, I rest my wea - ry
2. O Light that fol-lowest all my way, I yield my flick-ering
3. O Joy that seek - est me through pain, I can - not close my
4. O Cross that lift - est up my head, I dare not ask to

soul in Thee; I give Thee back the life I owe, That
torch to Thee; My heart re - stores its bor-rowed ray, That
heart to Thee; I trace the rain-bow through the rain, And
fly from Thee; I lay in dust life's glo - ry dead, And

in Thine o - cean depths its flow May rich - er, full - er be.
in Thy sun-shine's blaze its day May bright-er, fair - er be.
feel the prom - ise is not vain That morn shall tear - less be.
from the ground there blossoms red Life that shall end - less be. A-MEN.

aspiration and consecration

JESUS, MASTER, WHOSE I AM

ST. PETERSBURG. 7 7 7 7 7 7

Frances R. Havergal

Dimitri S. Bortniansky

1. Je - sus, Mas - ter, whose I am, Pur - chased Thine a-
2. Oth - er lords have long held sway; Now Thy name a-
3. Je - sus, Mas - ter, I am Thine. Keep me faith - ful,

lone to be By Thy blood, O spot - less Lamb,
lone to bear, Thy dear voice a - lone o - bey,
keep me near; Let Thy pres - ence in me shine,

Shed so will - ing - ly for me, Let my heart be
Is my dai - ly, hour - ly pray'r; Whom have I in
All my home - ward way to cheer. Je - sus, at Thy

all Thine own, Let me live to Thee a - lone.
heav'n but Thee? Noth - ing else my joy can be.
feet I fall; Oh, be Thou my all in all.

hymns of the christian life

make me a captive, Lord

PARADOXY. S.M.D.

George Matheson

Donald P. Hustad

141

1. Make me a cap - tive, Lord, And then I shall be free;
2. My heart is weak and poor Un - til it mas - ter find;
3. My pow'r is faint and low Till I have learned to serve:
4. My will is not my own Till Thou hast made it Thine;

Force me to ren - der up my sword, And I shall con-queror be;
It has no spring of ac - tion sure— It va - ries with the wind;
It wants the need - ed fire to glow, It wants the breeze to nerve;
If it would reach the monarch's throne It must its crown re - sign:

mp

I sink in life's a - larms When by my - self I stand;
It can - not free - ly move Till Thou has wrought its chain;
It can - not drive the world Un - til it - self be driv'n;
It on - ly stands un - bent, A - mid the clash - ing strife,

Im - pris - on me with - in Thine arms, And strong shall be my hand.
En-slave it with Thy match-less love, And death-less it shall reign.
Its flag can on - ly be un-furled When Thou shalt breathe from heav'n.
When on Thy bos - om it has leaned, And found in Thee its life. A-MEN.

aspiration and consecration

The story of this hymn is on page...37

142 LORD, SPEAK TO ME

CANONBURY. L.M.

Frances R. Havergal

Robert Schumann

1. Lord, speak to me, that I may speak In liv-ing ech-oes of Thy tone;
2. O teach me, Lord, that I may teach The pre-cious things Thou dost impart;
3. O fill me with Thy full-ness, Lord, Un-til my ver-y heart o'er-flow
4. O use me, Lord, use e-ven me, Just as Thou wilt, and when, and where;

As Thou hast sought, so let me seek Thy err-ing chil-dren lost and lone.
And wing my words, that they may reach The hid-den depths of many a heart.
In kindling thought and glow-ing word Thy love to tell, Thy praise to show.
Un-til Thy bless-ed face I see, Thy rest, Thy joy, Thy glo-ry share. AMEN.

143 I'LL LIVE FOR HIM

DUNBAR. 8 8 8 6 Ref.

Ralph E. Hudson

C. R. Dunbar

1. My life, my love I give to Thee, Thou Lamb of God who died for me;
2. I now be-lieve Thou dost re-ceive, For Thou hast died that I might live;
3. O Thou who died on Cal-va-ry, To save my soul and make me free,

REF. I'll live for Him who died for me, How hap-py then my life shall be!

D. C. Refrain

Oh, may I ev-er faith-ful be, My Sav-iour and my God!
And now hence-forth I'll trust in Thee, My Sav-iour and my God!
I'll con-se-crate my life to Thee, My Sav-iour and my God!

I'll live for Him who died for me, My Sav-iour and my God!

take thou our minds, dear lord   144

HALL. 10 10 10 10

William H. Foulkes

Calvin W. Laufer

1. Take Thou our minds, dear Lord, we hum - bly pray;
2. Take Thou our hearts, O Christ, they are Thine own;
3. Take Thou our wills, Most High! Hold Thou full sway;
4. Take Thou our - selves, O Lord, heart, mind, and will;

Give us the mind of Christ each pass - ing day;
Come Thou with - in our souls and claim Thy throne;
Have in our in - most souls Thy per - fect way;
Through our sur - ren - dered souls Thy plans ful - fill.

Teach us to know the truth that sets us free;
Help us to shed a - broad Thy death - less love;
Guard Thou each sa - cred hour from self - ish ease;
We yield our - selves to Thee— time, tal - ents, all!

Grant us in all our thoughts to hon - or Thee.
Use us to make the earth like heav'n a - bove.
Guide Thou our or - dered lives as Thou dost please.
We hear, and hence - forth heed, Thy sov - ereign call. A-MEN.

ASPIRATION AND CONSECRATION

145 I WOULD BE LIKE JESUS

WINONA LAKE. C.M. Ref.

James Rowe

Bentley D. Ackley

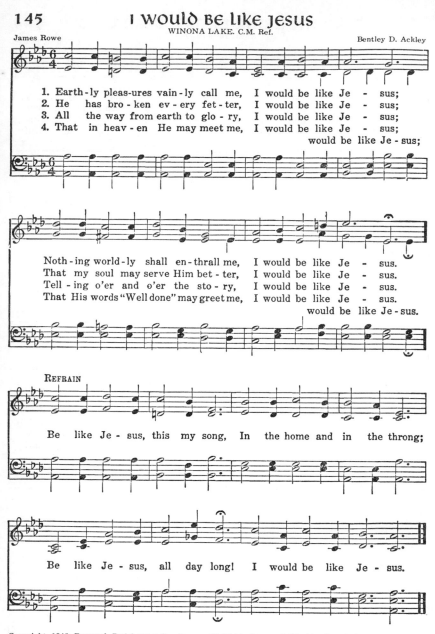

1. Earth-ly pleas-ures vain-ly call me, I would be like Je - sus;
2. He has bro - ken ev - ery fet - ter, I would be like Je - sus;
3. All the way from earth to glo - ry, I would be like Je - sus;
4. That in heav - en He may meet me, I would be like Je - sus;
   would be like Je - sus;

Noth - ing world-ly shall en-thrall me, I would be like Je - sus.
That my soul may serve Him bet - ter, I would be like Je - sus.
Tell - ing o'er and o'er the sto - ry, I would be like Je - sus.
That His words "Well done" may greet me, I would be like Je - sus.
would be like Je - sus.

REFRAIN

Be like Je - sus, this my song, In the home and in the throng;

Be like Je - sus, all day long! I would be like Je - sus.

oh, to be like thee

RONDINELLA. 10 9 10 9 Ref.

Thomas O. Chisholm

William J. Kirkpatrick

146

1. Oh, to be like Thee! bless-ed Re-deem-er, This is my con-stant
2. Oh, to be like Thee! full of com-pas-sion, Lov-ing, for-giv-ing,
3. Oh, to be like Thee! low-ly in spir-it, Ho-ly and harm-less,
4. Oh, to be like Thee! while I am plead-ing, Pour out Thy Spir-it,

long-ing and prayer. Glad-ly I'll for-feit all of earth's treas-ures,
ten-der and kind, Help-ing the help-less, cheer-ing the faint-ing,
pa-tient and brave; Meek-ly en-dur-ing cru-el re-proach-es,
fill with Thy love; Make me a tem-ple meet for Thy dwell-ing,

REFRAIN

Je-sus, Thy per-fect like-ness to wear.
Seek-ing the wan-dering sin-ner to find.   Oh, to be like Thee!
Will-ing to suf-fer oth-ers to save.
Fit me for life and heav-en a-bove.

Oh, to be like Thee, bless-ed Re-deem-er, pure as Thou art! Come in Thy

sweet-ness, come in Thy full-ness; Stamp Thine own im-age deep on my heart.

aspiration and consecration

147

Be thou my vision

SLANE. 10 10 10 10

Ancient Irish
Trans. by Mary E. Byrne
Versified by Eleanor H. Hull

Traditional Irish Melody
Harm. by David Evans

Unison

1. Be Thou my Vi - sion, O Lord of my heart;
2. Be Thou my Wis - dom, and Thou my true Word;
3. Rich - es I heed not, nor man's emp - ty praise,
4. High King of heav - en, my vic - to - ry won,

Nought be all else to me, save that Thou art—
I ev - er with Thee and Thou with me, Lord;
Thou mine in - her - it - ance, now and al - ways:
May I reach heav - en's joys, O bright heaven's Sun!

Thou my best thought, by day or by night,
Thou my great Fa - ther, I Thy true son;
Thou and Thou on - ly, first in my heart,
Heart of my own heart, what - ev - er be - fall,

Wak - ing or sleep - ing, Thy pres - ence my light.
Thou in me dwell - ing, and I with Thee one.
High King of heav - en, my Treas - ure Thou art.
Still be my Vi - sion, O Rul - er of all. A - MEN.

Words used by permission of Chatto and Windus Ltd. Music from "The Revised Church Hymnary" by permission of Oxford University Press.

hymns of the christian life

The story of this hymn is on page...87

Search Me, O God

MAORI. 10 10 10 10

J. Edwin Orr

Maori Melody
Arr. by Donald P. Hustad

1. Search me, O God, and know my heart to - day;
2. I praise Thee, Lord, for cleans-ing me from sin:
3. Lord, take my life, and make it whol - ly Thine:
4. O Ho - ly Ghost, re - vi - val comes from Thee:

Try me, O Sav - iour, know my thoughts, I pray:
Ful - fill Thy Word, and make me pure with - in;
Fill my poor heart with Thy great love di - vine;
Send a re - vi - val, start the work in me:

See if there be some wick - ed way in me:
Fill me with fire, where once I burned with shame:
Take all my will, my pas - sion, self and pride;
Thy Word de - clares Thou wilt sup - ply our need:

Cleanse me from ev - ery sin, And set me free.
Grant my de - sire to mag - ni - fy Thy name.
I now sur - ren - der: Lord, in me a - bide.
For bless - ing now, O Lord, I hum - bly plead.

ASPIRATION AND CONSECRATION

149 I NEED THEE EVERY HOUR

NEED. 6 4 6 4 Ref.

Annie S. Hawks and
Robert Lowry

Robert Lowry

1. I need Thee ev-ery hour, Most gra-cious Lord; No ten-der voice like
2. I need Thee ev-ery hour, Stay Thou near by; Temp-ta-tions lose their
3. I need Thee ev-ery hour, In joy or pain; Come quick-ly and a-
4. I need Thee ev-ery hour, Most Ho-ly One; O make me Thine in-

REFRAIN

Thine Can peace af-ford.
power When Thou art nigh. I need Thee, O I need Thee; Ev-ery hour I
bide, Or life is vain.
deed, Thou bless-ed Son!

need Thee; O bless me now, my Sav-iour, I come to Thee!

150 MORE LOVE TO THEE

MORE LOVE TO THEE. 6 4 6 4 6 6 4 4

Elizabeth P. Prentiss

William H. Doane

1. More love to Thee, O Christ, More love to Thee! Hear Thou the
2. Once earth-ly joy I craved, Sought peace and rest; Now Thee a-
3. Let sor-row do its work, Send grief and pain; Sweet are Thy
4. Then shall my lat-est breath Whis-per Thy praise; This be the

prayer I make On bend-ed knee; This is my ear-nest plea:
lone I seek, Give what is best; This all my prayer shall be:
mes-sen-gers, Sweet their re-frain, When they can sing with me:
part-ing cry My heart shall raise; This still its prayer shall be:

More love, O Christ, to Thee, More love to Thee, More love to Thee! A-MEN.

BENEATH THE CROSS OF JESUS
ST. CHRISTOPHER. 7 6 8 6 8 6 8 6
151

Elizabeth C. Clephane

Frederick C. Maker

1. Be - neath the cross of Je - sus I fain would take my stand—
2. Up - on that cross of Je - sus Mine eye at times can see
3. I take, O cross, thy shad - ow For my a - bid - ing - place;

The shad - ow of a might - y Rock With - in a wea - ry land;
The ver - y dy - ing form of One Who suf - fered there for me;
I ask no oth - er sun-shine than The sun - shine of His face;

A home with - in the wil - der - ness, A rest up - on the way,
And from my smit - ten heart with tears Two won - ders I con - fess—
Con - tent to let the world go by, To know no gain nor loss,

From the burn-ing of the noon-tide heat, And the bur-den of the day.
The won - ders of re-deem-ing love And my un - wor - thi-ness.
My sin - ful self my on - ly shame, My glo - ry all the cross. A-MEN.

Music copyright by The Psalms & Hymns Trust. Used by permission.

aspiration and consecration

LIVING FOR JESUS

LIVING. 10 10 10 10 Ref.

Thomas O. Chisholm

C. Harold Lowden

1. Liv-ing for Je-sus a life that is true, Striv-ing to please Him in
2. Liv-ing for Je-sus who died in my place, Bear-ing on Cal-vary my
3. Liv-ing for Je-sus wher-ev-er I am, Do-ing each du-ty in
4. Liv-ing for Je-sus through earth's little while, My dear-est treas-ure, the

all that I do; Yield-ing al-le-giance, glad-heart-ed and free,
sin and dis-grace; Such love con-strains me to an-swer His call,
His ho-ly name; Will-ing to suf-fer af-flic-tion and loss,
light of His smile; Seek-ing the lost ones He died to re-deem,

REFRAIN

This is the path-way of bless-ing for me.
Fol-low His lead-ing and give Him my all.
Deem-ing each tri-al a part of my cross. O Je-sus, Lord and
Bring-ing the wea-ry to find rest in Him.

Sav-iour, I give my-self to Thee, For Thou, in Thy a-tone-ment, Didst

give Thy-self for me; I own no oth-er Mas-ter, My heart shall be Thy

hymns of the christian life

throne; My life I give, hence-forth to live, O Christ, for Thee a - lone.

open my eyes, that I may see 153

SCOTT. Irregular.

Clara H. Scott

Clara H. Scott

1. O - pen my eyes, that I may see Glimps-es of truth Thou hast for me;
2. O - pen my ears, that I may hear Voic - es of truth Thou send-est clear;
3. O - pen my mouth, and let me bear Glad - ly the warm truth ev-ery-where;

Place in my hands the won-der - ful key That shall un-clasp, and set me free.
And while the wave-notes fall on my ear, Ev - ery-thing false will dis - ap-pear.
O - pen my heart, and let me pre-pare Love with Thy chil-dren thus to share.

Si - lent-ly now I wait for Thee, Read-y, my God, Thy will to see;

O - pen my eyes, il - lu - mine me, Spir - it di - vine!
O - pen my ears, il - lu - mine me, Spir - it di - vine!
O - pen my heart, il - lu - mine me, Spir - it di - vine! A - MEN.

aspiration and consecration

154 have thine own way, Lord

ADELAIDE. 5 4 5 4 D.

Adelaide A. Pollard

George C. Stebbins

1. Have Thine own way, Lord! Have Thine own way! Thou art the
2. Have Thine own way, Lord! Have Thine own way! Search me and
3. Have Thine own way, Lord! Have Thine own way! Wound-ed and
4. Have Thine own way, Lord! Have Thine own way! Hold o'er my

Pot - ter; I am the clay. Mould me and make me Aft - er Thy
try me, Mas-ter, to - day! Whit - er than snow, Lord, Wash me just
wea - ry, Help me, I pray! Pow - er— all pow - er— Sure - ly is
be - ing Ab - so - lute sway! Fill with Thy Spir - it Till all shall

will, While I am wait - ing, Yield - ed and still.
now, As in Thy pres - ence Hum - bly I bow.
Thine! Touch me and heal me, Sav - iour di - vine!
see Christ on - ly, al - ways, Liv - ing in me! A - MEN.

The story of this hymn is on page...91

155 breathe on me, breath of god

TRENTHAM. S.M.

Edwin Hatch

Robert Jackson

1. Breathe on me, Breath of God, Fill me with life a - new, That I may
2. Breathe on me, Breath of God, Un - til my heart is pure, Un - til with
3. Breathe on me, Breath of God, Till I am whol - ly Thine, Un - til this
4. Breathe on me, Breath of God, So shall I nev - er die, But live with

love   what Thou dost love,   And   do   what Thou wouldst do.
Thee   I   will   one will,   To   do   and to   en - dure.
earth - ly   part   of   me   Glows   with Thy fire   di - vine.
Thee   the   per - fect life   Of   Thine e - ter - ni - ty.   A - MEN.

REVIVE US AGAIN

REVIVE US AGAIN. 11 11 Ref.

156

William P. Mackay

John J. Husband

1. We praise Thee, O God, for the Son of Thy love,   For   Je - sus who
2. We praise Thee, O God, for Thy Spir - it of light,   Who has shown us our
3. All glo - ry and praise to the Lamb that was slain,   Who has borne all our
4. Re - vive us a - gain, fill each heart with Thy love;   May each soul be re-

REFRAIN

died and   is now gone a - bove.
Sav - iour and scat - tered our night.   Hal - le - lu - jah! Thine the glo - ry, Hal - le-
sins, and has cleansed ev - ery stain.
kin - dled with fire from a - bove.

lu - jah! A - men; Hal - le - lu - jah! Thine the glo - ry; Re - vive us a - gain.

aspiration and consecration

The story of this hymn is on page..121

157

MORE LIKE THE MASTER

HUTCHISON. 10 10 11 11 Ref.

Charles H. Gabriel

Charles H. Gabriel

1. More like the Mas - ter I would ev - er be, More of His meek-ness, more hu - mil - i - ty; More zeal to la - bor, more cour-age to be true, More con - se - cra - tion for work He bids me do. Take Thou my heart, I would be Thine a - lone; Take Thou my heart and make it all Thine own; Purge me from sin, O Lord, I now im-

2. More like the Mas - ter is my dai - ly prayer; More strength to car-ry cross - es I must bear; More ear-nest ef - fort to bring His king-dom in; More of His Spir - it, the wan - der - er to win. Take my heart, O take my heart, I would be Thine a-lone; Take my heart, O take my heart and make it all Thine own; Purge Thou me from ev - 'ry sin, O Lord, I

3. More like the Mas - ter I would live and grow; More of His love to oth - ers I would show; More self - de - ni - al, like His in Gal - i - lee, More like the Mas - ter I long to ev - er be.

REFRAIN

plore, Wash me and keep me Thine for - ev - er - more.
now im-plore, Wash and keep, O wash and keep me Thine for - ev - er - more.

saviour, my heart is thine 158
ORLEANS. 6 4 6 4 4 4 6 4

Source Unknown
Alt. by George C. Stebbins

George C. Stebbins

1. Sav - iour, my heart is Thine, Keep it for me; May ev - ery
2. Sav - iour, my will is Thine, Keep it for me; May ev - ery
3. Sav - iour, my life is Thine, Keep it for me; May ev - ery
4. Sav - iour, my all is Thine, Keep it for me; May all I

thought of mine Glo - ri - fy Thee. Glo - ri - fy Thee,
act of mine Be done for Thee. Be done for Thee,
hour of mine Be lived for Thee. Be lived for Thee,
have, O Lord, Be used for Thee. Be used for Thee,

Glo - ri - fy Thee; May ev - ery thought of mine Glo - ri - fy Thee.
Be done for Thee; May ev - ery act of mine Be done for Thee.
Be lived for Thee; May ev - ery hour of mine Be lived for Thee.
Be used for Thee; May all I have, O Lord, Be used for Thee. A-MEN.

aspiration and consecration

IS YOUR ALL ON THE ALTAR?

HOFFMAN. 12 9 12 9 Ref.

Elisha A. Hoffman

Elisha A. Hoffman

1. You have longed for sweet peace and for faith to in-crease, And have earn-est-ly,
2. Would you walk with the Lord in the light of His Word, And have peace and con-
3. Oh, we nev-er can know what the Lord will be-stow Of the bless-ings for
4. Who can tell all the love He will send from a-bove, And how hap-py our

fer-vent-ly prayed; But you can-not have rest, or be per-fect-ly blest,
tent-ment al - way? You must do His sweet will to be free from all ill,
which we have prayed, Till our bod-y and soul He doth ful-ly con-trol,
hearts will be made, Of the fel-low-ship sweet we shall share at His feet,

REFRAIN

Un - til all on the al - tar is laid.
On the al - tar your all you must lay.
And our all on the al - tar is laid.
When our all on the al - tar is laid.

Is your all on the al-tar of

sac - ri-fice laid? Your heart, does the Spir-it con - trol? You can on - ly be

blest and have peace and sweet rest, As you yield Him your bod - y and soul.

hymns of the christian life

DRAW ME NEARER

I AM THINE. 10 7 10 7 Ref.

Fanny J. Crosby

William H. Doane

1. I am Thine, O Lord, I have heard Thy voice, And it
2. Con - se - crate me now to Thy serv - ice, Lord, By the
3. Oh, the pure de - light of a sin - gle hour That be-
4. There are depths of love that I can - not know Till I

told Thy love to me; But I long to rise in the arms of faith,
power of grace di - vine; Let my soul look up with a stead-fast hope,
fore Thy throne I spend, When I kneel in prayer, and with Thee, my God,
cross the nar - row sea; There are heights of joy that I may not reach

REFRAIN

And be clos - er drawn to Thee.
And my will be lost in Thine.
I com - mune as friend with friend!
Till I rest in peace with Thee.

Draw me near - er, near - er, near - er, near - er, bless - ed Lord, To the cross where Thou hast died; Draw me near - er, near - er, near - er, bless - ed Lord, To Thy pre - cious, bleed - ing side.

160

aspiration and consecration

161

SAVIOUR, thy dying love

SOMETHING FOR THEE. 10 10 12 10

Sylvanus D. Phelps

Robert Lowry

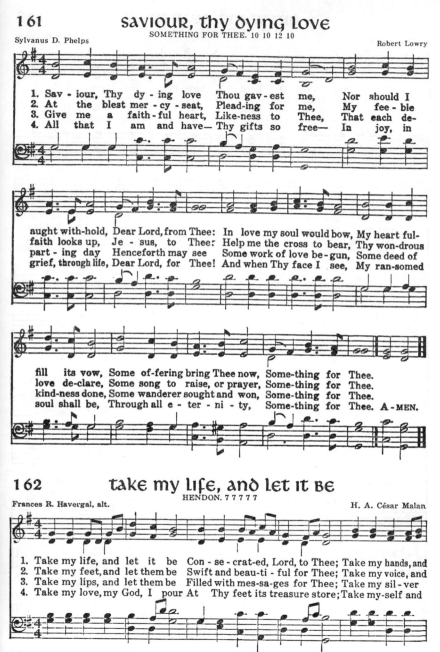

1. Sav - iour, Thy dy - ing love Thou gav - est me, Nor should I
2. At the blest mer - cy - seat, Plead - ing for me, My fee - ble
3. Give me a faith - ful heart, Like - ness to Thee, That each de -
4. All that I am and have— Thy gifts so free— In joy, in

aught with-hold, Dear Lord, from Thee: In love my soul would bow, My heart ful-
faith looks up, Je - sus, to Thee: Help me the cross to bear, Thy won-drous
part - ing day Henceforth may see Some work of love be - gun, Some deed of
grief, through life, Dear Lord, for Thee! And when Thy face I see, My ran-somed

fill its vow, Some of-fering bring Thee now, Some-thing for Thee.
love de-clare, Some song to raise, or prayer, Some-thing for Thee.
kind-ness done, Some wanderer sought and won, Some-thing for Thee.
soul shall be, Through all e - ter - ni - ty, Some-thing for Thee. A - MEN.

162

take my life, and let it be

HENDON. 7 7 7 7 7

Frances R. Havergal, alt.

H. A. César Malan

1. Take my life, and let it be Con - se - crat-ed, Lord, to Thee; Take my hands, and
2. Take my feet, and let them be Swift and beau-ti - ful for Thee; Take my voice, and
3. Take my lips, and let them be Filled with mes-sa-ges for Thee; Take my sil - ver
4. Take my love, my God, I pour At Thy feet its treasure store; Take my-self and

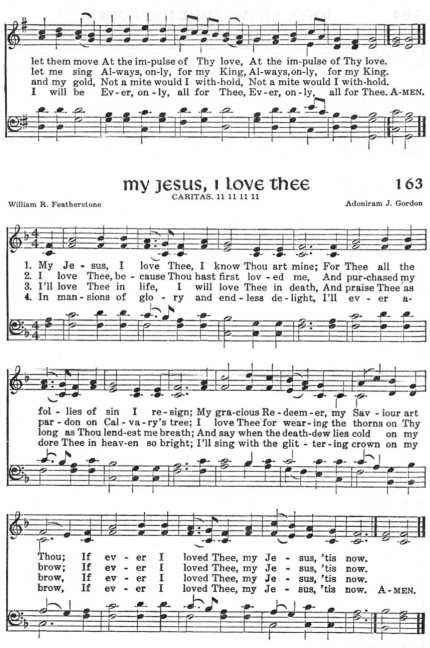

let them move At the im-pulse of Thy love, At the im-pulse of Thy love.
let me sing Al-ways, on-ly, for my King, Al-ways, on-ly, for my King.
and my gold, Not a mite would I with-hold, Not a mite would I with-hold.
I will be Ev-er, on-ly, all for Thee, Ev-er, on-ly, all for Thee. A-MEN.

my jesus, i love thee 163

CARITAS. 11 11 11 11

William R. Featherstone

Adoniram J. Gordon

1. My Je - sus, I love Thee, I know Thou art mine; For Thee all the
2. I love Thee, be - cause Thou hast first lov - ed me, And pur-chased my
3. I'll love Thee in life, I will love Thee in death, And praise Thee as
4. In man - sions of glo - ry and end - less de - light, I'll ev - er a-

fol - lies of sin I re-sign; My gra-cious Re-deem-er, my Sav - iour art
par - don on Cal - va-ry's tree; I love Thee for wear-ing the thorns on Thy
long as Thou lend-est me breath; And say when the death-dew lies cold on my
dore Thee in heav-en so bright; I'll sing with the glit - ter-ing crown on my

Thou; If ev - er I loved Thee, my Je - sus, 'tis now.
brow; If ev - er I loved Thee, my Je - sus, 'tis now.
brow, If ev - er I loved Thee, my Je - sus, 'tis now.
brow, If ev - er I loved Thee, my Je - sus, 'tis now. A - MEN.

aspiration and consecration

164 LORD, I HAVE SHUT THE DOOR

SANCTUARY. 6 4 6 4 D.

William M. Runyan

William M. Runyan

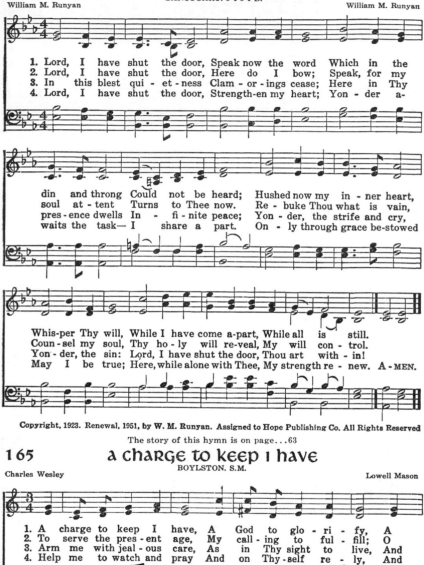

1. Lord, I have shut the door, Speak now the word Which in the
2. Lord, I have shut the door, Here do I bow; Speak, for my
3. In this blest qui - et - ness Clam - or - ings cease; Here in Thy
4. Lord, I have shut the door, Strength-en my heart; Yon - der a-

din and throng Could not be heard; Hushed now my in - ner heart,
soul at - tent Turns to Thee now. Re - buke Thou what is vain,
pres - ence dwells In - fi - nite peace; Yon - der, the strife and cry,
waits the task— I share a part. On - ly through grace be-stowed

Whis-per Thy will, While I have come a-part, While all is still.
Coun - sel my soul, Thy ho - ly will re-veal, My will con - trol.
Yon - der, the sin: Lord, I have shut the door, Thou art with - in!
May I be true; Here, while alone with Thee, My strength re - new. A - MEN.

The story of this hymn is on page...63

165 A CHARGE TO KEEP I HAVE

BOYLSTON. S.M.

Charles Wesley

Lowell Mason

1. A charge to keep I have, A God to glo - ri - fy, A
2. To serve the pres - ent age, My call - ing to ful - fill; O
3. Arm me with jeal - ous care, As in Thy sight to live, And
4. Help me to watch and pray And on Thy - self re - ly, And

hymns of the christian life

nev - er - dy - ing soul to save, And fit it for the sky.
may it all my powers en-gage, To do my Mas-ter's will!
O Thy serv - ant, Lord, pre-pare, A strict ac-count to give!
let me ne'er my trust be- tray, But press to realms on high. A - MEN.

NEARER, STILL NEARER 166
MORRIS. 9 10 9 10

Leila N. Morris   Leila N. Morris

1. Near-er, still near-er, close to Thy heart, Draw me, my Sav-iour, so pre-cious Thou
2. Near-er, still near-er, noth-ing I bring, Naught as an of-fering to Je - sus my
3. Near-er, still near-er, Lord, to be Thine, Sin, with its fol - lies, I glad - ly re-
4. Near-er, still near-er, while life shall last, Till safe in glo - ry my an - chor is

art; Fold me, O fold me close to Thy breast, Shel - ter me safe in that
King; On - ly my sin - ful, now con-trite heart, Grant me the cleansing Thy
sign; All of its pleas-ures, pomp and its pride, Give me but Je - sus, my
cast; Through endless a - ges, ev - er to be, Near - er, my Sav-iour, still

"Ha - ven of Rest," Shel-ter me safe in that "Ha - ven of Rest."
blood doth im-part, Grant me the cleansing Thy blood doth im-part.
Lord cru - ci - fied, Give me but Je - sus, my Lord cru - ci - fied.
near - er to Thee, Near-er, my Sav-iour, still near - er to Thee. A - MEN.

ASPIRATION AND CONSECRATION

my faith looks up to thee
OLIVET. 6 6 4 6 6 6 4

Ray Palmer   Lowell Mason

1. My faith looks up to Thee, Thou Lamb of Cal - va - ry,
2. May Thy rich grace im - part Strength to my faint - ing heart,
3. While life's dark maze I tread, And griefs a - round me spread,
4. When ends life's tran - sient dream, When death's cold, sul - len stream

Sav - iour di - vine! Now hear me while I pray, Take all my
My zeal in - spire; As Thou hast died for me, O may my
Be Thou my Guide; Bid dark - ness turn to day, Wipe sor - row's
Shall o'er me roll; Blest Sav - iour, then, in love, Fear and dis-

guilt a - way, O let me from this day Be whol - ly Thine!
love to Thee Pure, warm, and changeless be, A liv - ing fire!
tears a - way, Nor let me ev - er stray From Thee a - side.
trust re-move; O bear me safe a - bove, A ran-somed soul! A-MEN.

168

speak, lord, in the stillness
QUIETUDE. 6 5 6 5

E. May Grimes   Harold Green

1. Speak, Lord, in the still - ness, While I wait on Thee;
2. Speak, O bless - ed Mas - ter, In this qui - et hour;
3. For the words Thou speak - est, They are life in - deed;
4. All to Thee is yield - ed, I am not my own;
5. Speak, Thy ser - vant hear - eth, Be not si - lent, Lord;
6. Fill me with the know - ledge Of Thy glo - rious will;

By permission of the Africa Evangelical Fellowship — (previously known as the South Africa General Mission)

hymns of the christian life

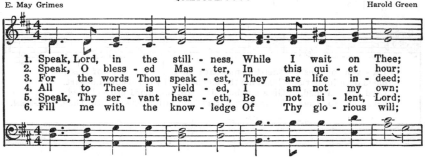

Hushed my heart to lis - ten, In ex - pect - an - cy.
Let me see Thy face, Lord, Feel Thy touch of power.
Liv - ing bread from hea - ven, Now my spi - rit feed!
Bliss - ful, glad sur - ren - der, I am Thine a - lone.
Waits my soul up - on Thee For the quick-ening word.
All Thine own good pleas - ure In Thy child ful - fill. A-MEN.

channels only 169

CHANNELS. 8 7 8 7 Ref.

Mary E. Maxwell

Ada Rose Gibbs

1. How I praise Thee, pre-cious Sav - iour, That Thy love laid hold of me;
2. Emp-tied that Thou should-est fill me, A clean ves - sel in Thy hand;
3. Wit-ness-ing Thy pow'r to save me, Set - ting free from self and sin;
4. Je - sus, fill now with Thy Spir - it Hearts that full sur - ren - der know;

Thou hast saved and cleansed and filled me That I might Thy chan-nel be.
With no pow'r but as Thou giv - est Gra-cious-ly with each com-mand.
Thou who bought-est to pos - sess me, In Thy full - ness, Lord, come in.
That the streams of liv - ing wa - ter From our in - ner man may flow.

REFRAIN

Chan-nels on - ly, bless-ed Mas - ter, But with all Thy won-drous pow'r

Flow-ing thro' us, Thou canst use us Ev - 'ry day and ev - 'ry hour.

aspiration and consecration

170 love divine, all loves excelling

BLAENWERN. 8 7 8 7 D.

Charles Wesley

William Penfro Rowlands

1. Love Di - vine, all loves ex - cel - ling, Joy of heav'n, to earth come down;
2. Breathe, O breathe Thy lov - ing Spir - it In - to ev - ery troub-led breast!
3. Come, al - might - y to de - liv - er, Let us all Thy life re - ceive;
4. Fin - ish then Thy new cre - a - tion, Pure and spot - less let us be;

Fix in us Thy hum - ble dwell - ing, All Thy faith-ful mer - cies crown:
Let us all in Thee in - her - it, Let us find that sec - ond rest.
Sud - den - ly re - turn, and nev - er, Nev - er - more Thy tem - ples leave:
Let us see Thy great sal - va - tion Per - fect - ly re - stored in Thee:

Je - sus, Thou art all com-pas - sion, Pure, un - bound - ed love Thou art:
Take a - way our bent to sin - ning, Al - pha and O - me - ga be;
Thee we would be al - ways bless-ing, Serve Thee as Thy hosts a - bove,
Changed from glo - ry in - to glo - ry, Till in heav'n we take our place,

Vis - it us with Thy sal - va - tion; En - ter ev - ery trem-bling heart.
End of faith, as its be - gin-ning, Set our hearts at lib - er - ty.
Pray and praise Thee with-out ceas-ing, Glo - ry in Thy per-fect love.
Till we cast our crowns before Thee, Lost in won - der, love and praise. A-MEN.

See alternate tune on opposite page

LORD, THOU LOV'ST THE CHEERFUL GIVER 171

BEECHER. 8 7 8 7 D.

Robert Murray

John Zundel

1. Lord, Thou lov'st the cheer-ful giv - er, Who with o - pen heart and hand
2. We are Thine, Thy mer - cy sought us, Found us in death's dread-ful way,
3. Blest by Thee with gifts and gra - ces, May we heed Thy church's call;
4. Sav - iour, Thou hast free-ly giv - en All the bless-ings we en - joy,

Bless-es free - ly, as a riv - er That re - fresh-es all the land.
To the fold in safe - ty brought us, Nev - er - more from Thee to stray.
Glad - ly in all times and pla - ces Give to Thee who giv - est all.
Earth-ly store and bread of heav - en, Love and peace with - out al - loy;

Grant us then the grace of giv - ing With a spir - it large and free,
Thine own life Thou free - ly gav - est As an off -'ring on the cross,
Thou hast bought us, and no long - er Can we claim to be our own;
Hum - bly now we bow be - fore Thee, And our all to Thee re - sign;

That our life and all our liv - ing We may con - se - crate to Thee.
For each sin - ner whom Thou sav - est From e - ter - nal shame and loss.
Ev - er free and ev - er strong-er, We shall serve Thee, Lord, a - lone.
For the king-dom, pow'r and glo - ry Are, O Lord, for - ev - er Thine. A-MEN.

ASPIRATION AND CONSECRATION

172 O JESUS, I HAVE PROMISED

ANGEL'S STORY. 7 6 7 6 D.

John E. Bode

Arthur H. Mann

1. O Je-sus, I have promised To serve Thee to the end; Be Thou for-ev - er
2. O let me feel Thee near me; The world is ev - er near; I   see the sights that
3. O Je-sus, Thou hast promised To all who fol-low Thee, That where Thou art in

near me, My Mas-ter and my Friend: I shall not fear the bat - tle If Thou art
daz - zle, The tempting sounds I hear: My foes are ev - er near me, A-round me
glo - ry, There shall Thy servant be; And, Je - sus, I have promised To serve Thee

by my side, Nor wan-der from the path-way If Thou wilt be my guide.
and with-in; But, Je-sus, draw Thou near-er, And shield my soul from sin.
to   the end; O give me grace to fol - low, My Mas-ter and my Friend. A-MEN.

Music used by permission of E. R. Goodliffe.

173 holy Ghost, with light divine

MERCY. 7 7 7 7

Andrew Reed

Louis M. Gottschalk
Arr. by Edwin P. Parker

1. Ho - ly Ghost, with light di - vine Shine up - on this heart of mine;
2. Ho - ly Ghost, with power di - vine Cleanse this guilt - y heart of mine;
3. Ho - ly Ghost, with joy di - vine Cheer this sad-dened heart of mine;
4. Ho - ly Spir - it, all di - vine, Dwell with - in this heart of mine;

Chase the shades of night a - way, Turn my dark-ness in - to day.
Long hath sin, with-out con-trol, Held do - min - ion o'er my soul.
Bid my man - y woes de - part, Heal my wound-ed, bleed-ing heart.
Cast down ev - ery i - dol-throne, Reign su - preme, and reign a-lone. A-MEN.

thy will, not mine, be done   174

VOLUNTAS DEI. 10 10 10 11

Joseph C. Macaulay   Joseph C. Macaulay

1. "Thy will, not mine, be done, Fa - ther, I pray," Deep in Geth-
2. "Thy will, not mine, be done," teach me to say, Not as un-
3. Thy will, not mine, be done, in life and death! Thy sov'reign
4. Thy will, not mine, be done! Je - sus, my Lord, Bind now my

sem - a - ne hear Je - sus say, Fac - ing the cross of shame, an-guish and
will - ing - ly, 'neath ty-rant's sway, But in sweet vas - sal-age, drawn by Thy
right I own, Who giv-est breath. Choose Thou my way, O Lord, Thou know-est
heart to Thee with love's strong cord; Teach me to self to die, to Thee to

woe, Drain - ing the cup of sor - row, life to be - stow.
grace, Glad - ly o - bey-ing till I look on Thy face.
best; On - ly in Thy blest will my soul finds its rest.
live, Help me, in glad sur - ren-der, my all to give. A-MEN.

aspiration and consecration

175 spirit of God, descend upon my heart

MORECAMBE. 10 10 10 10

George Croly

Frederick C. Atkinson

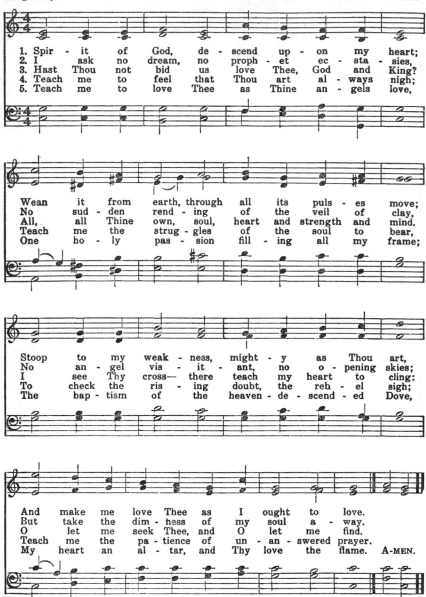

1. Spir - it of God, de - scend up - on my heart;
2. I ask no dream, no proph - et ec - sta - sies,
3. Hast Thou not bid us love Thee, God and King?
4. Teach me to feel that Thou art al - ways nigh;
5. Teach me to love Thee as Thine an - gels love,

Wean it from earth, through all its puls - es move;
No sud - den rend - ing of the veil of clay,
All, all Thine own, soul, heart and strength and mind.
Teach me the strug - gles of the soul to bear,
One ho - ly pas - sion fill - ing all my frame;

Stoop to my weak - ness, might - y as Thou art,
No an - gel vis - it - ant, no o - pening skies;
I see Thy cross— there teach my heart to cling;
To check the ris - ing doubt, the reb - el sigh;
The bap - tism of the heaven - de - scend - ed Dove,

And make me love Thee as I ought to love.
But take the dim - ness of my soul a - way.
O let me seek Thee, and O let me find.
Teach me the pa - tience of un - an - swered prayer.
My heart an al - tar, and Thy love the flame. A - MEN.

holy spirit, breathe on me 176

TRUETT. 7 6 8 6 Ref.

Edwin Hatch
Alt. by B. B. McKinney

B. B. McKinney

1. Ho - ly Spir - it, breathe on me, Un - til my heart is clean;
2. Ho - ly Spir - it, breathe on me, My stub-born will sub - due;
3. Ho - ly Spir - it, breathe on me, Fill me with pow'r di - vine;
4. Ho - ly Spir - it, breathe on me, Till I am all Thine own;

Let sun-shine fill its in - most part, With not a cloud be - tween.
Teach me in words of liv - ing flame What Christ would have me do.
Kin' - dle a flame of love and zeal With - in this heart of mine.
Un - til my will is lost in Thine, To live for Thee a - lone.

REFRAIN

Breathe on me, breathe on me, Ho - ly Spir - it, breathe on me;

Take Thou my heart, cleanse ev-ery part, Ho - ly Spir - it, breathe on me. A-MEN.

aspiration and consecration

The story of this hymn is on page...69

177

I SURRENDER ALL
SURRENDER. 8 7 8 7 Ref.

Judson W. VanDeVenter

Winfield S. Weeden
Arr. by Donald P. Hustad

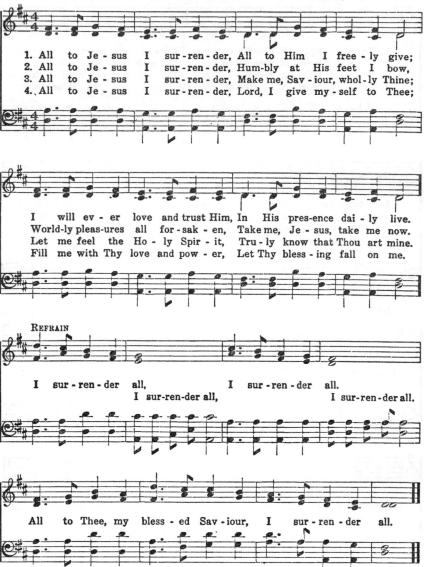

1. All to Je - sus I sur - ren - der, All to Him I free - ly give;
2. All to Je - sus I sur - ren - der, Hum-bly at His feet I bow,
3. All to Je - sus I sur - ren - der, Make me, Sav - iour, whol - ly Thine;
4. All to Je - sus I sur - ren - der, Lord, I give my - self to Thee;

I will ev - er love and trust Him, In His pres-ence dai - ly live.
World-ly pleas-ures all for - sak - en, Take me, Je - sus, take me now.
Let me feel the Ho - ly Spir - it, Tru - ly know that Thou art mine.
Fill me with Thy love and pow - er, Let Thy bless - ing fall on me.

REFRAIN

I sur - ren - der all, I sur - ren - der all.
I sur-ren-der all, I sur-ren-der all.

All to Thee, my bless - ed Sav - iour, I sur - ren - der all.

hymns of the christian life

The story of this hymn is on page. .117

all is well!
ALL IS WELL. 10 6 10 6 8 8 8 6

178

William Clayton
Alt. by Avis B. Christiansen

Adapted from J. T. White
The Sacred Harp, 1844

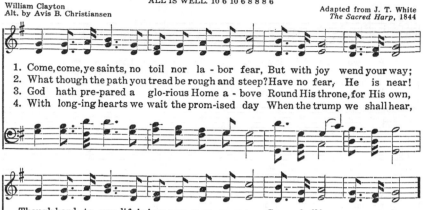

1. Come, come, ye saints, no toil nor la - bor fear, But with joy wend your way;
2. What though the path you tread be rough and steep? Have no fear, He is near!
3. God hath pre-pared a glo-rious Home a - bove Round His throne, for His own,
4. With long-ing hearts we wait the prom-ised day When the trump we shall hear,

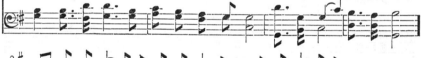

Though hard to you life's jour-ney may ap - pear, Grace shall be as your day.
His might-y arm un - to the end will keep; Soon His call you shall hear.
Where they may rest for - ev - er in His love, Toil and tears all un-known.
That sum-mons us from earth-ly cares a - way, At His side to ap-pear!

God's hand of love shall be your guide, And all your need He will pro-vide;
Then fol - low on, fresh cour-age take, For God His own will ne'er for-sake,
There they shall sing e - ter-nal praise To Him who saved them by His grace.
But un - til then we'll la-bor on In pa-tience till our course is run,

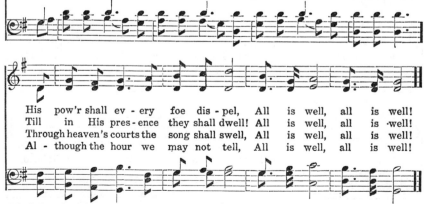

His pow'r shall ev - ery foe dis - pel, All is well, all is well!
Till in His pres - ence they shall dwell! All is well, all is well!
Through heaven's courts the song shall swell, All is well, all is well!
Al - though the hour we may not tell, All is well, all is well!

trust and assurance

he hideth my soul

KIRKPATRICK. 11 8 11 8 Ref.

Fanny J. Crosby

William J. Kirkpatrick

1. A won - der - ful Sav - iour is Je - sus my Lord, A won - der - ful
2. A won - der - ful Sav - iour is Je - sus my Lord, He tak - eth my
3. With num - ber-less bless - ings each mo - ment He crowns, And, filled with His
4. When clothed in His bright-ness, trans-port - ed I rise To meet Him in

Sav - iour to me; He hid - eth my soul in the cleft of the rock, Where
bur - den a - way; He hold - eth me up, and I shall not be moved, He
full - ness di - vine, I sing in my rap-ture, oh, glo - ry to God For
clouds of the sky, His per - fect sal - va - tion, His won - der - ful love, I'll

riv - ers of pleas-ure I see.
giv - eth me strength as my day.
such a Re-deem-er as mine!
shout with the millions on high.

REFRAIN

He hid - eth my soul in the cleft of the rock

That shadows a dry, thirst-y land; He hid-eth my life in the depths of His love,

And cov - ers me there with His hand, And cov - ers me there with His hand.

hymns of the christian life

how firm a foundation

FOUNDATION. 11 11 11 11

K. in Rippon's
A Selection of Hymns, 1787; alt.

Early American Melody

1. How firm a foun - da - tion, ye saints of the Lord,
2. "Fear not, I am with thee; O be not dis - mayed,
3. "When through fier - y tri - als thy path - way shall lie,
4. "The soul that on Je - sus hath leaned for re - pose,

Is laid for your faith in His ex - cel - lent Word;
For I am thy God, and will still give thee aid;
My grace, all - suf - fi - cient, shall be thy sup - ply;
I will not, I will not de - sert to his foes;

What more can He say than to you He hath said,
I'll strength - en thee, help thee, and cause thee to stand,
The flame shall not hurt thee; I on - ly de - sign
That soul, though all hell should en - deav - or to shake,

To you who for ref - uge to Je - sus have fled?
Up - held by my right - eous, om - nip - o - tent hand.
Thy dross to con - sume, and thy gold to re - fine.
I'll nev - er, no, nev - er, no, nev - er for - sake!" A - MEN.

For alternate tune, see No. 265

TRUST AND ASSURANCE

The story of this hymn is on page...79

181 TRUST AND OBEY

TRUST AND OBEY. 6 6 9 D. Ref.

John H. Sammis

Daniel B. Towner

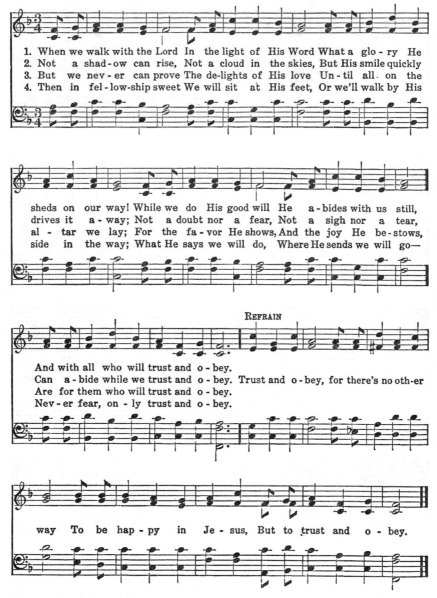

1. When we walk with the Lord In the light of His Word What a glo-ry He
2. Not a shad-ow can rise, Not a cloud in the skies, But His smile quickly
3. But we nev-er can prove The de-lights of His love Un-til all. on the
4. Then in fel-low-ship sweet We will sit at His feet, Or we'll walk by His

sheds on our way! While we do His good will He a-bides with us still,
drives it a-way; Not a doubt nor a fear, Not a sigh nor a tear,
al-tar we lay; For the fa-vor He shows, And the joy He be-stows,
side in the way; What He says we will do, Where He sends we will go—

REFRAIN

And with all who will trust and o-bey.
Can a-bide while we trust and o-bey. Trust and o-bey, for there's no oth-er
Are for them who will trust and o-bey.
Nev-er fear, on-ly trust and o-bey.

way To be hap-py in Je-sus, But to trust and o-bey.

hymns of the christian life

The story of this hymn is on page..111

God will take care of you

GOD CARES. C.M. Ref.

Civilla D. Martin

W. Stillman Martin

1. Be not dis-mayed what-e'er be-tide, God will take care of you;
2. Through days of toil when heart doth fail, God will take care of you;
3. All you may need He will pro-vide, God will take care of you;
4. No mat-ter what may be the test, God will take care of you;

Be-neath His wings of love a-bide, God will take care of you.
When dan-gers fierce your path as-sail, God will take care of you.
Noth-ing you ask will be de-nied, God will take care of you.
Lean, wea-ry one, up-on His breast, God will take care of you.

REFRAIN

God will take care of you, Through ev-ery day, O'er all the way;

He will take care of you, God will take care of you..........
take care of you.

TRUST AND ASSURANCE

TRUSTING JESUS
TRUSTING JESUS. 7 7 7 7 Ref.

Edgar P. Stites

Ira D. Sankey

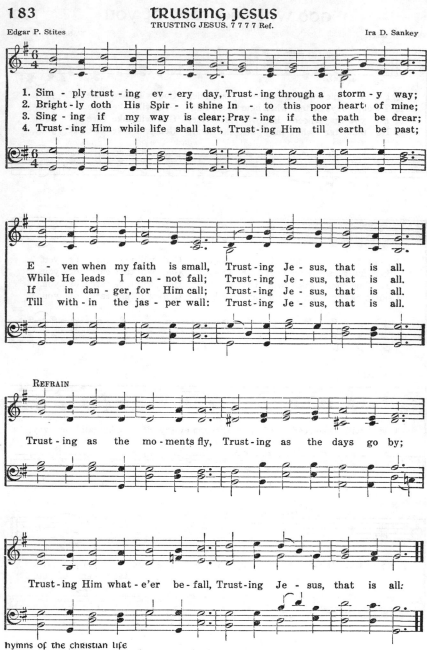

1. Sim - ply trust - ing ev - ery day, Trust - ing through a storm - y way;
2. Bright - ly doth His Spir - it shine In - to this poor heart of mine;
3. Sing - ing if my way is clear; Pray - ing if the path be drear;
4. Trust - ing Him while life shall last, Trust - ing Him till earth be past;

E - ven when my faith is small, Trust - ing Je - sus, that is all.
While He leads I can - not fall; Trust - ing Je - sus, that is all.
If in dan - ger, for Him call; Trust - ing Je - sus, that is all.
Till with - in the jas - per wall: Trust - ing Je - sus, that is all.

REFRAIN

Trust - ing as the mo - ments fly, Trust - ing as the days go by;

Trust - ing Him what - e'er be - fall, Trust - ing Je - sus, that is all:

hymns of the christian life

The story of this hymn is on page . . 129

moment by moment

WHITTLE. 10 10 10 10 Ref.

Daniel W. Whittle

May Whittle Moody

1. Dy - ing with Je - sus, by death reck-oned mine; Liv - ing with Je - sus, a
2. Nev - er a tri - al that He is not there, Nev - er a bur - den that
3. Nev - er a heart-ache and nev - er a groan, Nev - er a tear-drop and
4. Nev - er a weak-ness that He doth not feel, Nev - er a sick-ness that

new life di - vine; Look-ing to Je - sus till glo - ry doth shine, Mo-ment by
He doth not bear, Nev - er a sor-row that He doth not share, Mo-ment by
nev - er a moan; Nev - er a dan - ger, but there on the throne, Mo-ment by
He can - not heal; Mo - ment by mo-ment, in woe or in weal, Je - sus, my

REFRAIN

mo-ment, O Lord, I am Thine.
mo-ment I'm un - der His care; Mo-ment by mo-ment I'm kept in His love;
mo-ment, He thinks of His own.
Sav-iour, a-bides with me still.

Mo-ment by mo-ment I've life from a - bove; Look-ing to Je - sus till

glo - ry doth shine; Mo - ment by mo-ment, O Lord, I am Thine.

trust and assurance

185 WHAT A FRIEND WE HAVE IN JESUS

CONVERSE. 8 7 8 7 D.

Joseph Scriven

Charles C. Converse

1. What a Friend we have in Je - sus, All our sins and griefs to bear!
2. Have we tri - als and temp-ta - tions? Is there trou-ble an - y - where?
3. Are we weak and heav - y - la - den, Cum-bered with a load of care?

FINE

What a priv - i - lege to car - ry Ev - ery-thing to God in prayer!
We should nev - er be dis - cour-aged, Take it to the Lord in prayer.
Pre - cious Sav-iour, still our ref - uge— Take it to the Lord in prayer.

D.S.—All be - cause we do not car - ry Ev - ery-thing to God in prayer!
D.S.—Je - sus knows our ev - ery weak - ness, Take it to the Lord in prayer.
D.S.—In His arms He'll take and shield thee, Thou wilt find a sol - ace there.

D. S.

O what peace we oft - en for - feit, O what need-less pain we bear,
Can we find a friend so faith - ful Who will all our sor-rows share?
Do thy friends de-spise, for-sake thee? Take it to the Lord in prayer;

The story of this hymn is on page...39

186 COME, MY SOUL, THY SUIT PREPARE

HENDON. 7 7 7 7 7

John Newton

H. A. César Malan

1. Come, my soul, thy suit pre-pare, Je - sus loves to an-swer prayer; He Him-self has
2. Thou art com-ing to a King; Large pe-ti-tions with thee bring; For His grace and
3. Lord, I come to Thee for rest; Take pos-ses-sion of my breast; There Thy blood-bought
4. While I am a pil-grim here, Let Thy love my spir-it cheer: As my guide, my
5. Show me what I have to do; Ev - ery hour my strength renew; Let me live a

hymns of the christian life

bid thee pray, Therefore will not say thee nay, Therefore will not say thee nay.
power are such, None can ev-er ask too much, None can ev-er ask too much.
right maintain, And with-out a ri-val reign, And with-out a ri-val reign.
guard, my friend, Lead me to my journey's end, Lead me to my journey's end.
life of faith, Let me die Thy peo-ple's death, Let me die Thy people's death. A-MEN.

unto the hills

SANDON. 10 4 10 4 10 10

187

John D. S. Campbell
From Psalm 121

Charles H. Purday

1. Un-to the hills a-round do I lift up My long-ing eyes;
2. He will not suf-fer that thy foot be moved: Safe shalt thou be.
3. Je-ho-vah is Him-self thy keep-er true, Thy change-less shade;
4. From ev-er-y e-vil shall He keep thy soul, From ev-er-y sin;

O whence for me shall my sal-va-tion come, From whence a-rise? From God, the
No care-less slum-ber shall His eye-lids close, Who keep-eth thee. Be-hold, He
Je-ho-vah thy de-fense on thy right hand Him-self hath made. And thee no
Je-ho-vah shall pre-serve thy go-ing out, Thy com-ing in. A-bove thee

Lord, doth come my cer-tain aid, From God, the Lord, who heav'n and earth hath made.
sleep-eth not, He slumbereth ne'er, Who keep-eth Is-rael in His ho-ly care.
sun by day shall ev-er smite; No moon shall harm thee in the si-lent night.
watch-ing, He whom we a-dore Shall keep thee hence-forth, yea, for-ev-er-more.

TRUST AND ASSURANCE

LIKE A RIVER GLORIOUS

WYE VALLEY. 6 5 6 5 D. Ref.

Frances R. Havergal

James Mountain

1. Like a riv - er glo - rious Is God's per-fect peace, O - ver all vic - to - rious
2. Hid - den in the hol - low Of His bless-ed hand, Nev - er foe can fol - low,
3. Ev - ery joy or tri - al Fall-eth from a - bove, Traced up - on our di - al

In its bright in-crease; Per-fect, yet it flow - eth Full - er ev - ery day,
Nev - er trai - tor stand; Not a surge of wor - ry, Not a shade of care,
By the Sun of Love. We may trust Him ful - ly All for us to do;

REFRAIN

Per-fect, yet it grow-eth Deep - er all the way.
Not a blast of hur - ry Touch the spir - it there. Stayed up-on Je - ho - vah,
They who trust Him whol-ly Find Him whol - ly true.

Hearts are ful - ly blest; Find-ing, as He prom-ised, Per - fect peace and rest.

189 CHILDREN OF THE HEAVENLY FATHER

TRYGGARE KAN INGEN VARA. L.M.

Carolina V. (Sandell) Berg

Swedish Melody

1. Chil - dren of the heav'n-ly Fa - ther Safe - ly in His bos - om gath - er;
2. God His own doth tend and nour - ish, In His ho - ly courts they flour-ish;
3. Nei - ther life nor death can ev - er From the Lord His chil-dren sev - er;
4. What He takes or what He gives us Shows the Fa-ther's love so pre-cious;

Nest-ling bird nor star in heav-en Such a ref-uge e'er was giv-en.
Like a fa-ther kind He spares them, In His lov-ing arms He bears them.
For His love and deep com-pas-sion Com-forts them in trib-u-la-tion.
We may trust His pur-pose whol-ly—'Tis His chil-dren's wel-fare sole-ly.

The story of this hymn is on page..115

LEANING ON THE EVERLASTING ARMS 190

SHOWALTER. 10 9 10 9 Ref.

Elisha A. Hoffman   Anthony J. Showalter

1. What a fel-low-ship, what a joy di-vine, Lean-ing on the ev-er-last-ing arms;
2. Oh, how sweet to walk in this pilgrim way, Lean-ing on the ev-er-last-ing arms;
3. What have I to dread, what have I to fear, Lean-ing on the ev-er-last-ing arms?

What a bless-ed-ness, what a peace is mine, Lean-ing on the ev-er-last-ing arms.
Oh, how bright the path grows from day to day, Lean-ing on the ev-er-last-ing arms.
I have bless-ed peace with my Lord so near, Lean-ing on the ev-er-last-ing arms.

REFRAIN

Lean - ing, lean - ing, Safe and se-cure from all a-larms;
Lean-ing on Je-sus, lean-ing on Je-sus,

Lean - ing, lean - ing, Lean-ing on the ev-er-last-ing arms.
Lean-ing on Je-sus, lean-ing on Je-sus,

peace and comfort

191 come, ye Disconsolate

CONSOLATION (WEBBE). 11 10 11 10

Thomas Moore; 1, 2
Alt. by Thomas Hastings; 3

Samuel Webbe

1. Come, ye dis-con-so-late, wher-e'er ye lan-guish; Come to the
2. Joy of the des-o-late, light of the stray-ing, Hope of the
3. Here see the bread of life; see wa-ters flow-ing Forth from the

mer-cy-seat, fer-vent-ly kneel; Here bring your wounded hearts, here tell your
pen-i-tent, fade-less and pure, Here speaks the Com-fort-er, ten-der-ly
throne of God, pure from a-bove; Come to the feast of love; come, ev-er

an-guish; Earth has no sor-row that heaven can-not heal.
say-ing, "Earth has no sor-row that heaven can-not cure."
know-ing Earth has no sor-row but heaven can re-move. A-MEN.

192 peace, perfect peace

PAX TECUM. 4 6 10

Edward H. Bickersteth

George T. Caldbeck
Arr. by Charles J. Vincent

1. Peace, per-fect peace, in this dark world of sin?
2. Peace, per-fect peace, by throng-ing du-ties pressed?
3. Peace, per-fect peace, with sor-rows surg-ing round?
4. Peace, per-fect peace, our fu-ture all un-known?
5. Peace, per-fect peace, death shad-ow-ing us and ours?
6. It is e-nough: earth's strug-gles soon shall cease,

By permission of Church Society, London.

hymns of the christian life

The blood of Je - sus whis - pers peace with - in.
To do the will of Je - sus, this is rest.
On Je - sus' bos - om naught but calm is found.
Je - sus we know, and He is on the throne.
Je - sus has van-quished death and all its powers.
And Je - sus, call us to heaven's per - fect peace. A - MEN.

near to the heart of god 193

McAFEE. C.M. Ref.

Cleland B. McAfee

Cleland B. McAfee

1. There is a place of qui - et rest, Near to the heart of God,
2. There is a place of com - fort sweet, Near to the heart of God,
3. There is a place of full re - lease, Near to the heart of God,

A place where sin can - not mo - lest, Near to the heart of God.
A place where we our Sav - iour meet, Near to the heart of God.
A place where all is joy and peace, Near to the heart of God.

REFRAIN

O Je - sus, blest Re - deem - er, Sent from the heart of God,

Hold us, who wait be - fore Thee, Near to the heart of God.

peace and comfort

194 JESUS, I AM RESTING, RESTING

TRANQUILLITY. 8 7 8 5 D. Ref.

Jean S. Pigott

James Mountain

1. Je - sus, I am rest - ing, rest - ing In the joy of what Thou art;
2. Oh, how great Thy lov - ing kind - ness, Vast - er, broad-er than the sea!
3. Sim - ply trust - ing Thee, Lord Je - sus, I be - hold Thee as Thou art,
4. Ev - er lift Thy face up - on me, As I work and wait for Thee;

REFRAIN—Je - sus, I am rest - ing, rest - ing, In the joy of what Thou art,

FINE.

I am find - ing out the great - ness Of Thy lov - ing heart.
Oh, how mar - vel - lous Thy good - ness, Lav - ished all on me!
And Thy love, so pure, so change - less, Sat - is - fies my heart;
Rest-ing 'neath Thy smile, Lord Je - sus, Earth's dark shad - ows flee.

I am find - ing out the great - ness Of Thy lov - ing heart.

Thou hast bid me gaze up - on Thee, And Thy beau - ty fills my soul,
Yes, I rest in Thee, Be - lov - ed, Know what wealth of grace is Thine,
Sat - is - fies its deep - est long-ings, Meets, supplies its ev - ery need,
Brightness of my Fa - ther's glo - ry, Sun-shine of my Fa - ther's face,

D.C. Refrain

For by Thy trans-form - ing pow - er, Thou hast made me whole.
Know Thy cer - tain - ty of prom - ise, And have made it mine.
Com-pass - eth me round with bless-ings: Thine is love in - deed!
Keep me ev - er trust - ing, rest - ing, Fill me with Thy grace.

UNDER HIS WINGS

HINGHAM. 11 10 11 10 Ref.

William O. Cushing

Ira D. Sankey

1. Un - der His wings I am safe - ly a - bid - ing; Though the night
2. Un - der His wings, what a ref - uge in sor - row! How the heart
3. Un - der His wings, O what pre - cious en - joy - ment! There will I

deep - ens and tem - pests are wild, Still I can trust Him; I
yearn - ing - ly turns to His rest! Oft - en when earth has no
hide till life's tri - als are o'er; Shel - tered, pro - tect - ed, no

know He will keep me; He has re - deemed me, and I am His child.
balm for my heal - ing, There I find com - fort, and there I am blest.
e - vil can harm me; Rest - ing in Je - sus I'm safe ev - er - more.

REFRAIN

Un - der His wings, un - der His wings, Who from His love can sev - er?

Un - der His wings my soul shall a - bide, Safe - ly a - bide for - ev - er.

peace and comfort

196 In the Garden

GARDEN. Irregular. Ref.

C. Austin Miles

C. Austin Miles

1. I come to the gar-den a-lone, While the dew is still on the
2. He speaks, and the sound of His voice Is so sweet the birds hush their
3. I'd stay in the gar-den with Him Though the night a-round me be

ros - es; And the voice I hear, fall-ing on my ear; The
sing - ing, And the mel - o - dy that He gave to me, With-
fall - ing, But He bids me go; through the voice of woe, His

REFRAIN

Son of God dis - clos - es.
in my heart is ring - ing. And He walks with me, and He
voice to me is call - ing.

talks with me, And He tells me I am His own, And the

joy we share as we tar - ry there, None oth-er has ev - er known.

hymns of the christian life

The story of this hymn is on page...49

BE STILL, MY SOUL

FINLANDIA. 10 10 10 10 10 10

197

Katharina von Schlegel
From Psalm 46
Trans. by Jane L. Borthwick

Jean Sibelius
Arr. for *The Hymnal*, 1933

1. Be still, my soul: the Lord is on thy side; Bear pa-tient-ly the
2. Be still, my soul: thy God doth un-der-take To guide the fu-ture
3. Be still, my soul: the hour is has-t'ning on When we shall be for-

cross of grief or pain; Leave to thy God to or-der and pro-vide;
as He has the past. Thy hope, thy con-fi-dence let noth-ing shake;
ev-er with the Lord, When dis-ap-point-ment, grief, and fear are gone,

In ev-ery change He faith-ful will re-main. Be still, my soul: thy
All now mys-te-rious shall be bright at last. Be still, my soul: the
Sor-row for-got, love's pur-est joys re-stored. Be still, my soul: when

best, thy heav'n-ly Friend Thro' thorn-y ways leads to a joy-ful end.
waves and winds still know His voice who ruled them while He dwelt be-low.
change and tears are past, All safe and bless-ed we shall meet at last. A-MEN.

PEACE AND COMFORT

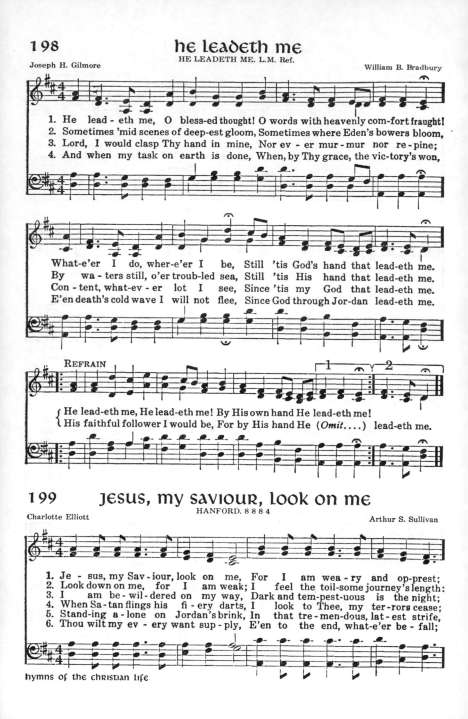

198
he leadeth me

HE LEADETH ME. L.M. Ref.

Joseph H. Gilmore

William B. Bradbury

1. He lead - eth me, O bless-ed thought! O words with heavenly com-fort fraught!
2. Sometimes 'mid scenes of deep-est gloom, Sometimes where Eden's bowers bloom,
3. Lord, I would clasp Thy hand in mine, Nor ev - er mur-mur nor re-pine;
4. And when my task on earth is done, When, by Thy grace, the vic-tory's won,

What-e'er I do, wher-e'er I be, Still 'tis God's hand that lead-eth me.
By wa-ters still, o'er troub-led sea, Still 'tis His hand that lead-eth me.
Con-tent, what-ev-er lot I see, Since 'tis my God that lead-eth me.
E'en death's cold wave I will not flee, Since God through Jor-dan lead-eth me.

REFRAIN

He lead-eth me, He lead-eth me! By His own hand He lead-eth me!
His faithful follower I would be, For by His hand He (*Omit....*) lead-eth me.

199
jesus, my saviour, look on me

HANFORD. 8 8 8 4

Charlotte Elliott

Arthur S. Sullivan

1. Je - sus, my Sav-iour, look on me, For I am wea-ry and op-prest;
2. Look down on me, for I am weak; I feel the toil-some journey's length:
3. I am be-wil-dered on my way, Dark and tem-pest-uous is the night;
4. When Sa-tan flings his fi-ery darts, I look to Thee, my ter-rors cease;
5. Stand-ing a-lone on Jordan's brink, In that tre-men-dous, lat-est strife,
6. Thou wilt my ev-ery want sup-ply, E'en to the end, what-e'er be-fall;

I come to cast my-self on Thee: Thou art my Rest.
Thine aid om-nip-o-tent I seek: Thou art my Strength.
O send Thou forth some cheer-ing ray! Thou art my Light.
Thy Cross a hid-ing-place im-parts: Thou art my Peace.
Thou wilt not suf-fer me to sink: Thou art my Life.
Through life, in death, e-ter-nal-ly, Thou art my All. A-MEN.

IT IS WELL WITH MY SOUL 200
VILLE DU HAVRE. 11 8 11 9 Ref.

Horatio G. Spafford

Philip P. Bliss

1. When peace, like a riv-er, at-tend-eth my way, When sor-rows like
2. Though Sa-tan should buf-fet, tho' tri-als should come, Let this blest as-
3. My sin— oh, the bliss of this glo-ri-ous thought, My sin— not in
4. And, Lord, haste the day when the faith shall be sight, The clouds be rolled

sea-bil-lows roll; What-ev-er my lot, Thou hast taught me to say,
sur-ance con-trol, That Christ has re-gard-ed my help-less es-tate,
part, but the whole, Is nailed to the cross and I bear it no more,
back as a scroll, The trump shall re-sound and the Lord shall de-scend,

REFRAIN

"It is well, it is well with my soul." It is well with my
And hath shed His own blood for my soul.
Praise the Lord, praise the Lord, O my soul!
"E - ven so"— it is well with my soul. It is well

soul, It is well, it is well with my soul.
with my soul,

peace and comfort

GIVE TO THE WINDS THY FEARS

DIADEMATA. S.M.D.

Paul Gerhardt
Trans. by John Wesley

George J. Elvey

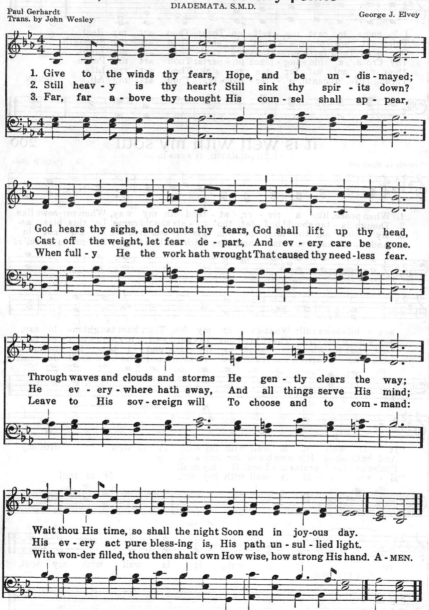

1. Give to the winds thy fears, Hope, and be un-dis-mayed;
2. Still heav-y is thy heart? Still sink thy spir-its down?
3. Far, far a-bove thy thought His coun-sel shall ap-pear,

God hears thy sighs, and counts thy tears, God shall lift up thy head,
Cast off the weight, let fear de-part, And ev-ery care be gone.
When full-y He the work hath wrought That caused thy need-less fear.

Through waves and clouds and storms He gen-tly clears the way;
He ev-ery-where hath sway, And all things serve His mind;
Leave to His sov-ereign will To choose and to com-mand:

Wait thou His time, so shall the night Soon end in joy-ous day.
His ev-ery act pure bless-ing is, His path un-sul-lied light.
With won-der filled, thou then shalt own How wise, how strong His hand. A-MEN.

standing on the promises

PROMISES. 11 11 11 9 Ref.

R. Kelso Carter   R. Kelso Carter

1. Stand-ing on the prom-is-es of Christ my King, Through e-ter-nal a-ges
2. Stand-ing on the prom-is-es that can-not fail, When the howl-ing storms of
3. Stand-ing on the prom-is-es of Christ the Lord, Bound to Him e-ter-nal-
4. Stand-ing on the prom-is-es I can-not fall, Lis-tening ev-ery mo-ment

let His prais-es ring; Glo-ry in the high-est, I will shout and sing,
doubt and fear as-sail, By the liv-ing word of God I shall pre-vail,
ly by love's strong cord, O-ver-com-ing dai-ly with the Spir-it's sword,
to the Spir-it's call, Rest-ing in my Sav-iour as my all in all,

REFRAIN

Stand ing on the prom-is-es of God. Stand - - ing, stand - - ing,
Standing on the promises, standing on the promises,

Stand-ing on the prom-is-es of God my Sav-iour; Stand - - ing,
Standing on the prom-is-es,

stand - - - ing, I'm stand-ing on the prom-is-es of God.
stand-ing on the prom-is-es,

the holy scriptures

203 Thy Word Have I Hid in My Heart

EOLA. 8 7 8 7 Ref.

Adapted by Ernest O. Sellers
From Psalm 119

Ernest O. Sellers

1. Thy Word is a lamp to my feet, A light to my path al-way,
2. For-ev-er, O Lord, is Thy Word Es-tab-lished and fixed on high;
3. At morn-ing, at noon, and at night I ev-er will give Thee praise;
4. Thro' Him whom Thy Word hath foretold, The Sav-iour and Morn-ing Star,

To guide and to save me from sin, And show me the heav'n-ly way.
Thy faith-ful-ness un-to all men A-bid-eth for-ev-er nigh.
For Thou art my por-tion, O Lord, And shall be thro' all my days!
Sal-va-tion and peace have been bro't To those who have strayed a-far.

REFRAIN

Thy Word have I hid in my heart (in my heart), That I might not

sin a-gainst Thee (a-gainst Thee); That I might not sin, that

I might not sin, Thy Word have I hid in my heart.

hymns of the christian life

thy word is like a garden, lord 204

SERAPH (BETHLEHEM). C.M.D.

Edwin Hodder

Gottfried W. Fink

1. Thy Word is like a gar - den, Lord, With flow - ers bright and fair;
2. Thy Word is like a star - ry host: A thou - sand rays of light
3. O may I love Thy pre - cious Word, May I ex - plore the mine,

And ev - ery one who seeks may pluck A love - ly clus - ter there.
Are seen to guide the trav - el - er, And make his path-way bright.
May I its fra-grant flow - ers glean, May light up - on me shine.

Thy Word is like a deep, deep mine; And jew - els rich and rare
Thy Word is like an ar - mor - y, Where sol-diers may re - pair,
O may I find my ar - mor there, Thy Word my trust - y sword;

Are hid-den in its might - y depths For ev - ery search-er there.
And find, for life's long bat - tle-day, All need-ful weap-ons there.
I'll learn to fight with ev - ery foe The bat - tle of the Lord. A-MEN.

The story of this hymn is on page...73

the holy scriptures

205 BREAK THOU THE BREAD OF LIFE

BREAD OF LIFE. 6 4 6 4 D.

Mary A. Lathbury

William F. Sherwin

1. Break Thou the bread of life, Dear Lord, to me, As Thou didst
2. Bless Thou the truth, dear Lord, To me, to me, As Thou didst
3. Thou art the bread of life, O Lord, to me, Thy ho - ly
4. O send Thy Spir - it, Lord, Now un - to me, That He may

break the loaves Be - side the sea; Be - yond the sa - cred page
bless the bread By Gal - i - lee; Then shall all bond - age cease,
Word the truth That sav - eth me; Give me to eat and live
touch my eyes, And make me see: Show me the truth con-cealed

I seek Thee, Lord, My spir - it pants for Thee, O liv - ing Word.
All fet - ters fall; And I shall find my peace, My All in all.
With Thee a - bove; Teach me to love Thy truth, For Thou art love.
With-in Thy Word, And in Thy Book re-vealed I see the Lord. A-MEN.

206 HOLY BIBLE, BOOK DIVINE

ALETTA. 7 7 7 7

John Burton

William B. Bradbury

1. Ho - ly Bi - ble, book di - vine, Pre - cious treas - ure, thou art mine;
2. Mine to chide me when I rove; Mine to show a Sav - iour's love;
3. Mine to com - fort in dis - tress, Suf - fering in this wil - der-ness;
4. Mine to tell of joys to come, And the reb - el sin - ner's doom;

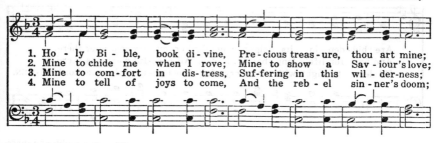

Mine to tell me whence I came; Mine to teach me what I am;
Mine thou art to guide and guard; Mine to pun-ish or re - ward;
Mine to show, by liv - ing faith, Man can tri - umph o - ver death;
O thou ho - ly book di - vine, Pre-cious trea-sure, thou art mine. A-MEN.

faith of our fathers! 207
ST. CATHERINE. 8 8 8 8 8 8

Frederick W. Faber

Henri F. Hemy
Alt. by James G. Walton

1. Faith of our fa - thers! liv - ing still In spite of dun-geon, fire and sword:
2. Our fa-thers, chained in pris - ons dark, Were still in heart and conscience free:
3. Faith of our fa - thers! we will strive To win all na - tions un - to thee,
4. Faith of our fa - thers! we will love Both friend and foe in all our strife:

O how our hearts beat high with joy When-e'er we hear that glo - rious word!
How sweet would be their chil-dren's fate, If they, like them, could die for thee!
And through the truth that comes from God Mankind shall then be tru - ly free.
And preach thee, too, as love knows how, By kind - ly words and vir - tuous life:

Faith of our fa-thers, ho - ly faith! We will be true to thee till death!
Faith of our fa-thers, ho - ly faith! We will be true to thee till death!
Faith of our fa-thers, ho - ly faith! We will be true to thee till death!
Faith of our fa-thers, ho - ly faith! We will be true to thee till death! A-MEN.

208 GLORIOUS THINGS OF THEE ARE SPOKEN
AUSTRIAN HYMN. 8,7 8 7 D.

John Newton

Franz Joseph Haydn

1. Glo - rious things of thee are spo - ken, Zi - on, cit - y of our God;
2. See, the streams of liv - ing wa - ters, Springing from e - ter - nal love,
3. Round each hab - i - ta - tion hov - ering, See the cloud and fire ap - pear

He whose word can - not be bro - ken Formed thee for His own a - bode;
Well sup - ply thy sons and daughters, And all fear of want re - move:
For a glo - ry and a cov - ering, Show - ing that the Lord is near!

On the Rock of A - ges found-ed, What can shake thy sure re - pose?
Who can faint, while such a riv - er Ev - er flows their thirst to assuage?
Glo-rious things of thee are spo - ken, Zi - on, cit - y of our God;

With sal-va-tion's walls sur-round-ed, Thou mayst smile at all thy foes.
Grace which, like the Lord, the Giv - er, Nev-er fails from age to age.
He, whose word can-not be bro - ken, Formed thee for His own a - bode. A-MEN.

the church's one foundation

AURELIA. 7 6 7 6 D.

Samuel J. Stone

Samuel S. Wesley

1. The Church's one Foun - da - tion Is Je - sus Christ her Lord;
2. E - lect from ev - ery na - tion, Yet one o'er all the earth,
3. 'Mid toil and trib - u - la - tion, And tu - mult of her war,
4. Yet she on earth hath un - ion With God the Three in One,

She is His new cre - a - tion, By wa - ter and the word:
Her char - ter of sal - va - tion, One Lord, one faith, one birth;
She waits the con - sum - ma - tion Of peace for - ev - er - more;
And mys - tic sweet com - mun - ion With those whose rest is won:

From heaven He came and sought her To be His ho - ly bride;
One ho - ly name she bless - es, Par - takes one ho - ly food,
Till with the vi - sion glo - rious Her long - ing eyes are blest,
O hap - py ones and ho - ly! Lord, give us grace that we,

With His own blood He bought her, And for her life He died.
And to one hope she press - es, With ev - ery grace en - dued.
And the great Church vic - to - rious Shall be the Church at rest.
Like them, the meek and low - ly, On high may dwell with Thee. A-MEN.

hymns of service
and challenge

The apostle Paul often describes the Christian's
daily life as a warfare against sin and the powers
of darkness, not only in our own personalities
but also in the social environment around us.

Soldiers of the twelfth century left family
and fortune to answer the call of the crusades.
Many lost their lives in those adventurous days.

"Deus vult" — "God wills it" — was their eager
response, and it is also ours today. These hymns
express a joyful willingness to give ourselves and
not to count the cost, in the service of our King.

RISE UP, O MEN OF GOD!

FESTAL SONG. S.M.

William P. Merrill

William H. Walter

1. Rise up, O men of God! Have done with less-er things;
2. Rise up, O men of God! His King-dom tar-ries long;
3. Rise up, O men of God! The Church for you doth wait,
4. Lift high the cross of Christ! Tread where His feet have trod;

Give heart and soul and mind and strength To serve the King of kings.
Bring in the day of broth-er-hood And end the night of wrong.
Her strength un-e-qual to her task; Rise up, and make her great!
As broth-ers of the Son of Man, Rise up, O men of God! A-MEN.

Words used by permission of "The Presbyterian Outlook"

O MASTER, LET ME WALK WITH THEE

211

MARYTON. L.M.

Washington Gladden

H. Percy Smith

1. O Mas-ter, let me walk with Thee In low-ly paths of serv-ice free;
2. Help me the slow of heart to move By some clear, winning word of love;
3. Teach me Thy patience! still with Thee In clos-er, dear-er com-pa-ny,
4. In hope that sends a shin-ing ray Far down the fu-ture's broad'ning way,

Tell me Thy se-cret; help me bear The strain of toil, the fret of care.
Teach me the wayward feet to stay, And guide them in the homeward way.
In work that keeps faith sweet and strong, In trust that tri-umphs o-ver wrong;
In peace that on-ly Thou canst give, With Thee, O Mas-ter, let me live. A-MEN.

212 he who would valiant be

ST. DUNSTAN'S. 11 11 12 11

Percy Dearmer
Adapted from John Bunyan

Charles W. Douglas

1. He who would val - iant be 'Gainst all dis - as - ter,
2. Who - so be - set him round With dis - mal sto - ries,
3. Since, Lord, thou dost de - fend Us with Thy Spir - it,

Let him in con - stan - cy Fol - low the Mas - ter.
Do but them - selves con - found, His strength the more is.
We know we at the end Shall life in - her - it.

There's no dis - cour - age - ment Shall make him once re - lent His
No foes shall stay his might; Though he with gi - ants fight, He
Then fan - cies, flee a - way! I'll fear not what men say, I'll

first a - vowed in - tent To be a pil - grim.
will make good his right To be a pil - grim.
la - bor night and day To be a pil - grim. A - MEN.

hymns of service and challenge

GUIDE ME, O THOU GREAT JEHOVAH

CWM RHONDDA. 8 7 8 7 8 7 7

213

From the Welsh
Trans. by Peter Williams and
William Williams

John Hughes

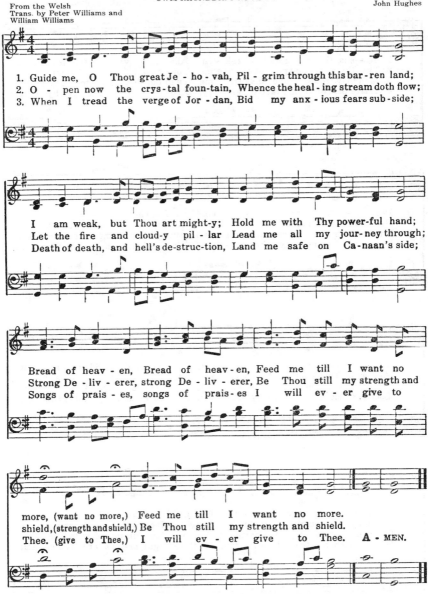

1. Guide me, O Thou great Je - ho - vah, Pil - grim through this bar - ren land;
2. O - pen now the crys - tal foun - tain, Whence the heal - ing stream doth flow;
3. When I tread the verge of Jor - dan, Bid my anx - ious fears sub - side;

I am weak, but Thou art might - y; Hold me with Thy power - ful hand;
Let the fire and cloud - y pil - lar Lead me all my jour - ney through;
Death of death, and hell's de - struc - tion, Land me safe on Ca - naan's side;

Bread of heav - en, Bread of heav - en, Feed me till I want no
Strong De - liv - erer, strong De - liv - erer, Be Thou still my strength and
Songs of prais - es, songs of prais - es I will ev - er give to

more, (want no more,) Feed me till I want no more.
shield, (strength and shield,) Be Thou still my strength and shield.
Thee. (give to Thee,) I will ev - er give to Thee. A - MEN.

The story of this hymn is on page...15

THE CHRISTIAN PILGRIM

214 JESUS, I MY CROSS HAVE TAKEN

ELLESDIE. 8 7 8 7 D.

Henry F. Lyte

Ascribed to Wolfgang A. Mozart
Arr. by Hubert P. Main

1. Je - sus, I my cross have tak - en, All to leave and fol - low Thee;
2. Let the world de-spise and leave me, They have left my Sav-iour, too;
3. Man may troub-le and dis - tress me, 'Twill but drive me to Thy breast;
4. Haste thee on from grace to glo - ry, Armed by faith and winged by prayer;

Des - ti - tute, de-spised, for - sak - en, Thou, from hence, my all shalt be:
Hu - man hearts and looks de - ceive me; Thou art not, like man, un - true;
Life with tri - als hard may press me, Heaven will bring me sweet - er rest.
Heaven's e-ter - nal day's be - fore thee, God's own hand shall guide thee there.

Per - ish ev - ery fond am - bi - tion, All I've sought, and hoped, and known;
And, while Thou shalt smile up - on me, God of wis - dom, love, and might,
O 'tis not in grief to harm me, While Thy love is left to me;
Soon shall close thy earth - ly mis - sion, Swift shall pass thy pil - grim days,

Yet how rich is my con-di - tion, God and heaven are still my own!
Foes may hate, and friends may shun me; Show Thy face, and all is bright.
O 'twere not in joy to charm me, Were that joy un-mixed with Thee.
Hope shall change to glad fru-i - tion, Faith to sight, and prayer to praise. AMEN.

WHEREVER HE LEADS I'LL GO

FALLS CREEK. 8 6 8 7 Ref.

B. B. McKinney

B. B. McKinney

1. "Take up thy cross and fol-low me," I heard my Mas-ter say;
2. He drew me clos-er to His side, I sought His will to know,
3. It may be through the shad-ows dim, Or o'er the storm-y sea,
4. My heart, my life, my all I bring To Christ who loves me so;

"I gave my life to ran-som thee, Sur-ren-der your all to-day."
And in that will I now a-bide, Wher-ev-er He leads I'll go.
I take my cross and fol-low Him, Wher-ev-er He lead-eth me.
He is my Mas-ter, Lord, and King, Wher-ev-er He leads I'll go.

REFRAIN

Wher-ev-er He leads I'll go, Wher-ev-er He leads I'll go,

I'll fol-low my Christ who loves me so, Wher-ev-er He leads I'll go.

THE CHRISTIAN PILGRIM

The story of this hymn is on page...99

216 SOLDIERS OF CHRIST, ARISE

DIADEMATA. S.M.D.

Charles Wesley

George J. Elvey

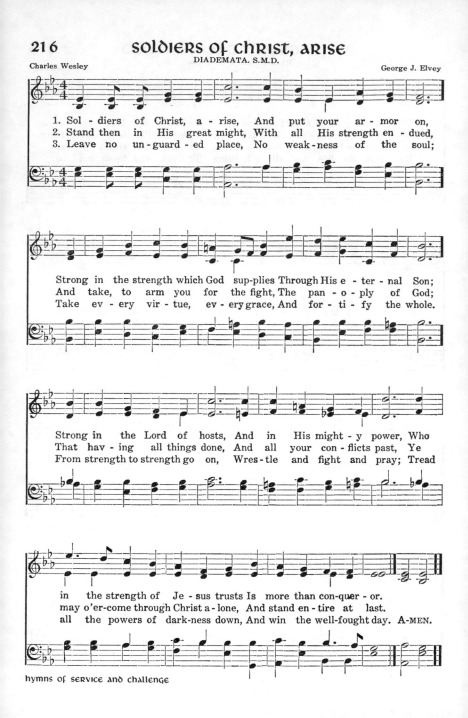

1. Sol - diers of Christ, a - rise, And put your ar - mor on,
2. Stand then in His great might, With all His strength en - dued,
3. Leave no un - guard - ed place, No weak - ness of the soul;

Strong in the strength which God sup-plies Through His e - ter - nal Son;
And take, to arm you for the fight, The pan - o - ply of God;
Take ev - ery vir - tue, ev - ery grace, And for - ti - fy the whole.

Strong in the Lord of hosts, And in His might - y power, Who
That hav - ing all things done, And all your con - flicts past, Ye
From strength to strength go on, Wres - tle and fight and pray; Tread

in the strength of Je - sus trusts Is more than con-quer - or.
may o'er-come through Christ a - lone, And stand en - tire at last.
all the powers of dark-ness down, And win the well-fought day. A-MEN.

hymns of service and challenge

ONWARD, CHRISTIAN SOLDIERS

ST. GERTRUDE. 6 5 6 5 D. Ref.

Sabine Baring-Gould

Arthur S. Sullivan

1. On-ward, Christian sol-diers, March-ing as to war, With the cross of Je - sus
2. Like a might-y ar - my Moves the Church of God; Brothers, we are tread-ing
3. Crowns and thrones may perish, Kingdoms rise and wane, But the Church of Je - sus
4. On-ward, then, ye peo - ple, Join our hap-py throng, Blend with ours your voic-es

Go - ing on be - fore: Christ the roy - al Mas - ter Leads a-gainst the foe;
Where the saints have trod; We are not di - vid - ed, All one bod - y we,
Con-stant will re - main; Gates of hell can nev - er 'Gainst that Church prevail;
In the tri-umph song; Glo - ry, laud, and hon - or Un - to Christ the King;

REFRAIN

For-ward in - to bat - tle, See, His banners go.
One in hope and doc - trine, One in char - i - ty. Onward, Christian sol - diers,
We have Christ's own promise, And that cannot fail.
This through countless a - ges Men and an-gels sing.

March-ing as to war, With the cross of Je - sus Go-ing on be - fore. A-MEN.

By permission of J. Curwen & Sons Ltd., 29 Maiden Lane, London, W. C. 2.

THE CHRISTIAN SOLDIER

lead on, o king eternal

LANCASHIRE. 7 6 7 6 D.

Ernest W. Shurtleff

Henry Smart

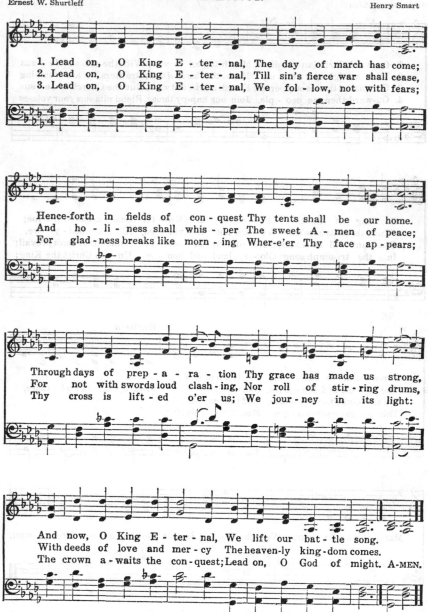

1. Lead on, O King E - ter - nal, The day of march has come;
2. Lead on, O King E - ter - nal, Till sin's fierce war shall cease,
3. Lead on, O King E - ter - nal, We fol - low, not with fears;

Hence-forth in fields of con - quest Thy tents shall be our home.
And ho - li - ness shall whis - per The sweet A - men of peace;
For glad - ness breaks like morn - ing Wher-e'er Thy face ap - pears;

Through days of prep - a - ra - tion Thy grace has made us strong,
For not with swords loud clash - ing, Nor roll of stir - ring drums,
Thy cross is lift - ed o'er us; We jour - ney in its light:

And now, O King E - ter - nal, We lift our bat - tle song.
With deeds of love and mer - cy The heaven-ly king - dom comes.
The crown a - waits the con - quest; Lead on, O God of might. A-MEN.

am I a soldier of the cross?

ARLINGTON. C.M.

Isaac Watts

Thomas A. Arne

1. Am I a sol - dier of the cross, A fol - lower of the Lamb,
2. Must I be car - ried to the skies On flow - ery beds of ease,
3. Are there no foes for me to face? Must I not stem the flood?
4. Sure I must fight, if I would reign; In - crease my cour - age, Lord;

And shall I fear to own His cause, Or blush to speak His name?
While oth - ers fought to win the prize, And sailed thro' blood - y seas?
Is this vile world a friend to grace, To help me on to God?
I'll bear the toil, en - dure the pain, Sup - port - ed by Thy word. A-MEN.

where cross the crowded ways of life 220

GERMANY. L.M.

Frank Mason North

William Gardiner's *Sacred Melodies*, 1815

1. Where cross the crowd-ed ways of life, Where sound the cries of race and clan,
2. In haunts of wretch-ed - ness and need, On shad-owed thresh-olds dark with fears,
3. The cup of wa - ter giv'n for Thee Still holds the fresh-ness of Thy grace;
4. O Mas-ter, from the moun-tain side, Make haste to heal these hearts of pain,
5. Till sons of men shall learn Thy love And fol-low where Thy feet have trod:

A - bove the noise of self - ish strife, We hear Thy voice, O Son of man!
From paths where hide the lures of greed, We catch the vi-sion of Thy tears.
Yet long these mul-ti-tudes to see The sweet com-pas-sion of Thy face.
A-mong these rest-less throngs a-bide, O tread the cit - y's streets a - gain;
Till glo-rious from Thy heaven a-bove Shall come the cit-y of our God. A-MEN.

the christian soldier

who is on the lord's side?

ARMAGEDDON. 6 5 6 5 D. Ref.

Frances R. Havergal

Traditional German Melody
Arr. by John Goss

1. Who is on the Lord's side? Who will serve the King? Who will be His
2. Not for weight of glo - ry, Not for crown and palm, En - ter we the
3. Je - sus, Thou hast bought us, Not with gold or gem, But with Thine own
4. Fierce may be the con - flict, Strong may be the foe, But the King's own

help - ers, Oth - er lives to bring? Who will leave the world's side?
ar - my, Raise the war - rior psalm; But for love that claim - eth
life - blood, For Thy di - a - dem. With Thy bless - ing fill - ing
ar - my None can o - ver - throw. Round His stand-ard rang - ing

Who will face the foe? Who is on the Lord's side? Who for
Lives for whom He died; He whom Je - sus nam - eth Must be
Each who comes to Thee, Thou hast made us will - ing, Thou hast
Vic - tory is se - cure; For His truth un-chang - ing Makes the

Him will go? By Thy call of mer - cy, By Thy grace di - vine,
on His side. By Thy love con-strain - ing, By Thy grace di - vine,
made us free. By Thy grand re - demp - tion, By Thy grace di - vine,
tri - umph sure. Joy-ful - ly en - list - ing By Thy grace di - vine,

We are on the Lord's side, Sav - iour, we are Thine. A - MEN.

See alternate tune on opposite page

hymns of service and challenge

ON OUR WAY REJOICING

HERMAS. 6 5 6 5 D. Ref.

222

John S. B. Monsell, alt.

Frances R. Havergal

1. On our way re - joic - ing, As we home-ward move, Heark-en to our
2. If with hon - est - heart - ed Love for God and man, Day by day Thou
3. On our way re - joic - ing Glad - ly let us go; Conquered hath our
4. Un - to God the Fa - ther Joy - ful songs we sing; Un - to God the

prais - es, O Thou God of love! Is there grief or sad - ness? Thou our
find us Do - ing all we can, Thou who giv'st the seed - time, Wilt give
Lead - er, Van-quished is our foe; Christ with-out, our safe - ty; Christ with-
Sav - iour Thank-ful hearts we bring; Un - to God the Spir - it Bow we

joy shalt be; Is our sky be - cloud - ed? There is light with Thee.
large in-crease, Crown the head with bless-ings, Fill the heart with peace.
in, our joy; Who, if we be faith - ful, Can our hope de - stroy?
and a - dore; On our way re - joic - ing Now and ev - er - more.

REFRAIN

On our way re - joic - ing, As we home-ward move,

Heark - en to our prais - es, O Thou God of love! A - MEN.

THE CHRISTIAN SOLDIER

223 THE SON OF GOD GOES FORTH TO WAR

ALL SAINTS, NEW. C.M.D.

Reginald Heber

Henry S. Cutler

1. The Son of God goes forth to war, A king-ly crown to gain;
2. The mar-tyr first, whose ea-gle eye Could pierce be-yond the grave,
3. A glo-rious band, the cho-sen few On whom the Spir-it came,
4. A no-ble ar-my, men and boys, The ma-tron and the maid,

His blood-red ban-ner streams a-far: Who fol-lows in His train?
Who saw his Mas-ter in the sky, And called on Him to save:
Twelve va-liant saints, their hope they knew, And mocked the cross and flame:
A-round the Sav-iour's throne re-joice, In robes of light ar-rayed:

Who best can drink his cup of woe, Tri-um-phant o-ver pain,
Like Him, with par-don on his tongue In midst of mor-tal pain,
They met the ty-rant's brandished steel, The li-on's go-ry mane;
They climbed the steep as-cent of heaven Through per-il, toil, and pain;

Who pa-tient bears his cross be-low, He fol-lows in His train.
He prayed for them that did the wrong: Who fol-lows in his train?
They bowed their necks the death to feel: Who fol-lows in their train?
O God, to us may grace be given To fol-low in their train. A-MEN.

the Battle is the Lord's!

LEONI. 6 6 8 4 D.

E. Margaret Clarkson

Hebrew Melody
Arr. by Meyer Lyon

224

1. The bat - tle is the Lord's! The har - vest fields are white:
2. The bat - tle is the Lord's! Not ours is strength or skill,
3. The bat - tle is the Lord's! The Vic - tor cru - ci - fied
4. The bat - tle is the Lord's! Stand still, my soul, and see

How few the reap - ing hands ap - pear, Their strength how slight!
But His a - lone, in sov - ereign grace, To work His will.
Must with the tra - vail of His soul Be sat - is - fied.
The great sal - va - tion God hath wrought Re - vealed for thee.

Yet vic - to - ry is sure— We face a van - quished foe;
Ours, count - ing not the cost, Un - flinch - ing, to o - bey;
The pow'rs of hell shall fail, And all God's will be done,
Then, rest - ing in His might, Lift high His tri - umph song,

Then for - ward with the ris - en Christ To bat - tle go!
And in His time His ho - ly arm Shall win the day.
Till ev - ery soul whom He hath giv'n To Christ be won.
For pow'r, do - min - ion, king - dom, strength To Christ be - long!

By permission of Christian Publications, Inc., Harrisburg, Pa.

the christian soldier

stand up, stand up for jesus

GEIBEL. 7 6 7 6 D. Ref.

George Duffield

Adam Geibel

Unison

1. Stand up, stand up for Je - sus, Ye sol - diers of the cross;
2. Stand up, stand up for Je - sus, The trump-et call o - bey;
3. Stand up, stand up for Je - sus, The strife will not be long;

Lift high His roy - al ban - ner, It must not suf - fer loss:
Forth to the might - y con - flict, In this His glo - rious day:
This day the noise of bat - tle, The next, the vic - tor's song:

From vic - tory un - to vic - tory His ar - my shall He lead,
"Ye that are men, now serve Him" A - gainst un - num-bered foes;
To him that o - ver - com - eth, A crown of life shall be:

Till ev - ery foe is van - quished, And Christ is Lord in - deed.
Let cour - age rise with dan - ger, And strength to strength op - pose.
He with the King of glo - ry Shall reign e - ter - nal - ly.

See alternate tune on opposite page

hymns of service and challenge

The story of this hymn is on page...19

Stand up for Je - sus, Ye sol - diers of the cross; ...
Stand up, stand up for Je - sus,

Lift high His roy-al ban - ner, It must not, it must not suf - fer loss.

the morning light is breaking 226
WEBB. 7 6 7 6 D.

Samuel F. Smith

George J. Webb

1. The morn-ing light is break-ing, The dark-ness dis-ap-pears; The sons of earth are
2. See hea-then na-tions bend-ing Be-fore the God we love, And thousand hearts as-
3. Blest riv - er of sal - va - tion, Pur-sue thine on-ward way; Flow thou to ev - ery

wak - ing To pen - i-ten-tial tears! Each breeze that sweeps the o-cean Brings ti-dings
cend - ing In grat - i - tude a-bove; While sin-ners, now con-fess-ing, The gos - pel
na - tion, Nor in thy rich-ness stay; Stay not till all the low - ly Tri - um-phant

from a - far, Of na-tions in com-mo - tion, Pre-pared for Zi-on's war.
call o - bey, And seek the Saviour's blessing, A na - tion in a day.
reach their home; Stay not till all the ho - ly Proclaim, "The Lord is come!" A-MEN.

RESCUE THE PERISHING

RESCUE. Irregular. Ref.

Fanny J. Crosby

William H. Doane

1. Res - cue the per - ish - ing, Care for the dy - ing, Snatch them in pit - y from
2. Though they are slighting Him, Still He is wait - ing, Wait - ing the pen - i - tent
3. Down in the hu - man heart, Crushed by the tempter, Feel - ings lie bur - ied that
4. Res - cue the per - ish - ing, Du - ty de - mands it; Strength for thy la - bor the

sin and the grave; Weep o'er the err - ing one, Lift up the fall - en.
child to re - ceive; Plead with them ear - nest - ly, Plead with them gen - tly,
grace can re - store; Touched by a lov - ing heart, Wak - ened by kind - ness,
Lord will pro - vide; Back to the nar - row way Pa - tient - ly win them;

REFRAIN

Tell them of Je - sus the migh - ty to save.
He will for - give if they on - ly be - lieve. Res - cue the per - ish - ing,
Chords that were bro - ken will vi - brate once more.
Tell the poor wan - derer a Sav - iour has died.

Care for the dy - ing; Je - sus is mer - ci - ful, Je - sus will save.

hark, the voice of Jesus calling
ELLESDIE. 8 7 8 7 D.

Daniel March

Ascribed to Wolfgang A. Mozart
Arr. by Hubert P. Main

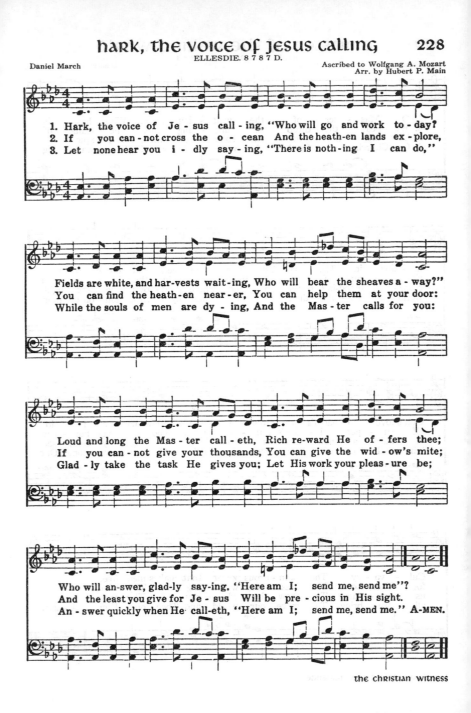

1. Hark, the voice of Je - sus call - ing, "Who will go and work to - day?
2. If you can - not cross the o - cean And the heath-en lands ex - plore,
3. Let none hear you i - dly say - ing, "There is noth-ing I can do,"

Fields are white, and har-vests wait-ing, Who will bear the sheaves a - way?"
You can find the heath-en near - er, You can help them at your door:
While the souls of men are dy - ing, And the Mas - ter calls for you:

Loud and long the Mas - ter call - eth, Rich re-ward He of - fers thee;
If you can - not give your thousands, You can give the wid - ow's mite;
Glad - ly take the task He gives you; Let His work your pleas - ure be;

Who will an-swer, glad-ly say-ing, "Here am I; send me, send me"?
And the least you give for Je - sus Will be pre - cious in His sight.
An - swer quickly when He call-eth, "Here am I; send me, send me." A-MEN.

O MASTER OF THE WAKING WORLD

ST. PETERSBURG. 8 8 8 8 8 8

Frank Mason North

Dimitri S. Bortniansky

1. O Mas - ter of the wak - ing world, Who hast the
2. We hear the throb of surg - ing life, The clank of
3. Thy wit - ness in the souls of men, Thy Spir - it's
4. O Church of God! A - wake! A - wake! The wak - ing

na - tions in Thy heart— The heart that bled and broke to send
chains, the curse of greed, The moan of pain, the fu - tile cries
cease - less, brood-ing power, In lands where shad - ows hide the light,
world is call - ing thee. Lift up thine eyes! Hear thou once more

God's love to earth's re - mot - est part— Show us a - new in
Of su - per - sti - tion's cru - el creed; The peo - ples hun - ger
A - wait a new cre - a - tive hour. O might - y God, set
The chal - lenge of hu - man - i - ty! O Christ, we come! Our

Cal - va - ry The won - drous power that makes men free.
for Thee, Lord, The isles are wait - ing for Thy Word.
us a - flame To show the glo - ries of Thy name.
all we bring, To serve our world and Thee, our King. A - MEN.

hymns of service and challenge

we've a story to tell to the nations

MESSAGE. Irregular. Ref.

H. Ernest Nichol

H. Ernest Nichol

1. We've a sto - ry to tell to the na - tions That shall
2. We've a song to be sung to the na - tions That shall
3. We've a mes - sage to give to the na - tions That the
4. We've a Sav - iour to show to the na - tions Who the

turn their hearts to the right, A sto - ry of truth and mer - cy,
lift their hearts to the Lord, A song that shall con - quer e - vil
Lord who reign - eth a - bove Hath sent us His Son to save us,
path of sor - row hath trod, That all of the world's great peo - ples

A sto - ry of peace and light, A sto - ry of peace and light.
And shat - ter the spear and sword, And shat - ter the spear and sword.
And show us that God is love, And show us that God is love.
Might come to the truth of God, Might come to the truth of God.

REFRAIN

For the dark - ness shall turn to dawn - ing, And the dawn - ing to noon-day bright,

And Christ's great king - dom shall come to earth, The king-dom of love and light.

the christian witness

231 the call for reapers

CLEMM. 8 7-8 7 Ref.

John O. Thompson

J.B.O. Clemm

1. Far and near the fields are teem-ing With the waves of ri-pened grain;
2. Send them forth with morn's first beaming, Send them in the noon-tide's glare;
3. O thou, whom thy Lord is send-ing, Gath-er now the sheaves of gold;

Far and near their gold is gleam-ing O'er the sun-ny slope and plain.
When the sun's last rays are gleam-ing, Bid them gath-er ev-ery-where.
Heavenward then at eve-ning wend-ing, Thou shalt come with joy un-told.

D.S.—*Send them now the sheaves to gath-er, Ere the har-vest-time pass by.*

REFRAIN

Lord of har-vest, send forth reap-ers! Hear us, Lord, to Thee we cry;

232 Jesus shall Reign

DUKE STREET. L.M.

Isaac Watts
From Psalm 72

John Hatton

1. Je-sus shall reign wher-e'er the sun Does his suc-ces-sive jour-neys run;
2. From north to south the prin-ces meet To pay their hom-age at His feet;
3. To Him shall end-less prayer be made, And end-less prais-es crown His head;
4. Peo-ple and realms of ev-ery tongue Dwell on His love with sweet-est song,

hymns of service and challenge

His kingdom spread from shore to shore, Till moons shall wax and wane no more.
While west-ern em-pires own their Lord, And sav-age tribes at-tend His word.
His name like sweet per-fume shall rise With ev-ery morn-ing sac-ri- fice.
And in-fant voic-es shall pro-claim Their ear-ly bless-ings on His name. A-MEN.

let the lower lights be burning 233
LOWER LIGHTS. 8 7 8 7 Ref.

Philip P. Bliss

Philip P. Bliss

1. Bright-ly beams our Fa-ther's mer-cy From His light-house ev-er-more,
2. Dark the night of sin has set-tled, Loud the an-gry bil-lows roar;
3. Trim your fee-ble lamp, my broth-er; Some poor sail-or tem-pest tossed,

But to us He gives the keep-ing Of the lights a-long the shore.
Ea-ger eyes are watch-ing, long-ing, For the lights a-long the shore.
Try-ing now to make the har-bor, In the dark-ness may be lost.

REFRAIN

Let the low-er lights be burn-ing! Send a gleam a-cross the wave!

Some poor faint-ing, strug-gling sea-man You may res-cue, you may save.

The christian witness

The story of this hymn is on page...85

234

to all the world

WIMBY. 8 7 8 7 8 8 8 7 Ref.

Joseph C. Macaulay

Wendell P. Loveless

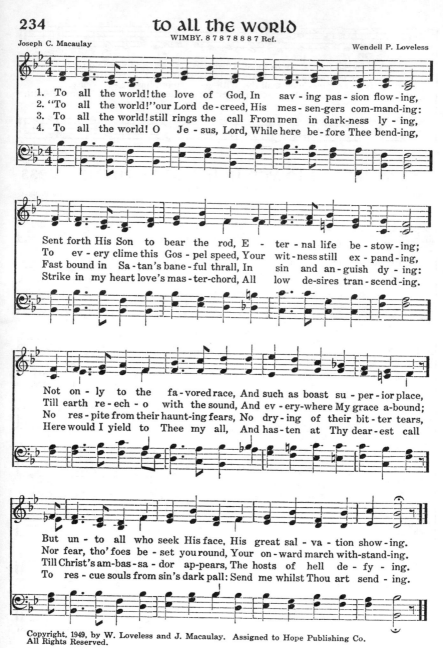

1. To all the world! the love of God, In sav-ing pas-sion flow-ing,
2. "To all the world!" our Lord de-creed, His mes-sen-gers com-mand-ing:
3. To all the world! still rings the call From men in dark-ness ly-ing,
4. To all the world! O Je-sus, Lord, While here be-fore Thee bend-ing,

Sent forth His Son to bear the rod, E - ter-nal life be-stow-ing;
To ev-ery clime this Gos - pel speed, Your wit-ness still ex-pand-ing,
Fast bound in Sa-tan's bane-ful thrall, In sin and an-guish dy-ing:
Strike in my heart love's mas-ter-chord, All low de-sires tran-scend-ing.

Not on - ly to the fa-vored race, And such as boast su-per-ior place,
Till earth re-ech-o with the sound, And ev-ery-where My grace a-bound;
No res-pite from their haunt-ing fears, No dry-ing of their bit-ter tears,
Here would I yield to Thee my all, And has-ten at Thy dear-est call

But un-to all who seek His face, His great sal-va-tion show-ing.
Nor fear, tho' foes be-set you round, Your on-ward march with-stand-ing.
Till Christ's am-bas-sa-dor ap-pears, The hosts of hell de-fy - ing.
To res-cue souls from sin's dark pall: Send me whilst Thou art send-ing.

hymns of service and challenge

REFRAIN

To all the world! O word of love di-vine! To all the world! This is Thy

blest de-sign; To all the world! and lo, the task is mine, Send me! O Lord, send me.

I GAVE MY LIFE FOR THEE — 235

KENOSIS. Irregular. Ref.

Frances R. Havergal

Philip P. Bliss

1. I gave My life for thee, My pre - cious blood I shed,
2. My Fa - ther's house of light, My glo - ry - cir - cled throne
3. I suf - fered much for thee, More than thy tongue can tell,
4. And I have brought to thee, Down from My home a - bove,

That thou might'st ran-somed be, And quick - ened from the dead;
I left for earth - ly night, For wan - derings sad and lone;
Of bit - terest ag - o - ny, To res - cue thee from hell;
Sal - va - tion full and free, My par - don and My love;

I gave, I gave My life for thee, What hast thou given for Me?
I left, I left it all for thee, Hast thou left aught for Me?
I've borne, I've borne it all for thee, What hast thou borne for Me?
I bring, I bring rich gifts to thee, What hast thou brought to Me?

the christian witness

make me a blessing

SCHULER. 10 7 10 7 Ref.

Ira B. Wilson

George S. Schuler

1. Out in the highways and byways of life, Man-y are weary and sad;
   are wea-ry and sad;
2. Tell the sweet story of Christ and His love, Tell of His power to forgive;
   His power to for-give;
3. Give as 'twas giv-en to you in your need, Love as the Master loved you;
   the Mas-ter loved you;

Car - ry the sunshine where darkness is rife, Mak - ing the sor-row-ing glad.
Oth-ers will trust Him if on - ly you prove True, ev - ery mo-ment you live.
Be to the help-less a help - er in-deed, Un - to your mis-sion be true.

REFRAIN *Men or Unison* *Women*

Make me a bless - ing, Make me a bless - ing, Out of my

Unison

life may Je - sus shine; Make me a bless - ing,

Men Out of my life

Women *Parts*

O Sav - iour, I pray, Make me a bless-ing to some-one to - day.
I pray Thee, my Saviour,

Tenors

hymns of service and challenge

TIDINGS. 11 10 11 10 Ref.

Mary A. Thomson

James Walch

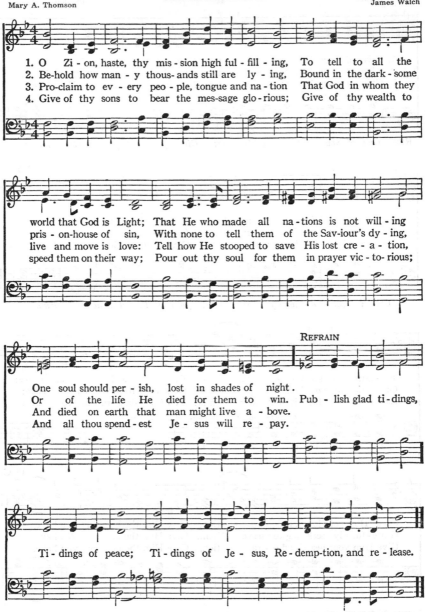

1. O Zi - on, haste, thy mis - sion high ful - fill - ing, To tell to all the
2. Be-hold how man - y thous- ands still are ly - ing, Bound in the dark - some
3. Pro-claim to ev - ery peo - ple, tongue and na - tion That God in whom they
4. Give of thy sons to bear the mes-sage glo - rious; Give of thy wealth to

world that God is Light; That He who made all na - tions is not will - ing
pris - on-house of sin, With none to tell them of the Sav-iour's dy - ing,
live and move is love: Tell how He stooped to save His lost cre - a - tion,
speed them on their way; Pour out thy soul for them in prayer vic - to - rious;

REFRAIN

One soul should per - ish, lost in shades of night.
Or   of   the life He died for them to win. Pub - lish glad ti - dings,
And died on earth that man might live a - bove.
And all thou spend-est Je - sus will re - pay.

Ti - dings of peace; Ti - dings of Je - sus, Re - demp-tion, and re - lease.

the christian witness

238 GIVE OF YOUR BEST TO THE MASTER

BARNARD. 8 7 8 7 D. Ref.

Howard B. Grose

Charlotte A. Barnard

1. Give of your best to the Mas - ter; Give of the strength of your youth;
2. Give of your best to the Mas - ter; Give Him first place in your heart;
3. Give of your best to the Mas - ter; Naught else is wor - thy His love;

Ref.—*Give of your best to the Mas - ter; Give of the strength of your youth;*

FINE

Throw your soul's fresh, glowing ar - dor In - to the bat-tle for truth.
Give Him first place in your serv - ice, Con-se - crate ev - ery part.
He gave Him - self for your ran - som, Gave up His glo - ry a - bove:

Clad in sal - va - tion's full ar - mor, Join in the bat - tle for truth.

Je - sus has set the ex - am - ple; Daunt-less was He, young and brave;
Give, and to you shall be giv - en; God His be - lov - ed Son gave;
Laid down His life with-out mur - mur, You from sin's ru - in to save;

D. C.

Give Him your loy - al de - vo - tion, Give Him the best that you have.
Grate - ful - ly seek - ing to serve Him, Give Him the best that you have.
Give Him your heart's ad-o - ra - tion, Give Him the best that you have.

hymns of service and challenge

hymns of the christian hope

The physical objective of the historic crusades
was the city of Jerusalem at the heart of the Holy
Land. The travelers hoped that the site of Jesus'
death and resurrection might be reclaimed from
those who occupied it.

The goal of the modern crusader is the "new
Jerusalem" — the eternal dwelling place which
Christ has prepared for us. Heaven is the
eagerly-anticipated home of the Christian, where
we will enjoy endless spiritual growth and activity
in the presence of the Saviour whom we love.

This "blessed hope" has inspired many of our
most joyful songs.

what if it were today?

SECOND COMING. Irregular. Ref.

Leila N. Morris

Leila N. Morris

1. Je - sus is com - ing to earth a - gain, What if it were to - day?
2. Sa - tan's do - min - ion will soon be o'er, Oh, that it were to - day!
3. Faith-ful and true would He find us here, If He should come to - day?

Com - ing in pow - er and love to reign, What if it were to - day?
Sor - row and sigh - ing shall be no more, Oh, that it were to - day!
Watch-ing in glad - ness and not in fear, If He should come to - day?

Com - ing to claim His cho - sen Bride, All the re - deemed and pu - ri - fied,
Then shall the dead in Christ a - rise, Caught up to meet Him in the skies,
Signs of His com - ing mul - ti - ply, Morning light breaks in east - ern sky,

rit. *a tempo*

O - ver this whole earth scat-tered wide, What if it were to - day?
When shall these glo - ries meet our eyes? What if it were to - day?
Watch, for that time is draw - ing nigh, What if it were to - day?

REFRAIN

Glo - ry, glo - ry! Joy to my heart 'twill bring;
Joy to my heart 'twill bring;

hymns of the christian hope

Glo - ry, glo - ry! When we shall crown Him King;
When we shall crown Him King;

Glo - ry, glo - ry! Haste to pre-pare the way;
Haste to pre - pare the way;

Glo - ry, glo - ry! Je - sus will come some day.

the king shall come when morning dawns 240
ST. STEPHEN. C.M.

Ancient Greek
Trans. by John Brownlie

William Jones

1. The King shall come when morn-ing dawns, And light tri - um - phant breaks;
2. Not as of old a lit - tle child To bear, and fight, and die,
3. O bright-er than the ris - ing morn When He, vic - to - rious, rose,
4. O bright-er than that glo-rious morn Shall this fair morn-ing be,
5. The King shall come when morn-ing dawns, And light and beau-ty brings:

When beau - ty gilds the east - ern hills, And life to joy a - wakes.
But crowned with glo - ry like the sun That lights the morn-ing sky.
And left the lone-some place of death, De - spite the rage of foes—
When Christ, our King, in beau - ty comes, And we His face shall see!
Hail, Christ the Lord! Thy peo - ple pray, Come quick-ly, King of kings! A-MEN.

hymns of the christian hope

241 OUR GOD IS SOVEREIGN STILL

SOVEREIGNTY. 9 9 9 6 Ref.

E. Margaret Clarkson

E. Margaret Clarkson

1. A - mid the fears that op-press our day, A - cross the clouds that ob-
2. Though wars may rise, and though king-doms fall, Though ills may threat-en, and
3. Though fierce the fight 'gainst the hosts of wrong, His Word is sure, and His
4. When Christ shall come to re - ceive His own, When His the king-dom, the

scure our way, One gold - en truth sheds its shin - ing ray— Our
fears en - thrall, Our God still lives, and He hears our call— Our
arm is strong; The day is His: raise His tri - umph song— Our
pow'r, the throne, E - ter - nal King He shall reign a - lone— Our

REFRAIN

God is sov-ereign still.
God is sov-ereign still.
God is sov-ereign still. His ho - ly pur - pose un-chang-ing stands, The
God is sov-ereign still.

stars still turn at their Lord's com-mands; He holds the world in His

hymns of the christian hope

might-y hands—Our God is sov-ereign still! Our God is sov-ereign still!

when we all get to heaven

HEAVEN. 8 7 8 7 Ref.

Eliza E. Hewitt

Emily D. Wilson

1. Sing the won-drous love of Je - sus, Sing His mer - cy and His grace;
2. While we walk the pil - grim pathway, Clouds will o - ver-spread the sky;
3. Let us then be true and faith-ful, Trust-ing, serv - ing ev - ery day;
4. On-ward to the prize be - fore us! Soon His beau-ty we'll be - hold;

In the man - sions bright and bless - ed, He'll pre - pare for us a place.
But when trav-'ling days are o - ver, Not a shad-ow, not a sigh.
Just one glimpse of Him in glo - ry Will the toils of life re-pay.
Soon the pearl - y gates will o - pen, We shall tread the streets of gold.

REFRAIN

When we all get to heaven, What a day of re-joicing that will be!
When we all   What a day of rejoicing that will be!

When we all see Je-sus, We'll sing and shout the victory.
When we all   and shout the vic-to-ry.

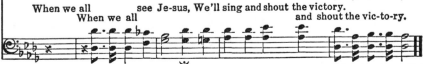

hymns of the christian hope

JESUS, JESUS, WE ARE WAITING

TOCCOA. 8 7 8 7 D.

George Shaw, alt.

George Shaw
Arr. by Ruth E. Marsden

1. Je - sus, Je - sus, we are wait-ing, Wait-ing for e - ter - nal day;
2. Je - sus, Je - sus, we are long-ing, As we wait with quick-ened pace,
3. Je - sus, Je - sus, we are hop-ing For that day of love di - vine,
4. Je - sus, Je - sus, we will own Thee, As our Proph-et, Priest, and King;

Wait - ing till the morn - ing dawn-eth With the light of sin - less ray.
In our hearts God's peace a-bound-ing, Till with joy we see Thy face.
When, with hearts a - blaze with glo - ry, We in Christ's own im - age shine.
In this world of Thy re - ject - ion, We to Thee our treas-ures bring.

Joy e - ter - nal, joy e - ter - nal, When the night has passed a - way!
Peace e - ter - nal, peace e - ter - nal, Through Thy sac - ri - fice and grace!
Love e - ter - nal, love e - ter - nal, In our hearts for - ev - er Thine!
Praise e - ter - nal, praise e - ter - nal, Ran-somed men with an - gels sing!

rit.

Joy e - ter - nal, joy e - ter - nal, When the night has passed a - way!
Peace e - ter - nal, peace e - ter - nal, Through Thy sac - ri - fice and grace!
Love e - ter - nal, love e - ter - nal, In our hearts for - ev - er Thine!
Praise e - ter - nal, praise e - ter - nal, Ran-somed men with an - gels sing!

hymns of the christian hope

the sands of time are sinking

RUTHERFORD. 7 6 7 6 7 6 7 5

Anne Ross Cousin

Chrétien Urhan
Arr. by Edward F. Rimbault

244

1. The sands of time are sink - ing, The dawn of heav - en breaks;
2. O Christ, He is the foun - tain, The deep, sweet well of love!
3. With mer - cy and with judg - ment My web of time He wove,

The sum - mer morn I've sighed for, The fair, sweet morn, a - wakes;
The streams on earth I've tast - ed More deep I'll drink a - bove:
And aye the dews of sor - row Were lus - tered by His love.

Dark, dark hath been the mid - night, But day - spring is at hand,
There to an o - cean full - ness His mer - cy doth ex - pand,
I'll bless the hand that guid - ed, I'll bless the heart that planned,

And glo - ry, glo - ry dwell - eth In Im - man - uel's land.
And glo - ry, glo - ry dwell - eth In Im - man - uel's land.
When throned where glo - ry dwell - eth In Im - man - uel's land. A-MEN.

hymns of the christian hope

FOR ALL THE SAINTS

SINE NOMINE. 10 10 10 Alleluias

William W. How   R. Vaughan Williams

1. For all the saints who from their la-bors rest, Who Thee by faith be-
2. Thou wast their rock, their fortress and their might; Thou, Lord, their cap-tain
6. But lo! there breaks a yet more glo-rious day; The saints tri-um-phant
7. From earth's wide bounds, from o-cean's far-thest coast, Thro' gates of pearl stream

fore the world con-fessed, Thy name, O Je - sus, be for-ev-er blest.
in the well-fought fight; Thou, in the dark - ness drear, their one true light.
rise in bright ar-ray; The King of Glo - ry pass-es on His way.
in the count-less host, Sing-ing to Fa - ther, Son, and Ho-ly Ghost.

(after stanza 7)

Al - le - lu - ia! Al - le - lu - ia! A - MEN.

HARMONY, *stanzas 3, 4, 5*

3. O blest com-mun - ion, fel - low-ship di - vine! We fee - bly strug - gle;
4. And when the strife is fierce, the war-fare long, Steals on the ear the
5. The gold-en eve - ning bright-ens in the west; Soon, soon to faith - ful

they in glo - ry shine. Yet all are one in Thee, for all are Thine.
dis - tant tri-umph song, And hearts are brave a - gain and arms are strong.
war-riors com - eth rest; And sweet the calm of Par - a - dise, the blest.

Music from "The English Hymnal." Used by permission of the Oxford University Press.

hymns of the christian hope

The story of this hymn is on page...97

(Sop.) Al - le - lu - ia! D. C. stanzas 6 and 7

Al - le - lu - ia! Al - le - lu - ia!

face to face

FACE TO FACE. 8 7 8 7 Ref.

246

Carrie E. Breck

Grant Colfax Tullar

1. Face to face with Christ my Sav - iour, Face to face—what will it be—
2. On - ly faint-ly now I see Him, With the dark-ling veil be-tween;
3. What re - joic-ing in His pres - ence, When are ban-ished grief and pain;
4. Face to face! O bliss-ful mo - ment! Face to face—to see and know;

When with rap-ture I be - hold Him, Je - sus Christ Who died for me?
But a bless - ed day is com - ing, When His glo - ry shall be seen.
When the crook-ed ways are straightened, And the dark things shall be plain.
Face to face with my Re-deem - er, Je - sus Christ Who loves me so.

REFRAIN

Face to face I shall be-hold Him, Far be-yond the star-ry sky;

Face to face in all His glo - ry, I shall see Him by and by!

hymns of the christian hope

247 when I can read my title clear

PISGAH. 8 6 8 6 6 6 8 6

Isaac Watts

Ascribed to J. C. Lowry

1. When I can read my ti - tle clear To man - sions in the skies,
2. Should earth a - gainst my soul en - gage, And fi - ery darts be hurled,
3. Let cares like a wild del - uge come, And storms of sor - row fall!
4. There shall I bathe my wea - ry soul In seas of heaven-ly rest,

I'll bid fare-well to ev - ery fear, And wipe my weep - ing eyes.
Then I can smile at Sa - tan's rage, And face a frown-ing world.
So I but safe - ly reach my home, My God, my heaven, my all.
And not a wave of troub-le roll A - cross my peace-ful breast.

And wipe my weep - ing eyes, And wipe my weep - ing eyes,
And face a frown-ing world, And face a frown - ing world,
My God, my heaven, my all, My God, my heaven, my all,
A - cross my peace-ful breast, A - cross my peace - ful breast,

I'll bid fare-well to ev - ery fear, And wipe my weep-ing eyes.
Then I can smile at Sa - tan's rage, And face a frown-ing world.
So I but safe - ly reach my home, My God, my heaven, my all.
And not a wave of troub-le roll A - cross my peace-ful breast. A-MEN.

hymns of the christian hope

my saviour first of all

I SHALL KNOW HIM. 14 11 14 11 Ref.

248

Fanny J. Crosby

John R. Sweney

1. When my life-work is end-ed, and I cross the swell-ing tide, When the bright and glo-rious morn-ing I shall see; I shall know my Re-deem-er when I reach the oth-er side, And His smile will be the first to wel-come me.

2. Oh, the soul-thrill-ing rap-ture when I view His bless-ed face, And the lus-ter of His kind-ly beam-ing eye; How my full heart will praise Him for the mer-cy, love, and grace, That pre-pare for me a man-sion in the sky.

3. Oh, the dear ones in glo-ry, how they beck-on me to come, And our part-ing at the riv-er I re-call; To the sweet vales of E-den they will sing my wel-come home; But I long to meet my Sav-iour first of all.

4. Thro' the gates to the cit-y in a robe of spot-less white, He will lead me where no tears will ev-er fall; In the glad song of a-ges I shall min-gle with de-light; But I long to meet my Sav-iour first of all.

REFRAIN

I shall know Him, I shall know Him, And redeemed by His side I shall stand,
I shall know Him, I shall know Him By the print of the nails in His hand.

249 the king in his beauty

NEW HAMPTON. 9 8 9 8 Ref.

Adoniram J. Gordon   Adoniram J. Gordon

1. I shall see the King in His beau-ty, In the land that is far a-way,
2. To be-hold the Chief of Ten Thousand, Ah! my soul, this were joy e-nough;
3. Who can tell the rap-tur-ous meet-ing, When the Lord shall bring home His own?
4. Oh! to none will the King be a stranger Of the throngs who sur-round His seat;
5. I shall see Him, I shall be like Him, By one glance of His face transformed;

When the shad-ows at length have lift-ed, And the dark-ness has turned to day.
'Twill suf-fice for the bliss of hea-ven, That the Lamb is the light there-of.
With one sight all His saints are ravished, The Lamb in the midst of the throne.
For the hearts of the saved will know Him, By the prints of the nails in His feet.
And this bod-y of sin and dark-ness To the im-age of Christ con-formed.

REFRAIN

I shall see Him in the glo-ry, The Lamb that once was slain;

How I'll then re-sound the sto-ry, With all the ran-somed train!

Hal-le-lu-jah, Hal-le-lu-jah! To the Lamb that once was slain;

hymns of the christian hope

Hal - le - lu - jah, Hal - le - lu - jah, Hal - le - lu - jah! A - men.

he the pearly gates will open 250

HAN SKALL OPPNA PARLEPORTEN. 8 7 8 7 Ref.

Fred Blom
Trans. by N. Carlson

Elsie Ahlwén

1. Love di - vine, so great and won - drous, Deep and might-y, pure, sub - lime;
2. Like a dove when hunt-ed, fright-ened, As a wound-ed fawn was I;
3. Love di - vine, so great and won-drous—All my sins He then for - gave,
4. In life's e - ven-tide, at twi - light, At His door I'll knock and wait;

Com - ing from the heart of Je - sus—Just the same through tests of time.
Bro - ken heart-ed, yet He healed me—He will heed the sin - ner's cry.
I will sing His praise for - ev - er, For His blood, His pow'r to save.
By the pre-cious love of Je - sus, I shall en - ter heav-en's gate.

REFRAIN

He the pearl - y gates will o - pen, So that I may en - ter in;

For He pur-chased my re - demp - tion, And for-gave me all my sin.

hymns of the christian hope

The story of this hymn is on page . . 135

251

CHRIST RETURNETH

CHRIST RETURNETH. Irregular. Ref.

H. L. Turner

James McGranahan

1. It may be at morn, when the day is a - wak - ing, When sun-light through darkness and shad - ow is break-ing, That Je - sus will come in the full-ness of glo - ry, To re-ceive from the world "His own."

2. It may be at mid - day, it may be at twi - light, It may be, per-chance, that the black-ness of mid-night Will burst in - to light in the blaze of His glo - ry, When Je - sus re - ceives "His own."

3. While its hosts cry Ho - san - na, from heav - en de-scend-ing, With glo - ri - fied saints and the an - gels at - tend-ing, With grace on His brow, like a ha - lo of glo - ry, Will Je - sus re - ceive "His own."

4. Oh, joy! oh, de - light! should we go with - out dy - ing, No sick-ness, no sad - ness, no dread and no cry - ing, Caught up through the clouds with our Lord in - to glo - ry, When Je - sus re - ceives "His own."

REFRAIN

O Lord Je - sus, how long, how long Ere we shout the glad song, Christ re-

rit.

turn-eth! Hal-le - lu - jah! hal-le - lu - jah! A - men, Hal-le - lu - jah! A - men.

hymns of the christian hope

O that will be glory

GLORY SONG. 10 10 10 10 Ref.

Charles H. Gabriel

Charles H. Gabriel

1. When all my la-bors and tri-als are o'er, And I am safe on that beau-ti-ful shore, Just to be near the dear Lord I a-dore,

2. When, by the gift of His in-fi-nite grace, I am ac-cord-ed in heav-en a place, Just to be there and to look on His face,

3. Friends will be there I have loved long a-go; Joy like a riv-er a-round me will flow; Yet, just a smile from my Sav-iour, I know,

REFRAIN

Will through the a-ges be glo-ry for me. O that will be glo-ry for me, Glo-ry for me, glo-ry for me; When by His grace

O that will be glo-ry for me, Glo-ry for me, glo-ry for me;

I shall look on His face, That will be glo-ry, be glo-ry for me.

hymns of the christian hope

The story of this hymn is on page..139

253

in heaven above
HAUGE. 8 6 8 6 8 8 6

Laurentius Laurentii Laurinus
Revised, Johan Astrom
Trans. by William Maccall

Norwegian Folk Melody

1. In heav'n a - bove, in heav'n a - bove, Where God our Fa - ther dwells,
2. In heav'n a - bove, in heav'n a - bove, What glo - ry deep and bright!
3. In heav'n a - bove, in heav'n a - bove, No tears of pain are shed;
4. In heav'n a - bove, in heav'n a - bove, God hath a joy pre -pared,

How bound-less there the bless - ed - ness! No tongue its great-ness tells;
The splen - dor of the noon - day sun Grows pale be - fore its light;
There noth - ing e'er shall fade or die; Life's full - ness 'round is spread,
Which mor - tal ear hath nev - er heard, Nor mor - tal vis - ion shared,

There face to face, and full and free, Ev - er and
That might - y Sun that ne'er goes down, Be - fore whose
And, like an o - cean, joy o'er - flows, And with im -
Which nev - er en - tered mor - tal breast, By mor - tal

ev - er - more we see— We see the Lord of hosts!
face clouds nev - er frown, Is God the Lord of hosts.
mor - tal mer - cy glows, Our God the Lord of hosts.
lips was ne'er ex - pressed, 'Tis God, the Lord of hosts!

hymns of the christian hope

hymns of all seasons

Many of the early Christian songs were Christmas
carols. They were composed and sung joyfully
in chapel as well as in cathedral, in peasant hut
as well as in moated castle. During the Middle
Ages, Easter carols were also popular.

Today the Christian crusader can sing and enjoy
special hymns for all the festivals of the church
year, and for Thanksgiving, New Year's Day and
national holidays as well.

"I will bless the Lord at all times: His praise
shall continually be in my mouth." Psalm 34:1

WE GATHER TOGETHER

KREMSER. Irregular.

Source Unknown
Trans. by Theodore Baker

Netherlands Folk Song
Arr. by Edward Kremser

1. We gath-er to-geth-er to ask the Lord's bless-ing;
2. Be-side us to guide us, our God with us join-ing,
3. We all do ex-tol Thee, Thou Lead-er tri-um-phant,

He chas-tens and has-tens His will to make known;
Or-dain-ing, main-tain-ing His king-dom di-vine;
And pray that Thou still our De-fend-er wilt be.

The wick-ed op-press-ing now cease from dis-tress-ing,
So from the be-gin-ning the fight we were win-ning:
Let Thy con-gre-ga-tion es-cape trib-u-la-tion:

Sing prais-es to His Name: He for-gets not His own.
Thou, Lord, wast at our side, all glo-ry be Thine!
Thy Name be ev-er praised! O Lord, make us free! A-MEN.

ALTERNATE ENDING (after third stanza)

Lord, make us free.

hymns of all seasons

come, ye thankful people, come

ST. GEORGE'S, WINDSOR. 7 7 7 7. D.

Henry Alford

George J. Elvey

1. Come, ye thank-ful peo-ple, come, Raise the song of har-vest-home:
2. All the world is God's own field, Fruit un-to His praise to yield;
3. For the Lord our God shall come, And shall take His har-vest home;
4. E-ven so, Lord, quick-ly come To Thy fi-nal har-vest-home;

All is safe-ly gath-ered in, Ere the win-ter storms be-gin;
Wheat and tares to-geth-er sown, Un-to joy or sor-row grown;
From His field shall in that day All of-fens-es purge a-way;
Gath-er Thou Thy peo-ple in, Free from sor-row, free from sin;

God, our Ma-ker, doth pro-vide For our wants to be sup-plied:
First the blade, and then the ear, Then the full corn shall ap-pear:
Give His an-gels charge at last In the fire the tares to cast;
There, for-ev-er pu-ri-fied, In Thy pres-ence to a-bide:

Come to God's own tem-ple, come, Raise the song of har-vest-home.
Lord of har-vest, grant that we Whole-some grain and pure may be.
But the fruit-ful ears to store In His gar-ner ev-er-more.
Come, with all Thine an-gels, come, Raise the glo-rious har-vest-home. A-MEN.

thanksgiving

256   now thank we all our god

NUN DANKET. 6 7 6 7 6 6 6 6

Martin Rinkart
Trans. by Catherine Winkworth

Johann Crüger
Harm. by Felix Mendelssohn

1. Now thank we all our God With heart and hands and voic - es,
2. O may this boun - teous God, Through all our life be near us,
3. All praise and thanks to God The Fa - ther now be giv - en,

Who won-drous things hath done, In whom His world re - joic - es;
With ev - er joy - ful hearts And bless - ed peace to cheer us;
The Son, and Him who reigns With them in high - est heav - en,

Who, from our moth - er's arms, Hath blessed us on our way
And keep us in His grace, And guide us when per - plexed,
The one e - ter - nal God, Whom earth and heaven a - dore;

With count-less gifts of love, And still is ours to - day.
And free us from all ills In this world and the next.
For thus it was, is now, And shall be ev - er - more. A-MEN.

hymns of all seasons

The story of this hymn is on page..123

thanks to God for my Redeemer

TACK, O GUD. 8 7 8 7 D.

257

August Ludvig Storm
Trans. by Carl E. Backstrom

J. A. Hultman

1. Thanks to God for my Re-deem - er, Thanks for all Thou dost pro - vide!
2. Thanks for prayers that Thou hast answered, Thanks for what Thou dost de - ny!
3. Thanks for ros - es by the way-side, Thanks for thorns their stems con-tain!

Thanks for times now but a mem - 'ry, Thanks for Je - sus by my side!
Thanks for storms that I have weath-ered, Thanks for all Thou dost sup - ply!
Thanks for homes and thanks for fire - side, Thanks for hope, that sweet re - frain!

Thanks for pleas - ant, balm - y spring-time, Thanks for dark and drear - y fall!
Thanks for pain, and thanks for plea - sure, Thanks for com - fort in de - spair!
Thanks for joy and thanks for sor - row, Thanks for heav'n-ly peace with Thee!

Thanks for tears by now for - got - ten, Thanks for peace with - in my soul!
Thanks for grace that none can meas - ure, Thanks for love be - yond com-pare!
Thanks for hope in the to - mor - row, Thanks thro' all e - ter - ni - ty!

thanksGIVING

HARK, THE HERALD ANGELS SING

MENDELSSOHN. 7 7 7 7 D. Ref.

Charles Wesley, alt.

Felix Mendelssohn
Arr. by William H. Cummings

1. Hark! the her-ald an-gels sing, "Glo-ry to the new-born King:
2. Christ, by high-est heaven a - dored; Christ, the Ev - er - last-ing Lord!
3. Hail the heaven-born Prince of Peace! Hail the Sun of Right-eous-ness!

Peace on earth, and mer-cy mild, God and sin-ners rec - on-ciled!"
Late in time be-hold Him come, Off - spring of the Vir-gin's womb:
Light and life to all He brings, Risen with heal - ing in His wings.

Joy - ful, all ye na - tions, rise, Join the tri-umph of the skies;
Veiled in flesh the God-head see; Hail th' In-car-nate De - i - ty,
Mild He lays His glo-ry by, Born that man no more may die,

With th' an - gel - ic host pro-claim, "Christ is born in Beth-le-hem!"
Pleased as man with men to dwell, Je - sus, our Em-man-u - el.
Born to raise the sons of earth, Born to give them sec - ond birth.

Hark! the her-ald an-gels sing, "Glo-ry to the new-born King." A-MEN.

Music used by permission of Novello & Co., Ltd.

hymns of all seasons

The story of this hymn is on page..157

thou didst leave thy throne

MARGARET. Irregular. Ref.

259

Emily E. S. Elliott

Timothy R. Matthews

1. Thou didst leave Thy throne and Thy king-ly crown When Thou cam-est to earth for me; But in Beth-le-hem's home was there found no room For Thy ho-ly na-tiv-i-ty:
2. Heav-en's arch-es rang when the an-gels sang, Pro-claim-ing Thy roy-al de-gree; But in low-ly birth didst Thou come to earth, And in great hu-mil-i-ty:
3. Thou cam-est, O Lord, with the liv-ing Word That should set Thy peo-ple free; But with mock-ing scorn, and with crown of thorn, They bore Thee to Cal-va-ry:
4. When the heav-ens shall ring, and the an-gels sing, At Thy com-ing to vic-to-ry, Let Thy voice call me home, say-ing, "Yet there is room, There is room at My side for thee:"

REFRAIN

1-3. O come to my heart, Lord Je-sus! There is room in my heart for Thee.
4. My heart shall rejoice, Lord Je-sus! When Thou comest and call-est for me. A-MEN.

christmas

angels we have heard on high

GLORIA. 7 7 7 7 Ref.

Source Unknown

Old French Carol

1. An - gels we have heard on high, Sweet - ly sing - ing o'er the plains,
2. Shepherds, why this ju - bi - lee? Why your joy - ous strains pro - long?
3. Come to Beth - le - hem, and see Him whose birth the an - gels sing;
4. See with - in a man - ger laid Je - sus, Lord of heav'n and earth!

And the moun-tains in re - ply Ech - o back their joy - ous strains.
Say what may the ti - dings be, Which in - spire your heav'n-ly song?
Come, a - dore on bend - ed knee Christ the Lord, the new - born King.
Ma - ry, Jo - seph, lend your aid, With us sing our Sav - iour's birth.

REFRAIN

Glo - - - - - - - - - - - - - - - ri - a

in ex - cel - sis De - o, Glo - - - - - - -

- - - - ri - a in ex - cel - sis De - o. A-MEN.

what child is this, who, laid to rest 261

CHRIST THE KING. 8 7 8 7 Ref.

Traditional
Arr. by William C. Dix

Old English Melody

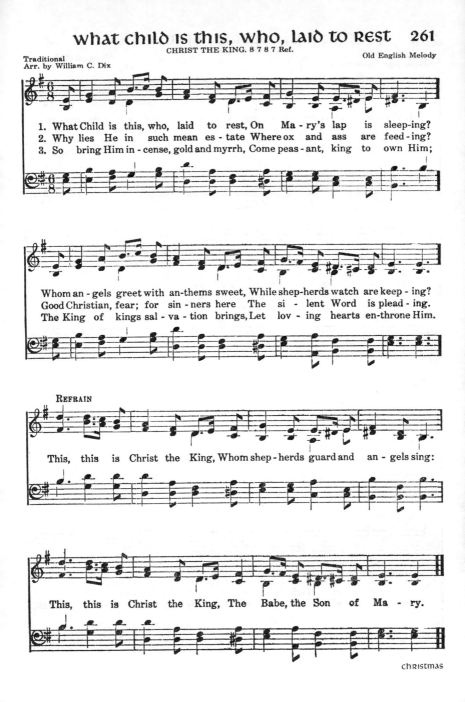

1. What Child is this, who, laid to rest, On Ma-ry's lap is sleep-ing?
2. Why lies He in such mean es-tate Where ox and ass are feed-ing?
3. So bring Him in-cense, gold and myrrh, Come peas-ant, king to own Him;

Whom an-gels greet with an-thems sweet, While shep-herds watch are keep-ing?
Good Christian, fear; for sin-ners here The si-lent Word is plead-ing.
The King of kings sal-va-tion brings, Let lov-ing hearts en-throne Him.

REFRAIN

This, this is Christ the King, Whom shep-herds guard and an-gels sing:

This, this is Christ the King, The Babe, the Son of Ma-ry.

christmas

262 O come, o come, emmanuel

VENI EMMANUEL. 8 8 8 8 8 8

Latin Hymn
Trans. by John Mason Neale

Ancient Plainsong

1. O come, O come, Em - man - u - el, And ran - som cap - tive
2. O come, Thou Rod of Jes - se, free Thine own from Sa - tan's
3. O come, Thou Day-spring, come and cheer Our spir - its by Thine
4. O come, Thou Key of Da - vid, come, And o - pen wide our

Is - ra - el, That mourns in lone - ly ex - ile here
tyr - an - ny; From depths of hell Thy peo - ple save
ad - vent here; And drive a - way the shades of night,
heaven - ly home; Make safe the way that leads on high,

Un - til the Son of God ap - pear. Re - joice! re - joice! Em -
And give them vic - tory o'er the grave. Re - joice! re - joice! Em -
And pierce the clouds and bring us light! Re - joice! re - joice! Em -
And close the path to mis - er - y. Re - joice! re - joice! Em -

man - u - el Shall come to thee, O Is - - ra - el!
man - u - el Shall come to thee, O Is - - ra - el!
man - u - el Shall come to thee, O Is - - ra - el!
man - u - el Shall come to thee, O Is - - ra - el! A-MEN.

The story of this hymn is on page . . 145

GOOD CHRISTIAN MEN, REJOICE

263

IN DULCI JUBILO. Irregular.

Medieval Latin Hymn
Trans. by John Mason Neale

German Melody, 14th Century

1. Good Chris-tian men, re - joice, With heart and soul and voice;
2. Good Chris-tian men, re - joice, With heart and soul and voice;
3. Good Chris-tian men, re - joice, With heart and soul and voice!

Give ye heed to what we say: Je - sus Christ is born to - day;
Now ye hear of end - less bliss; Je - sus Christ was born for this!
Now ye need not fear the grave; Je - sus Christ was born to save!

Ox and ass be - fore Him bow, And He is in the man - ger now.
He hath oped the heaven-ly door, And man is bless - ed ev - er -more.
Calls you one and calls you all To gain His ev - er - last - ing hall.

Christ is born to - day! Christ is born to - day!
Christ was born for this! Christ was born for this!
Christ was born to save! Christ was born to save!

christmas

264 THERE'S A SONG IN THE AIR

CHRISTMAS SONG. 6 6 6 6 12 12

Josiah G. Holland

Karl P. Harrington

1. There's a song in the air! There's a star in the sky!
2. There's a tu - mult of joy O'er the won - der - ful birth,
3. In the light of that star Lie the a - ges im - pearled,
4. We re - joice in the light, And we ech - o the song

There's a mo - ther's deep prayer, And a ba - by's low cry!
For the Vir - gin's sweet boy Is the Lord of the earth.
And that song from a - far Has swept o - ver the world.
That comes down through the night From the heav - en - ly throng.

And the star rains its fire while the beau - ti - ful sing,
Ay! the star rains its fire while the beau - ti - ful sing,
Ev - ery heart is a - flame, and the beau - ti - ful sing,
Ay! we shout to the love - ly e - van - gel they bring,

For the man - ger of Beth - le - hem cra - dles a King!
For the man - ger of Beth - le - hem cra - dles a King!
In the homes of the na - tions that Je - sus is King!
And we greet in His cra - dle our Sav - iour and King! A-MEN.

hymns of all seasons

O come, all ye faithful

ADESTE FIDELES. Irregular. Ref.

Latin Hymn, 18th Century
Trans. by Frederick Oakeley

John F. Wade's *Cantus Diversi*

265

1. O come, all ye faith - ful, Joy - ful - ly tri - um - phant,
2. Sing, choirs of an - gels, Sing in ex - ul - ta - tion!
3. Yea, Lord, we greet Thee, Born this hap - py morn - ing,

O come ye, O come ye to Beth - le - hem!
O sing, all ye bright hosts of heaven a - bove;
Je - sus, to Thee be all glo - ry given;

Come and be - hold Him, Born the King of an - gels;
Glo - ry to God, all Glo - ry in the high - est;
Word of the Fa - ther, Now in flesh ap - pear - ing;

REFRAIN

O come, let us a - dore Him, O come, let us a - dore Him,

O come, let us a - dore Him, Christ the Lord. A - MEN.

christmas

266 O little town of Bethlehem
ST. LOUIS. 7 6 8 6 D.

Phillips Brooks

Lewis H. Redner

1. O   lit-tle town of Beth-le-hem, How still we see thee lie! A - bove thy deep and
2. For Christ is born of Ma - ry, And gathered all a - bove, While mortals sleep, the
3. How si-lent-ly, how si-lent-ly, The wondrous gift is given! So God im-parts to
4. O   ho-ly Child of Beth-le-hem! De-scend to us, we pray; Cast out our sin, and

dreamless sleep The si - lent stars go by. Yet in thy dark streets shineth The ev - er -
an - gels keep Their watch of wondering love. O morn-ing stars, to-geth - er Proclaim the
human hearts The blessings of His heaven. No ear may hear His com-ing, But in this
en - ter in; Be born in us to - day. We hear the Christmas an-gels The great glad

last-ing Light; The hopes and fears of all the years Are met in thee to-night.
ho - ly birth! And prais-es sing to God the King, And peace to men on earth.
world of sin, Where meek souls will receive Him still, The dear Christ enters in.
ti - dings tell; O come to us, a - bide with us, Our Lord Em-man-u - el. A-MEN.

267 While shepherds watched their flocks
CHRISTMAS. C.M.

Nahum Tate

George F. Handel, arr.

1. While shepherds watched their flocks by night, All seat-ed on the ground, The an - gel
2. "Fear not!" said he; for might-y dread Had seized their troubled mind, "Glad ti-dings
3. "To   you, in Dav-id's town this day, Is born of Da - vid's line,   The Sav-iour
4. "The heavenly Babe you there shall find To hu-man view dis-played, All mean-ly
5. "All glo - ry be to God on high, And to the earth be peace: Good will hence-

hymns of all seasons

of the Lord came down, And glo-ry shone a-round, And glo-ry shone a-round.
of great joy I bring To you and all man-kind, To you and all man-kind.
who is Christ, the Lord, And this shall be the sign: And this shall be the sign:
forth from heaven to men, Be-gin and nev-er cease, Be-gin and nev-er cease. "A-MEN.

silent night! holy night!

STILLE NACHT. Irregular.

268

Joseph Mohr

Franz Gruber

1. Si - lent night! ho - ly night! All is calm, all is bright
2. Si - lent night! ho - ly night! Shep-herds quake at the sight,
3. Si - lent night! ho - ly night! Son of God, Love's pure light,
4. Si - lent night! ho - ly night! All is dark save the light

'Round yon vir - gin mo-ther and Child, Ho - ly In-fant so ten-der and mild,
Glo - ries stream from heav-en a - far, Heavenly hosts sing Al-le-lu - ia;
Ra-diant beams from Thy ho-ly face, With the dawn of re - deem-ing grace,
Yon - der, where they sweet vi - gils keep O'er the Babe who in si - lent sleep

Sleep in heav - en - ly peace, Sleep in heav - en - ly peace.
Christ the Sav - iour is born, Christ the Sav - iour is born.
Je - sus, Lord, at Thy birth, Je - sus, Lord, at Thy birth.
Rests in heav - en - ly peace, Rests in heav - en - ly peace. A-MEN.

269

WHEN, HIS SALVATION BRINGING

TOURS. 7 6 7 6 D.

John King

Berthold Tours

1. When, His sal - va - tion bring - ing, To Zi - on Je - sus came,
2. And since the Lord re - tain - eth His love for chil - dren still,
3. For should we fail pro - claim - ing Our great Re - deem - er's praise,

The chil - dren all stood sing - ing Ho - san - na to His name;
Though now as King He reign - eth On Zi - on's heaven - ly hill,
The stones, our si - lence sham - ing, Would their ho - san - nas raise.

Nor did their zeal of - fend Him, But, as He rode a - long,
We'll flock a - round His ban - ner Who sits up - on the throne,
But shall we on - ly ren - der The trib - ute of our words?

He bade them still at - tend Him, And smiled to hear their song.
And cry a - loud, "Ho - san - na To Da - vid's roy - al Son!"
No! while our hearts are ten - der, They, too, shall be the Lord's. A - MEN.

all glory, laud, and honor
ST. THEODULPH. 7 6 7 6 D. Ref.

270

Theodulph of Orleans
Trans. by John Mason Neale

Melchior Teschner

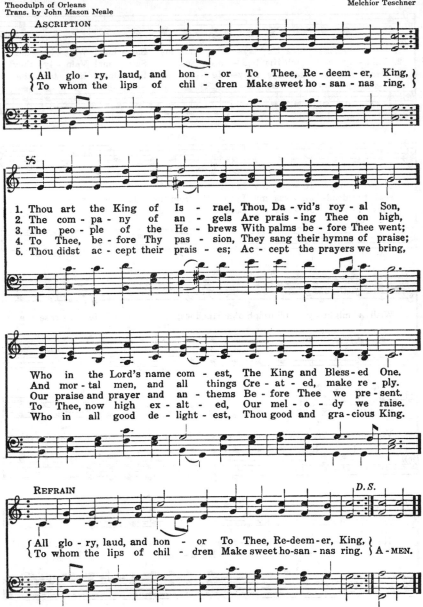

ASCRIPTION

{ All glo - ry, laud, and hon - or To Thee, Re - deem - er, King,
  To whom the lips of chil - dren Make sweet ho - san - nas ring. }

1. Thou art the King of Is - rael, Thou, Da - vid's roy - al Son,
2. The com - pa - ny of an - gels Are prais - ing Thee on high,
3. The peo - ple of the He - brews With palms be - fore Thee went;
4. To Thee, be - fore Thy pas - sion, They sang their hymns of praise;
5. Thou didst ac - cept their prais - es; Ac - cept the prayers we bring,

Who in the Lord's name com - est, The King and Bless - ed One.
And mor - tal men, and all things Cre - at - ed, make re - ply.
Our praise and prayer and an - thems Be - fore Thee we pre - sent.
To Thee, now high ex - alt - ed, Our mel - o - dy we raise.
Who in all good de - light - est, Thou good and gra - cious King.

REFRAIN

D. S.

{ All glo - ry, laud, and hon - or To Thee, Re - deem - er, King,
  To whom the lips of chil - dren Make sweet ho - san - nas ring. } A - MEN.

The story of this hymn is on page...43

palm sunday

CHRIST AROSE

CHRIST AROSE. 6 5 6 4 Ref.

Robert Lowry

Robert Lowry

1. Low in the grave He lay— Je - sus my Sav - iour! Wait - ing the
2. Vain - ly they watch His bed— Je - sus my Sav - iour! Vain - ly they
3. Death can-not keep his prey— Je - sus my Sav - iour! He tore the

REFRAIN

com - ing day— Je - sus my Lord! Up from the grave He a - rose,
seal the dead— Je - sus my Lord! He a - rose,
bars a - way— Je - sus my Lord!

With a might - y tri - umph o'er His foes; He a - rose a
He a - rose!

Vic - tor from the dark do-main, And He lives for - ev - er with His saints to reign.

He a - rose! He a - rose! Hal - le - lu - jah! Christ a-rose!
He a - rose! He a - rose!

thine is the glory

JUDAS MACCABEUS. 10 11 11 11 Ref.

Edmond L. Budry
Trans. by R. Birch Hoyle

George F. Handel

1. Thine is the glo - ry, Ris - en, con-qu'ring Son; End - less is the
2. Lo! Je - sus meets thee, Ris - en, from the tomb; Lov - ing - ly He
3. No more we doubt Thee, Glo - rious Prince of Life! Life is nought with-

vic - t'ry Thou o'er death hast won. An - gels in bright rai - ment
greets thee, Scat-ters fear and gloom; Let His church with glad - ness
out Thee; Aid us in our strife; Make us more than con - qu'rors,

Rolled the stone a - way, Kept the fold - ed grave - clothes
Hymns of tri - umph sing, For her Lord now liv - eth;
Through Thy death - less love; Bring us safe through Jor - dan

REFRAIN

Where Thy bod - y lay.
Death hath lost its sting. Thine is the glo - ry, Ris-en, con-qu'ring Son;
To Thy home a - bove.

End - less is the vic - t'ry Thou o'er death hast won. A - MEN.

This hymn is taken from "Cantate Domino" with the permission of the World Student Christian Federation, Geneva, Switzerland.

EASTER

273 I know that my Redeemer liveth

HANNAH. 9 8 9 8 Ref.

Jessie B. Pounds

James H. Fillmore

1. I know that my Redeemer liv-eth, And on the earth a-gain shall stand;
2. I know His promise never fail-eth, The word He speaks, it can-not die;
3. I know my mansion He pre-par-eth, That where He is there I may be;

1. And on the earth again shall stand;

I know e-ter-nal life He giv-eth, That grace and pow'r are in His hand.
Tho' cru-el death my flesh as-sail-eth, Yet I shall see Him by and by.
O won-drous tho't, for me He careth, And He at last will come for me.

1. That grace and pow'r are in His hand.

REFRAIN

I know, I know that Je-sus liv-eth, And on the
I know, I know

earth a-gain shall stand; I know, I know
And on the earth I know, I know

that life He giv-eth, That grace and pow'r are in His hand.
That grace and pow'r

hymns of all seasons

CHRIST THE LORD IS RISEN TODAY 274

EASTER HYMN (WORGAN). 7 7 7 7 Alleluias.

Charles Wesley

Arr. from *Lyra Davidica*, 1708

1. Christ the Lord is risen to - day, Al - - - - le - lu - ia!
2. Love's re - deem - ing work is done, Al - - - - le - lu - ia!
3. Lives a - gain our glo - rious King; Al - - - - le - lu - ia!
4. Soar we now where Christ has led, Al - - - - le - le - ia!

Sons of men and an - gels say: Al - - - - le - lu - ia!
Fought the fight, the bat - tle won; Al - - - - le - lu - ia!
Where, O death, is now thy sting? Al - - - - le - lu - ia!
Fol - lowing our ex - alt - ed Head; Al - - - - le - lu - ia!

Raise your joys and tri - umphs high, Al - - - - le - lu - ia!
Death in vain for - bids Him rise; Al - - - - le - lu - ia!
Dy - ing once, He all doth save: Al - - - - le - lu - ia!
Made like Him, like Him we rise; Al - - - - le - lu - ia!

Sing, ye heavens, and earth re - ply, Al - - - - le - lu - ia!
Christ has o - pened Par - a - dise. Al - - - - le - lu - ia!
Where thy vic - to - ry, O grave? Al - - - - le - lu - ia!
Ours the cross, the grave, the skies. Al - - - - le - lu - ia! A-MEN.

275

the strife is o'er

VICTORY. 8 8 8 4 Alleluias

From the Latin
Trans. by Francis Pott

Giovanni P. da Palestrina
Adapted by W. H. Monk

Al - le - lu - ia! Al - le - lu - ia! Al - le - lu - ia!

Org.

1. The strife is o'er, the bat - tle done; The vic - to - ry of life is won;
2. The powers of death have done their worst, But Christ their le - gions hath dis-persed:
3. The three sad days have quick - ly sped; He ris - es glo - rious from the dead:
4. He closed the yawn-ing gates of hell; The bars from heaven's high por - tals fell:
5. Lord, by the stripes which wounded Thee, From death's dread sting Thy serv-ants free,

The song of tri - umph has be - gun. Al - le - lu - ia!
Let shouts of ho - ly joy out-burst. Al - le - lu - ia!
All glo - ry to our ris - en Head! Al - le - lu - ia!
Let hymns of praise His tri - umphs tell. Al - le - lu - ia!
That we may live and sing to Thee. Al - le - lu - ia! A-MEN.

276

lift up, lift up your voices now

WALTHAM. L.M.

John Mason Neale

J. Baptiste Calkin

1. Lift up, lift up your voic - es now! The whole wide world re-joic - es now;
2. In vain with stone the cave they barred; In vain the watch kept ward and guard;
3. And all He did, and all He bare, He gives us as our own to share;
4. O Vic - tor, aid us in the fight, And lead through death to realms of light;

hymns of all seasons

The Lord hath triumphed glo-rious-ly, The Lord shall reign vic-to-rious-ly.
Ma - jes-tic from the spoil-ed tomb, In pomp of tri-umph Christ is come.
And hope, and joy, and peace be-gin, For Christ has won, and man shall win.
We safe-ly pass where Thou hast trod; In Thee we die to rise to God. A-MEN.

jesus lives, and so shall i

ZUVERSICHT. 7 8 7 8 7 7

277

Christian F. Gellert
Trans. by Philip Schaff

Johann Crüger

1. Je - sus lives, and so shall I. Death! thy sting is gone for - ev - er.
2. Je - sus lives and reigns supreme; And, His king-dom still re - main-ing,
3. Je - sus lives, I know full well, Naught from Him my heart can sev - er,
4. Je - sus lives, and death is now But my en - trance in - to glo - ry.

He who deigned for me to die, Lives, the bands of death to sev - er.
I shall al - so be with Him, Ev - er liv - ing, ev - er reign-ing.
Life nor death nor powers of hell, Joy nor grief, hence-forth for - ev - er.
Cour - age, then, my soul, for thou Hast a crown of life be - fore thee;

He shall raise me with the just: Je - sus is my Hope and Trust.
God has promised: be it must; Je - sus is my Hope and Trust.
None of all His saints is lost; Je - sus is my Hope and Trust.
Thou shalt find thy hopes were just; Je - sus is the Christian's Trust. A-MEN.

EASTER

another year is dawning

SALVATORI. 7 6 7 6 D.

Frances R. Havergal

Arr. from J. Michael Haydn

1. An - oth - er year is dawn - ing! Dear Fa - ther, let it be,
2. An - oth - er year of mer - cies, Of faith - ful - ness and grace;
3. An - oth - er year of serv - ice, Of wit - ness for Thy love;

In work - ing or in wait - ing, An - oth - er year with Thee;
An - oth - er year of glad - ness In the shin - ing of Thy face;
An - oth - er year of train - ing For ho - lier work a - bove.

An - oth - er year of lean - ing Up - on Thy lov - ing breast,
An - oth - er year of prog - ress, An - oth - er year of praise,
An - oth - er year is dawn - ing! Dear Fa - ther, let it be

An - oth - er year of trust - ing, Of qui - et, hap - py rest.
An - oth - er year of prov - ing Thy pres - ence all the days.
On earth, or else in heav - en, An - oth - er year for Thee. A-MEN.

I WITH THEE WOULD BEGIN

LAT MIG BÖRJA MED DIG. Irregular.

From the Swedish
Trans. by A. Samuel Wallgren

W. Theodor Söderberg

279

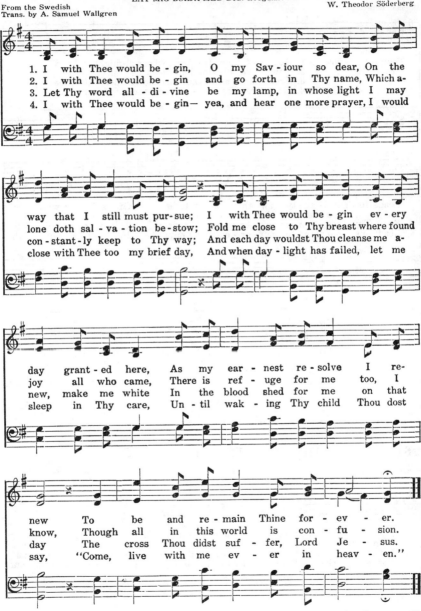

1. I with Thee would be - gin, O my Sav - iour so dear, On the
2. I with Thee would be - gin and go forth in Thy name, Which a-
3. Let Thy word all - di - vine be my lamp, in whose light I may
4. I with Thee would be - gin— yea, and hear one more prayer, I would

way that I still must pur - sue; I with Thee would be - gin ev - ery
lone doth sal - va - tion be - stow; Fold me close to Thy breast where found
con - stant - ly keep to Thy way; And each day wouldst Thou cleanse me a-
close with Thee too my brief day, And when day - light has failed, let me

day grant - ed here, As my ear - nest re - solve I re-
joy all who came, There is ref - uge for me too, I
new, make me white In the blood shed for me on that
sleep in Thy care, Un - til wak - ing Thy child Thou dost

new To be and re - main Thine for - ev - er.
know, Though all in this world is con - fu - sion.
day The cross Thou didst suf - fer, Lord Je - sus.
say, "Come, live with me ev - er in heav - en."

the changing year

The story of this hymn is on page....3

280   GOD OF OUR FATHERS, WHOSE ALMIGHTY HAND

NATIONAL HYMN. 10 10 10 10

Daniel C. Roberts

George W. Warren

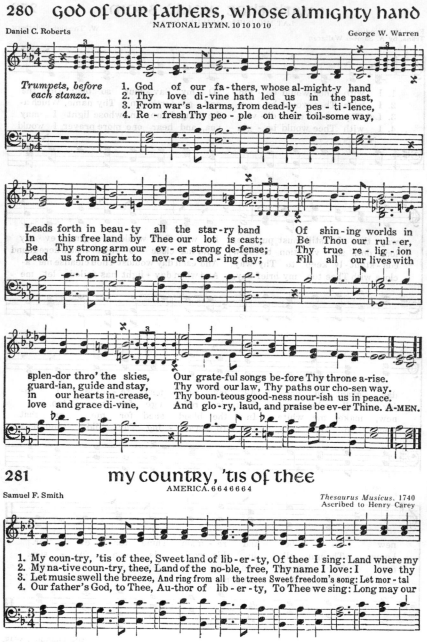

Trumpets, before
each stanza.

1. God of our fa - thers, whose al-might-y hand
2. Thy love di-vine hath led us in the past,
3. From war's a-larms, from dead-ly pes - ti-lence,
4. Re - fresh Thy peo - ple on their toil-some way,

Leads forth in beau - ty all the star - ry band   Of shin - ing worlds in
In this free land by Thee our lot is cast;   Be Thou our rul - er,
Be Thy strong arm our ev - er strong de-fense;   Thy true re - lig - ion
Lead us from night to nev - er - end - ing day;   Fill all our lives with

splen-dor thro' the skies,   Our grate-ful songs be-fore Thy throne a-rise.
guard-ian, guide and stay,   Thy word our law, Thy paths our cho-sen way.
in our hearts in-crease,   Thy boun-teous good-ness nour-ish us in peace.
love and grace di-vine,   And glo-ry, laud, and praise be ev-er Thine. A-MEN.

281   MY COUNTRY, 'TIS OF THEE

AMERICA. 6 6 4 6 6 6 4

Samuel F. Smith

Thesaurus Musicus. 1740
Ascribed to Henry Carey

1. My coun-try, 'tis of thee, Sweet land of lib - er - ty, Of thee I sing: Land where my
2. My na-tive coun-try, thee, Land of the no-ble, free, Thy name I love: I love thy
3. Let music swell the breeze, And ring from all the trees Sweet freedom's song: Let mor - tal
4. Our father's God, to Thee, Au-thor of lib - er - ty, To Thee we sing: Long may our

fa-thers died, Land of the pilgrim's pride, From ev - ery moun-tain side Let free-dom ring!
rocks and rills, Thy woods and templed hills; My heart with rapture thrills, Like that a - bove.
tongues awake; Let all that breathe partake; Let rocks their silence break, The sound prolong.
land be bright With freedom's ho-ly light; Pro-tect us by Thy might, Great God, our King! A-MEN.

GOD SAVE AMERICA!   282
RUSSIAN HYMN. 11 10 11 10

Henry F. Chorley; 1, 2
John Ellerton; 3, 4   Alexis F. Lvov

1. God save A - mer - i - ca! New world of glo - ry, New - born to
2. God save A - mer - i - ca! Here may all ra - ces Min - gle to-
3. God save A - mer - i - ca! Bear - ing the ol - ive, Hers be the
4. God save A - mer - i - ca! 'Mid all her splen - dors, Save her from

free - dom and knowl - edge and power, Lift - ing the towers of her
geth - er as chil - dren of God, Found - ing an em - pire on
bless - ing the peace - mak - ers prove, Call - ing the na - tions to
pride and from lux - u - ry; Throne in her heart the un-

light - ning - lit cit - ies Where the flood tides of hu - man - i - ty roar!
broth - er - ly kind - ness, E - qual in lib - er - ty, made of one blood!
glad fed - er - a - tion, Lead - ing the world in the tri - umph of love!
seen and e - ter - nal; Right be her might and the truth make her free! A-MEN.

283 O BEAUTIFUL FOR SPACIOUS SKIES

MATERNA. C.M.D.

Katharine Lee Bates

Samuel A. Ward

1. O beau-ti-ful for spa-cious skies, For am-ber waves of grain,
2. O beau-ti-ful for pil-grim feet, Whose stern, im-pas-sioned stress
3. O beau-ti-ful for he-roes proved In lib-er-at-ing strife,
4. O beau-ti-ful for pa-triot dream That sees be-yond the years

For pur-ple moun-tain maj-es-ties A-bove the fruit-ed plain!
A thor-ough-fare for free-dom beat A-cross the wil-der-ness!
Who more than self their coun-try loved, And mer-cy more than life!
Thine al-a-bas-ter cit-ies gleam, Un-dimmed by hu-man tears!

A-mer-i-ca! A-mer-i-ca! God shed His grace on thee,
A-mer-i-ca! A-mer-i-ca! God mend thine ev-ery flaw,
A-mer-i-ca! A-mer-i-ca! May God thy gold re-fine
A-mer-i-ca! A-mer-i-ca! God shed His grace on thee,

And crown thy good with broth-er-hood From sea to shin-ing sea!
Con-firm thy soul in self-con-trol, Thy lib-er-ty in law!
Till all suc-cess be no-ble-ness And ev-ery gain di-vine!
And crown thy good with broth-er-hood From sea to shin-ing sea! A-MEN.

hymns of all seasons

The story of this hymn is on page...81

BATTLE HYMN OF THE REPUBLIC

BATTLE HYMN. 15 15 15 6 Ref.

Julia Ward Howe   John William Steffe

1. Mine   eyes have seen the glo - ry of the com - ing of the Lord; He is
2. I have seen Him in the watch-fires of a hun-dred cir-cling camps;They have
3. He has sound-ed forth the trum-pet that shall nev - er sound re-treat; He is
4. In the beau-ty of the lil - ies Christ was born a-cross the sea, With a

tram-pling out the vin-tage where the grapes of wrath are stored;He hath loosed the
build - ed Him an al - tar in the eve-ning dews and damps;I can read His
sift - ing out the hearts of men be-fore His judg-ment seat. O be swift, my
glo - ry in His bos-om that trans-fig-ures you and me; As He died to

fate - ful light-ning of His ter - ri - ble swift sword;His truth is march-ing on.
right-eous sen-tence by the dim and flar - ing lamps;His day is march-ing on.
soul, to an-swer Him! be ju - bi-lant, my feet! Our God is march-ing on.
make men ho - ly, let us die to make men free; While God is march-ing on.

REFRAIN

Glo - ry! glo - ry, hal - le - lu - jah! Glo - ry! glo - ry, hal - le - lu - jah!

Glo - ry! glo - ry, hal - le - lu - jah! Our God is march-ing on.

national days

SCRIPTURE READINGS

The readings are in consecutive scriptural order with relation to the beginning passage of each reading. The text used is the King James Version, 1611, with a few exceptions, when the American Standard Version, 1901, is used for easier congregational participation.

The hymns listed at the bottom of each column are appropriate for singing in connection with that Scripture Reading.

285   GOD THE CREATOR

In the beginning God created the heaven and the earth.

And the earth was without form, and void; and darkness was upon the face of the deep.

And the Spirit of God moved upon the face of the waters. And God said, Let there be light: and there was light.

And God saw the light, that it was good: and God divided the light from the darkness.

And God called the light Day, and the darkness he called Night.

And the evening and the morning were the first day. — Genesis 1: 1-5.

By the word of the Lord were the heavens made; and all the host of them by the breath of his mouth.

He gathereth the waters of the sea together as an heap: he layeth up the depth in storehouses.

Let all the earth fear the Lord: let all the inhabitants of the world stand in awe of him.

For he spake, and it was done; he commanded, and it stood fast.
— Psalm 33: 6-9.

Let us come before his presence with thanksgiving, and make a joyful noise unto him with psalms.

For the Lord is a great God, and a great King above all gods.

In his hand are the deep places of the earth: the strength of the hills is his also.

The sea is his, and he made it: and his hands formed the dry land.

O come, let us worship and bow down: let us kneel before the Lord our maker.

For he is our God; and we are the people of his pasture, and the sheep of his hand. — Psalm 95: 2-7.

Hymns: 1, 5, 16, 18, 44, 48

286   GOD'S COMMANDMENTS

And the Lord came down upon Mount Sinai, on the top of the mount: and the Lord called Moses up to the top of the mount; and Moses went up. — Exodus 19:20.

And God spake all these words saying, I am the Lord thy God which have brought thee out of the land of Egypt, out of the house of bondage.

Thou shalt have no other Gods before me.

Thou shalt not make unto thee any graven image. Thou shalt not bow down thyself to them, nor serve them.

Thou shalt not take the name of the Lord thy God in vain.

Remember the sabbath day to keep it holy.

Honor thy father and thy mother.

Thou shalt not kill.

Thou shalt not commit adultery.

Thou shalt not steal.

Thou shalt not bear false witness against thy neighbor.

Thou shalt not covet.

— Exodus 20:1-7 (Abridged).

Then one of them, which was a lawyer, asked him a question, tempting him, and saying, Master, which is the great commandment in the law?

Jesus said unto him, Thou shalt love the Lord thy God with all thy heart, and with all thy soul, and with all thy mind. This is the first and great commandment.

And the second is like unto it. Thou shalt love thy neighbor as thyself.

On these two commandments hand all the law and the prophets.
— Matthew 22:35-40.

Hymns: 165, 181, 203, 207

287   THE WAY OF LIFE

Blessed is the man that walketh not in the counsel of the ungodly, nor standeth in the way of sinners, nor sitteth in the seat of the scornful.

But his delight is in the law of the Lord; and in his law doth he meditate day and night.

And he shall be like a tree planted by the rivers of water, that bringeth forth his fruit in his season; his leaf also shall not wither; and whatsoever he doeth shall prosper.

The ungodly are not so: but are like the chaff which the wind driveth away.

Therefore the ungodly shall not stand in the judgment, nor sinners in the congregation of the righteous.

For the Lord knoweth the way of the righteous: but the way of the ungodly shall perish. — Psalm 1.

Enter ye in at the strait gate: for wide is the gate, and broad is the way, that leadeth to destruction, and many there be which go in thereat:

Because strait is the gate, and narrow is the way, which leadeth unto life, and few there be that find it.

Hymns 55, 111, 117, 125   — Matthew 7: 13, 14.

288   THE SHEPHERD PSALM

The Lord is my shepherd; I shall not want.

He maketh me to lie down in green pastures: he leadeth me beside the still waters.

He restoreth my soul: he leadeth me in the paths of righteousness for his name's sake.

Yea, though I walk through the valley of the shadow of death, I will fear no evil:

For thou art with me; thy rod and thy staff they comfort me.

Thou preparest a table before me in the presence of mine enemies:

Thou anointest my head with oil; my cup runneth over.

Surely goodness and mercy shall follow me all the days of my life; and I will dwell in the house of the Lord for ever. — Psalm 23.

Hymns: 40, 133, 189, 198

289   DIVINE PROVIDENCE

I will bless the Lord at all times: his praise shall continually be in my mouth.

My soul shall make her boast in the Lord: the humble shall hear thereof, and be glad.

O magnify the Lord with me, and let us exalt his name together.

I sought the Lord, and he heard me, and delivered me from all my fears.

They looked unto him, and were lightened; and their faces were not ashamed.

This poor man cried, and the Lord heard him, and saved him out of all his troubles.

The angel of the Lord encampeth round about them that fear him, and delivereth them.

O taste and see that the Lord is good: blessed is the man that trusteth in him.

O fear the Lord, ye his saints; for there is no want to them that fear him.

The young lions do lack, and suffer hunger; but they that seek the Lord shall not want any good thing.

The eyes of the Lord are upon the righteous, and his ears are open unto their cry.

The face of the Lord is against them that do evil, to cut off the remembrance of them from the earth.

The righteous cry, and the Lord heareth, and delivereth them out of all their troubles.

The Lord is nigh unto them that are of a broken heart; and saveth such as be of a contrite spirit.

Many are the afflictions of the righteous: but the Lord delivereth him out of them all.

The Lord redeemeth the soul of his servants; and none of them that trust in him shall be desolate.

— Psalm 34: 1-10, 15-19, 22.

Hymns: 12, 19, 33, 182, 187

290 PRAYER OF PENITENCE

Have mercy upon me, O God, according to thy lovingkindness:

According unto the multitude of thy tender mercies blot out my transgressions.

Wash me thoroughly from mine iniquity, and cleanse me from my sin.

For I acknowledge my transgressions; and my sin is ever before me.

Against thee, thee only, have I sinned, and done this evil in thy sight; that thou mightest be justified when thou speakest, and be clear when thou judgest.

Purge me with hyssop, and I shall be clean: wash me, and I shall be whiter than snow.

Make me to hear joy and gladness; that the bones which thou hast broken may rejoice.

Hide thy face from my sins, and blot out all mine iniquities.

Create in me a clean heart, O God; and renew a right spirit within me.

Cast me not away from thy presence; and take not thy holy spirit from me.

Restore unto me the joy of thy salvation; and uphold me with thy free spirit.

Then will I teach transgressors thy ways; and sinners shall be converted unto thee.

Deliver me from bloodguiltiness, O God, thou God of my salvation; and my tongue shall sing aloud of thy righteousness.

O Lord, open thou my lips; and my mouth shall show forth thy praise.

For thou desirest not sacrifice; else would I give it: thou delightest not in burnt offering.

The sacrifices of God are a broken spirit: a broken and a contrite heart, O God, thou wilt not despise.

— From Psalm 51.

Hymns: 57, 71, 76, 84

291 OBEDIENCE TO GOD

Blessed are the undefiled in the way, who walk in the law of the Lord.

Blessed are they that keep his testimonies, and that seek him with the whole heart.

They also do no iniquity: they walk in his ways.

Thou hast commanded us to keep thy precepts diligently.

O that my ways were directed to keep thy statutes!

Then shall I not be ashamed, when I have respect unto all thy commandments.

I will praise thee with uprightness of heart, when I shall have learned thy righteous judgments.

I will keep thy statutes: O forsake me not utterly.

Wherewithal shall a young man cleanse his way? By taking heed thereto according to thy word.

With my whole heart have I sought thee: O let me not wander from thy commandments.

Thy word have I hid in mine heart, that I might not sin against thee.

Blessed art thou, O Lord: teach me thy statutes.

With my lips have I declared all the judgments of thy mouth.

I have rejoiced in the way of thy testimonies, as much as in all riches.

I will meditate in thy precepts, and have respect unto thy ways.

I will delight myself in thy statutes: I will not forget thy word.

Deal bountifully with thy servant, that I may live, and keep thy word.

Open thou mine eyes, that I may behold wondrous things out of thy law.

— Psalm 119: 1-18.

Hymns: 137, 146, 153, 165, 181

292 GOD'S OMNISCIENCE

O Lord, thou hast searched me, and known me.

Thou knowest my downsitting and mine uprising; thou understandest my thought afar off.

Thou compassest my path and my lying down, and art acquainted with all my ways.

For there is not a word in my tongue, but, lo, O Lord, thou knowest it altogether.

Thou has beset me behind and before, and laid thine hand upon me.

Such knowledge is too wonderful for me; it is high, I cannot attain unto it.

Whither shall I go from thy spirit? or whither shall I flee from thy presence?

If I ascend up into heaven, thou art there: if I make my bed in sheol, behold, thou art there.

If I take the wings of the morning, and dwell in the uttermost parts of the sea;

Even there shall thy hand lead me, and thy right hand shall hold me.

If I say, Surely the darkness shall cover me; even the night shall be light about me.

Yea, the darkness hideth not from thee; but the night shineth as the day: the darkness and the light are both alike to thee.

I will praise thee; for I am fearfully and wonderfully made:

Marvellous are thy works; and that my soul knoweth right well.

Search me, O God, and know my heart: try me, and know my thoughts;

And see if there be any wicked way in me, and lead me in the way everlasting. — From Psalm 139.

Hymns: 9, 38, 43, 241.

293 TRUE WISDOM

Happy is the man that findeth wisdom, and the man that getteth understanding.

For the merchandise of it is better than the merchandise of silver, and the gain thereof than fine gold.

She is more precious than rubies: and all the things thou canst desire are not to be compared unto her.

Length of days is in her right hand; and in her left hand riches and honour.

Her ways are ways of pleasantness, and all her paths are peace.

She is a tree of life to them that lay hold upon her: and happy is every one that retaineth her.

The Lord by wisdom hath founded the earth; by understanding hath he established the heavens.

By his knowledge the depths are broken up, and the clouds drop down the dew.

My son, let not them depart from thine eyes; keep sound wisdom and discretion:

So shall they be life unto thy soul, and grace to thy neck.

Then shalt thou walk in thy way safely, and thy foot shall not stumble.

When thou liest down thou shalt not be afraid: yea, thou shalt lie down, and thy sleep shall be sweet.

Be not afraid of sudden fear, neither of the desolation of the wicked, when it cometh.

For the Lord shall be thy confidence, and shall keep thy foot from being taken.

Trust in the Lord with all thine heart; and lean not unto thine own understanding.

In all thy ways acknowledge him, and he shall direct thy paths.

— Proverbs 3: 13-26, 5, 6.

Hymns: 48, 135, 144, 180, 198

294 ADORATION OF THE MAGI

Now when Jesus was born in Bethlehem of Judea in the days of Herod the king, behold, there came wise men from the east to Jerusalem, saying,

Where is he that is born King of the Jews? for we have seen his star in the east, and are come to worship him.

When Herod the king had heard these things, he was troubled, and all Jerusalem with him.

And when he had gathered all the chief priests and scribes of the people together, he demanded of them where Christ should be born.

And they said unto him, In Bethlehem of Judea: for thus it is written by the prophet,

And thou Bethlehem, in the land of Judah, art not the least among the princes of Judah: for out of thee shall come a governor, that shall rule my people Israel.

Then Herod, when he had privily called the wise men, enquired of them diligently what time the star appeared. And he sent them to Bethlehem, and said,

Go and search diligently for the young child; and when ye have found him, bring me word again, that I may come and worship him also.

When they had heard the king, they departed; and, lo, the star, which they saw in the east, went before them, till it came and stood over where the young child was.

When they saw the star, they rejoiced with exceeding great joy.

And when they were come into the house, they saw the young child with Mary his mother, and fell down, and worshipped him:

And when they had opened their treasures, they presented unto him gifts; gold, and frankincense, and myrrh. — Matthew 2: 1-11.

Hymns: 258-268.

295 THE BEATITUDES

And seeing the multitudes, he went up into the mountain: and when he was set, his disciples came unto him:

And he opened his mouth, and taught them, saying,

Blessed are the poor in spirit: for theirs is the kingdom of heaven.

Blessed are they that mourn: for they shall be comforted.

Blessed are the meek: for they shall inherit the earth.

Blessed are they which do hunger and thirst after righteousness: for they shall be filled.

Blessed are the merciful: for they shall obtain mercy.

Blessed are the pure in heart: for they shall see God.

Blessed are the peacemakers: for they shall be called the children of God.

Blessed are they which are persecuted for righteousness' sake: for theirs is the kingdom of heaven.

Blessed are ye, when men shall revile you, and persecute you, and shall say all manner of evil against you falsely, for my sake.

Rejoice, and be exceeding glad: for great is your reward in heaven: for so persecuted they the prophets which were before you.

Ye are the salt of the earth: but if the salt have lost his savour, wherewith shall it be salted?

It is thenceforth good for nothing, but to be cast out, and to be trodden under foot of men.

Ye are the light of the world. A city that is set on an hill cannot be hid.

Let your light so shine before men, that they may see your good works, and glorify your Father which is in heaven. — Matthew 5: 1-14, 16.

Hymns: 142, 145, 150, 157, 236

296   THE WHITENED HARVEST

And Jesus went about all the cities and villages, teaching in their synagogues, and preaching the gospel of the kingdom, and healing every sickness and every disease among the people.

But when he saw the multitudes, he was moved with compassion on them, because they fainted, and were scattered abroad, as sheep having no shepherd.

Then saith he unto his disciples, The harvest truly is plenteous, but the labourers are few;

Pray ye therefore the Lord of the harvest, that he will send forth labourers into his harvest.

— Matthew 9: 35-38.

For there is no difference between the Jew and the Greek: for the same Lord over all is rich unto all that call upon him.

For whosoever shall call upon the name of the Lord shall be saved.

How then shall they call on him in whom they have not believed? and how shall they believe in him of whom they have not heard? and how shall they hear without a preacher?

And how shall they preach, except they be sent? as it is written, How beautiful are the feet of them that preach the gospel of peace, and bring glad tidings of good things!

— Romans 10: 12-15.

Say not ye, There are yet four months, and then cometh harvest? behold, I say unto you, Lift up your eyes, and look on the fields; for they are white already to harvest.

— John 4: 35.

He that goeth forth and weepeth, bearing precious seed, shall doubtless come again with rejoicing, bringing his sheaves with him. — Psalm 126:6.

Hymns: 215, 228, 230, 231, 237

297   THE LAST SUPPER

Now the first day of the feast of unleavened bread the disciples came to Jesus, saying unto him, Where wilt thou that we prepare for thee to eat the passover?

And he said, Go into the city to such a man, and say unto him, The Master saith, My time is at hand; I will keep the passover at thy house with my disciples.

And the disciples did as Jesus had appointed them; and they made ready the passover.

Now when the even was come, he sat down with the twelve.

And as they did eat, he said, Verily I say unto you, that one of you shall betray me.

And they were exceeding sorrowful, and began every one of them to say unto him, Lord, is it I?

And he answered and said, He that dippeth his hand with me in the dish, the same shall betray me.

The Son of man goeth as it is written of him: but woe unto that man by whom the Son of man is betrayed! it had been good for that man if he had not been born.

Then Judas, which betrayed him, answered and said, Master, is it I? He said unto him, Thou hast said.

And as they were eating, Jesus took bread, and blessed it, and brake it, and gave it to the disciples, and said, Take, eat; this is my body.

And he took the cup, and gave thanks, and gave it to them, saying, Drink ye all of it; For this is my blood of the new testament, which is shed for many for the remission of sins.

But I say unto you, I will not drink henceforth of this fruit of the vine, until that day when I drink it new with you in my Father's kingdom.

— Matthew 26: 17-29.

Hymns: 34, 70, 78, 88, 124

298 THE RISEN LORD

In the end of the sabbath, as it began to dawn toward the first day of the week, came Mary Magdalene and the other Mary to see the sepulchre.

And, behold, there was a great earthquake; for the angel of the Lord descended from heaven, and came and rolled back the stone from the door, and sat upon it.

His countenance was the lightning, and his raiment white as snow: **And for fear of him the keepers did shake, and became as dead men.**

And the angel answered and said unto the women, Fear not ye: for I know that ye seek Jesus, which was crucified.

He is not here; for he is risen, as he said. Come, see the place where the Lord lay.

And go quickly, and tell his disciples that he is risen from the dead; and, behold, he goeth before you into Galilee; there shall ye see him: lo, I have told you.

And they departed quickly from the sepulchre with fear and great joy; and did run to bring his disciples word.

And as they went to tell his disciples, behold, Jesus met them, saying, All hail. And they came and held him by the feet, and worshipped him.

Then said Jesus unto them, Be not afraid: go tell my brethren that they go into Galilee, and there shall they see me. — Matthew 28: 1-10.

Then the same day at evening, being the first day of the week, when the doors were shut where the disciples were assembled for fear of the Jews, came Jesus and stood in the midst, and saith unto them, Peace be unto you.

And when he had so said, he shewed unto them his hands and his side. Then were the disciples glad, when they saw the Lord.

Hymns: 89, 126, 271-277 — John 20: 19, 20.

299 THE GREAT COMMISSION

Then the eleven disciples went away into Galilee, into a mountain where Jesus had appointed them.

And when they saw him, they worshipped him: but some doubted.

And Jesus came and spake unto them, saying, All power is given unto me in heaven and in earth.

Go ye therefore, and teach all nations, baptizing them in the name of the Father, and of the Son, and of the Holy Ghost:

Teaching them to observe all things whatsoever I have commanded you: and, lo, I am with you alway, even unto the end of the world.

Jesus said unto them, Thus it is written, and thus it behoved Christ to suffer, and to rise from the dead the third day:

And that repentance and remission of sins should be preached in his name among all nations, beginning at Jerusalem.

And ye are witnesses of these things.

And, behold, I send the promise of my Father upon you: but tarry ye in the city of Jerusalem, until ye be endued with power from on high.
— Luke 24: 46-49.

They asked of him, saying, Lord, wilt thou at this time restore again the kingdom to Israel?

And he said unto them, It is not for you to know the times or the seasons, which the Father hath put in his own power:

But ye shall receive power, after that the Holy Ghost is come upon you:

And ye shall be witnesses unto me both in Jerusalem, and in all Judaea, and in Samaria, and unto the uttermost part of the earth.

And when he had spoken these things, while they beheld, he was taken up; and a cloud received him out of their sight. — Acts 1: 6-9.

Hymns: 142, 155, 224, 226, 234

300 THE TRIUMPHAL ENTRY

And when they came nigh to Jerusalem, unto Bethphage and Bethany, at the mount of Olives, he sendeth forth two of his disciples, and saith unto them,

Go your way into the village over against you: and as soon as ye be entered into it, ye shall find a colt tied, whereon never man sat; loose him, and bring him.

And if any man say unto you, Why do ye this? say ye that the Lord hath need of him; and straightway he will send him hither.

And they went their way, and found the colt tied by the door without in a place where two ways met; and they loose him.

And certain of them that stood there said unto them, What do ye, loosing the colt?

And they said unto them even as Jesus had commanded: and they let them go.

And they brought the colt to Jesus, and cast their garments on him; and he sat upon him.

And many spread their garments in the way; and others cut down branches off the trees, and strawed them in the way.

And they that went before, and they that followed, cried, saying, Hosanna; Blessed is he that cometh in the name of the Lord:

Blessed be the kingdom of our father David, that cometh in the name of the Lord: Hosanna in the highest. And Jesus entered into Jerusalem, and into the temple.
— Mark 11: 1-11.

And when he was come into Jerusalem, all the city was moved, saying, Who is this?

And the multitude said, This is Jesus the prophet of Nazareth of Galilee. — Matthew 21: 10, 11.

Hymns: 28, 35, 269, 270

301 THE SAVIOUR'S ADVENT

And there were in the same country shepherds abiding in the field, keeping watch over their flock by night.

And, lo, the angel of the Lord came upon them, and the glory of the Lord shone round about them: and they were sore afraid.

And the angel said unto them, Fear not: for, behold, I bring you good tidings of great joy, which shall be to all people.

For unto you is born this day in the city of David a Saviour, which is Christ the Lord.

And this shall be a sign unto you; Ye shall find the babe wrapped in swaddling clothes, lying in a manger.

And suddenly there was with the angel a multitude of the heavenly host praising God, and saying,

Glory to God in the highest, and on earth peace, good will toward men.

And it came to pass, as the angels were gone away from them into heaven, the shepherds said one to another,

Let us now go even unto Bethlehem, and see this thing which is come to pass, which the Lord hath made known unto us.

And they came with haste, and found Mary, and Joseph, and the babe lying in a manger.

And when they had seen it, they made known abroad the saying which was told them concerning this child.

And all they that heard it wondered at those things which were told them by the shepherds.

But Mary kept all these things, and pondered them in her heart.

And the shepherds returned, glorifying and praising God for all the things that they had heard and seen, as it was told unto them. — Luke 2: 8-20.

Hymns: 258-268

302 CHRIST TEACHES PRAYER

And it came to pass, that, as he was praying in a certain place, when he ceased, one of his disciples said unto him, Lord, teach us to pray, as John also taught his disciples.

And he said unto them, When ye pray, say, Our Father which art in heaven, Hallowed be thy name. Thy kingdom come. Thy will be done, as in heaven, so in earth.

Give us day by day our daily bread.

And forgive us our sins; for we also forgive every one that is indebted to us.

And lead us not into temptation; but deliver us from evil.

And he said unto them, Which of you shall have a friend, and shall go unto him at midnight, and say unto him, Friend, lend me three loaves;

For a friend of mine in his journey is come to me, and I have nothing to set before him?

And he from within shall answer and say, Trouble me not: the door is now shut, and my children are with me in bed; I cannot rise and give thee.

I say unto you, Though he will not rise and give him because he is his friend, yet because of his importunity he will rise and give him as many as he needeth.

And I say unto you, Ask, and it shall be given you; seek, and ye shall find; knock, and it shall be opened unto you.

For every one that asketh receiveth; and he that seeketh findeth; and to him that knocketh it shall be opened.

If ye then, being evil, know how to give good gifts unto your children: how much more shall your heavenly Father give the Holy Spirit to them that ask him?
— Luke 11: 1-10, 13.

Hymns: 164, 168, 175, 185, 186

303 THE INCARNATE CHRIST

In the beginning was the Word, and the Word was with God, and the Word was God.

The same was in the beginning with God.

All things were made by him; and without him was not anything made that was made.

In him was life; and the life was the light of men.

And th light shineth in darkness; and the darkness comprehended it not.

There was a man sent from God, whose name was John.

The same came for a witness, to bear witness of the Light, that all men through him might believe.

He was not that Light, but was sent to bear witness of that Light.

That was the true Light, which lighteth every man that cometh into the world.

He was in the world, and the world was made by him, and the world knew him not.

He came unto his own, and his own received him not.

But as many as received him, to them gave he power to become the sons of God, even to them that believe on his name:

Which were born, not of blood, nor of the will of the flesh, nor of the will of man, but of God.

And the Word was made flesh, and dwelt among us, and we beheld his glory, the glory as of the only begotten of the Father, full of grace and truth.

For God so loved the world, that he gave his only begotten Son, that whosoever believeth in him should not perish, but have everlasting life.

For God sent not his Son into the world to condemn the world; but that the world through him might be saved.
— John 1: 1-14; 3: 16, 17.

Hymns: 4, 17, 42, 83, 262

304 THE HOLY SPIRIT

And it shall come to pass afterward, that I will pour out my spirit upon all flesh; and your sons and your daughters shall prophesy, your old men shall dream dreams, your young men shall see visions:

And also upon the servants and upon the handmaids in those days will I pour out my spirit. — Joel 2: 28, 29.

And I will pray the Father, and he shall give you another Comforter, that he may abide with you for ever;

Even the Spirit of truth; whom the world cannot receive, because it seeth him not, neither knoweth him: but ye know him; for he dwelleth with you, and shall be in you.
— John 14: 16, 17.

Nevertheless I tell you the truth: It is expedient for you that I go away: for if I go not away, the Comforter will not come unto you;

But if I depart, I will send him unto you. And when he is come, he will reprove the world of sin, and of righteousness, and of judgment.
— John 16: 7, 8.

But ye shall receive power, after that the Holy Ghost is come upon you:

And ye shall be witnesses unto me both in Jerusalem, and in all Judaea, and in Samaria, and unto the uttermost part of the earth.
— Acts 1: 8.

And when the day of Pentecost was fully come, they were all with one accord in one place.

And suddenly there came a sound from heaven as of a rushing mighty wind, and it filled all the house where they were sitting.

And there appeared unto them cloven tongues like as of fire, and it sat upon each of them.

And they were all filled with the Holy Ghost, and began to speak with other tongues, as the Spirit gave them utterance. — Acts 2: 1-4.

Hymns: 154, 155, 173, 175, 176

305 CHRISTIAN ASSURANCE

As many as are led by the Spirit of God, they are the sons of God.

For ye have not received the spirit of bondage again to fear; but ye have received the Spirit of adoption, whereby we cry, Abba, Father.

The Spirit itself beareth witness with our spirit, that we are the children of God:

And if children, then heirs; heirs of God, and joint-heirs with Christ; if so be that we suffer with him, that we may be also glorified together.

For I reckon that the sufferings of this present time are not worthy to be compared with the glory which shall be revealed in us.

And we know that all things work together for good to them that love God, to them who are the called according to his purpose.

What shall we then say to these things? If God be for us, who can be against us?

He that spared not his own Son, but delivered him up for us all, how shall he not with him also freely give us all things?

Who shall separate us from the love of Christ? shall tribulation, or distress, or persecution, or famine, or nakedness, or peril, or sword?

Nay, in all these things we are more than conquerors through him that loved us.

For I am persuaded, that neither death, nor life, nor angels, nor principalities, nor powers, nor things present, nor things to come.

Nor height, nor depth, nor any other creature, shall be able to separate us from the love of God, which is in Christ Jesus our Lord.
— Romans 8: 14-18, 28, 31, 32, 35, 37-39.

Hymns: 22, 123, 131, 179, 180

306   THE LOVE CHAPTER

Though I speak with the tongues of men and of angels, and have not love, I am become as sounding brass, or a tinkling cymbal.

And though I have the gift of prophecy, and understand all mysteries, and all knowledge; and though I have all faith, so that I could remove mountains, and have not love, I am nothing.

And though I bestow all my goods to feed the poor, and though I give my body to be burned, and have not love, it profiteth me nothing.

Love suffereth long, and is kind; love envieth not; love vaunteth not itself, is not puffed up.

Doth not behave itself unseemly, seeketh not her own, is not easily provoked, thinketh no evil;

Rejoiceth not in iniquity, but rejoiceth in the truth;

Beareth all things, believeth all things, hopeth all things, endureth all things.

Love never faileth: but whether there be prophecies, they shall fail; whether there be tongues, they shall cease; whether there be knowledge, it shall vanish away.

For we know in part, and we prophesy in part.

But when that which is perfect is come, then that which is in part shall be done away.

When I was a child, I spake as a child, I understood as a child, I thought as a child: but when I became a man, I put away childish things.

For now we see through a glass, darkly; but then face to face:

Now I know in part; but then shall I know even as also I am known.

And now abideth faith, hope, love, these three; but the greatest of these is love.   —I Corinthians 13.

Hymns: 52, 74, 150, 170

307   SPIRITUAL WARFARE

Finally, my brethren, be strong in the Lord, and in the power of his might.

Put on the whole armour of God, that ye may be able to stand against the wiles of the devil.

For we wrestle not against flesh and blood, but against principalities, against powers, against the rulers of the darkness of this world, against spiritual wickedness in high places.

Wherefore take unto you the whole armour of God, that ye may be able to withstand in the evil day, and having done all, to stand.

Stand therefore, having your loins girt about with truth, and having on the breastplate of righteousness; and your feet shod with the preparation of the gospel of peace;

Above all, taking the shield of faith, wherewith ye shall be able to quench all the fiery darts of the wicked.

And take the helmet of salvation, and the sword of the Spirit, which is the word of God:

Praying always with all prayer and supplication in the Spirit, and watching thereunto with all perseverance and supplication for all saints.   —Ephesians 6: 10-18.

Thou therefore endure hardness as a good soldier of Jesus Christ.

No man that warreth entangleth himself with the affairs of this life; that he may please him who hath chosen him to be a soldier.
   —II Timothy 2: 3, 4.

I have fought a good fight, I have finished my course, I have kept the faith:

Henceforth there is laid up for me a crown of righteousness, which the Lord, the righteous judge, shall give me at that day: and not to me only, but unto all them also that love his appearing.   —II Timothy 4: 7, 8.

Hymns: 216, 218, 219, 223, 225

308 THE RETURN OF CHRIST

But I would not have you to be ignorant, brethren, concerning them which are asleep, that ye sorrow not, even as others which have no hope.

For if we believe that Jesus died and rose again, even so them also which sleep in Jesus will God bring with him.

For this we say unto you by the word of the Lord, that we which are alive and remain unto the coming of the Lord shall not precede them which are asleep.

For the Lord himself shall descend from heaven with a shout, with the voice of the archangel, and with the trump of God: and the dead in Christ shall rise first.

Then we which are alive and remain shall be caught up together with them in the clouds, to meet the Lord in the air: and so shall we ever be with the Lord.

Wherefore comfort one another with these words.

But of the times and the seasons, brethren, ye have no need that I write unto you.

For yourselves know perfectly that the day of the Lord so cometh as a thief in the night.

But ye, brethren, are not in darkness, that that day should overtake you as a thief. Ye are all the children of the day: we are not of the night, nor of darkness.

Therefore let us not sleep, as do others; but let us watch and be sober.

For God hath not appointed us to wrath, but to obtain salvation by our Lord Jesus Christ,

Who died for us, that, whether we wake or sleep, we should live together with him.

— I Thessalonians 4: 13-18; 5: 1, 2, 4-6, 9, 10.

Hymns: 239, 240, 241, 243, 251

309 THE HOLY SCRIPTURES

Knowing this first, that no prophecy of the scripture is of any private interpretation.

For the prophecy came not in old time by the will of man: but holy men of God spake as they were moved by the Holy Ghost.

— II Peter 1: 20, 21.

All scripture is given by inspiration of God, and is profitable for doctrine, for reproof, for correction, for instruction in righteousness:

That the man of God may be perfect, thoroughly furnished unto all good works. — II Timothy 3: 16, 17.

Study to show thyself approved unto God, a workman that needeth not to be ashamed, rightly dividing the word of truth. — II Timothy 2: 15.

For the word of God is quick, and powerful, and sharper than any two-edged sword, piercing even to the dividing asunder of soul and spirit, and of the joints and marrow, and is a discerner of the thoughts and intents of the heart. — Hebrews 4: 12.

But these are written, that ye might believe that Jesus is the Christ, the Son of God; and that believing ye might have life through his name. — John 20: 31.

For whatsoever things were written aforetime were written for our learning, that we through patience and comfort of the scriptures might have hope. — Romans 15: 4.

Teach me, O Lord, the way of thy statutes; and I shall keep it unto the end.

Give me understanding, and I shall keep thy law; yea, I shall observe it with my whole heart.

The entrance of thy words giveth light; it giveth understanding unto the simple.

Great peace have they which love thy law: and nothing shall offend them. — Psalm 119: 33, 34, 130, 165.

Hymns: 101, 153, 202-206

310 BLESSINGS FROM GOD

Bless the Lord, O my soul; and all that is within me, bless his holy name.

Bless the Lord, O my soul, and forget not all his benefits:

Who forgiveth all thine iniquities; who healeth all thy diseases;

Who redeemeth thy life from destruction; who crowneth thee with lovingkindness and tender mercies;

Who satisfieth thy mouth with good things; so that thy youth is renewed like the eagle's.

The Lord executeth righteousness and judgment for all that are oppressed.

He made known his ways unto Moses, his acts unto the children of Israel.

The Lord is merciful and gracious, slow to anger, and plenteous in mercy.

He will not always chide; neither will he keep his anger for ever.

He hath not dealt with us after our sins, nor rewarded us according to our iniquities.

For as the heaven is high above the earth, so great is his mercy toward them that fear him.

As far as the east is from the west, so far hath he removed our transgressions from us.

Like as a father pitieth his children, so the Lord pitieth them that fear him.

For he knoweth our frame; he remembereth that we are dust.

As for man, his days are as grass; as a flower of the field, so he flourisheth.

For the wind passeth over it, and it is gone; and the place thereof shall know it no more.

But the mercy of the Lord is from everlasting to everlasting upon them that fear him, and his righteousness unto children's children;

Bless the Lord, all his works, in all places of his dominion: bless the Lord, O my soul.   From Psalm 103.

Hymns: 1, 13, 22, 32, 52

311 COMFORT FROM CHRIST

Let not your heart be troubled: ye believe in God, believe also in me.

In my Father's house are many mansions: if it were not so, I would have told you. I go to prepare a place for you.

And if I go and prepare a place for you, I will come again, and receive you unto myself; that where I am, there ye may be also.

And whither I go ye know, and the way ye know.

Thomas saith unto him, Lord, we know not whither thou goest; and how can we know the way?

Jesus saith unto him, I am the way, the truth, and the life: no man cometh unto the Father, but by me.

If ye had known me, ye should have known my Father also: and from henceforth ye know him, and have seen him.

Philip saith unto him, Lord, show us the Father, and it sufficeth us.

Jesus saith unto him, Have I been so long time with you, and yet hast thou not known me, Philip? he that hath seen me hath seen the Father; and how sayest thou then, Show us the Father?

Believest thou not that I am in the Father, and the Father in me? the words that I speak unto you I speak not of myself: but the Father that dwelleth in me, he doeth the works.

Verily, verily, I say unto you, He that believeth on me, the works that I do shall he do also; and greater works than these shall he do; because I go unto my Father.

Peace I leave with you, my peace I give unto you: not as the world giveth, give I unto you. Let not your heart be troubled, neither let it be afraid.   —John 14: 1-12, 27.

Hymns: 188, 192, 245, 252, 253

inδex of authors, composers, anδ sources

index of authors, composers, and sources

Grimes, Katherine A. (b. 1877); 137.
Grose, Howard Benjamin (1851-1939); 238.
Gruber, Franz Xaver (1787-1863); 268.

h

Hanby, Benjamin Russell (1833-1867); 15.
Handel, George Frederick (1685-1759); 267, 272.
Hankey, Arabella Catherine (1834-1911); 95, 96.
Harkness, Robert (1880-1961); 4.
Harrington, Karl Pomeroy (1861-1953); 264.
Harrison, Ralph (1748-1810); 13.
Hart, Joseph (1712-1768); 53.
Hassler, Hans Leo (1564-1612); 34.
Hastings, Thomas (1784-1872); 191.
Hatch, Edwin (1835-1889); 155, 176.
Hatton, John (1710-1793); 232.
Havergal, Frances Ridley (1836-1879); 102, 140, 142,
   162, 188, 221, 222, 235, 278.
Hawks, Annie Sherwood (1836-1918); 149.
Haydn, Franz Joseph (1732-1809); 208.
Haydn, Johann Michael (1737-1806); 48, 278.
Hayford, Jack W. (b. 1934); 14.
Hearn, Marianne (1834-1909); 66.
Heber, Reginald (1783-1826); 8, 223.
Hebrew Melody, Anonymous; 38, 224.
Hedge, Frederick Henry (1805-1890); 32.
Hemy, Henri Frederick (1818-1888); 207.
Herbert, George (1593-1632); 36.
Hewitt, Eliza Edmunds (1851-1920); 61, 242.
Hickman, Roger M. (b. 1888); 110.
Hine, Stuart K. (b. 1899); 1.
Hodder, Edwin (1837-1904); 204.
Hoffman, Elisha Albright (1839-1929); 42, 159, 190.
Holden, Oliver (1765-1844); 35.
Holland, Josiah Gilbert (1819-1881); 264.
How, William Walsham (1823-1897); 65, 245.
Howe, Julia Ward (1819-1910); 284.
Hoyle, Richard Birch (1875-1939); 272.
Hudson, Ralph E. (1843-1901); 88, 107, 143.
Hughes, John (1873-1932); 213
Hull, Eleanor Henrietta (1860-1935); 147.
Hultman, John Alfred (1861-1942); 257.
Husband, Edward (1843-1908); 65.
Husband, John Jenkins (1760-1825); 156.
Hussey, Jennie Evelyn (1874-1958); 67.
Hustad, Donald Paul (b. 1918); 20, 22, 86, 98, 115,
   141, 148, 177.

i

Ingall's "Christian Harmony", 1805; 37.
Irish Text, Anonymous; 147.
Irish Melody, Anonymous; 147.
Irvine, Jessie Seymour (1836-1887); 40.

j

Jackson, H. G. (19th Century); 62.
Jackson, Robert (1842-1914); 155.
John F. Wade's "Cantus Diversi", 1751; 265.
Johnston, Julia Harriette (1849-1919); 76.
Jones, William (1726-1800); 240.
Judah, Daniel ben (14th Century); 38.

k

K. in Rippon's "A Selection of Hymns", 1787; 180.
"Katholisches Gesangbuch", 1774; 11.
Kelly, Thomas (1769-1855); 23.
Ken, Thomas (1637-1711); 50.
Ketchum, Albert Allen (20th Century); 118.
Kethe, William (d. ca. 1593); 51.
Kidder, Mary Ann (1820-1905); 69.
King, John (1789-1858); 269.
Kirkpatrick, William James (1838-1921); 61, 67, 83,
   87, 99, 109, 111, 146, 179.
Knapp, Phoebe Palmer (1839-1908); 97.
Knecht, Justin Heinrich (1752-1817); 65.
Kocher, Conrad (1786-1872); 18.
Kremser, Edward (1838-1869); 254.

l

Langran, James (1835-1909); 45.
Lathbury, Mary Artemisia (1841-1913); 205.
Latin Text, Anonymous; 262, 263, 265, 275.
Laufer, Calvin Weiss (1874-1938); 144.
Laurinus, Laurentius Laurentii (1573-1655); 253.
Lester, John Henry (19th Century); 138.
Lillenas, Haldor (1885-1959); 106.
Loes, Harry Dixon (1892-1965); 113.
Longstaff, William Dunn (1822-1894); 136.
Loveless, Wendell P. (b. 1892); 234.
Lowden, Carl Harold (b. 1883); 152.
Lowry, Joseph C. (19th Century); 247.
Lowry, Robert (1826-1899); 149, 161, 271.
Luther, Martin (1483-1546); 32.
Lvov, Alexis F. (ca. 1799-1870); 282.
Lyne, J. L. (19th Century); 148.
Lyon, Meyer (1751-1799); 38, 224.

m

McAfee, Cleland Boyd (1866-1944); 193.
McCutchan, Robert Guy (1877-1958); 36.
McDaniel, Rufus Henry (1850-1940); 120.
McGranahan, James (1840-1907); 55, 123, 126, 251.
McKinney, Baylus Benjamin (1886-1952); 176, 215.
Macaulay, Joseph C. (b. 1900); 174, 234.
Maccall, William (1812-1888); 253.
Mackay, William Paton (1839-1885); 156.
Main, Hubert Platt (1839-1925); 214, 228.
Maker, Frederick Charles (1844-1927); 59, 151.
Malan, Henri Abraham César (1787-1864); 162, 186.
Mann, Arthur Henry (1850-1929); 172.
Maori Melody (Traditional); 148.
March, Daniel (1816-1909); 228.
Marsden, Ruth E. (20th Century); 243.
Marsh, Charles Howard (1886-1956); 116.
Marsh, Simeon Butler (1798-1875); 78.
Martin, Civilla Durfee (1866-1948); 182.
Martin, Walter Stillman (1862-1935); 182.
Mason, Lowell (1792-1872); 24, 49, 71, 81, 128, 165,
   167.
Matheson, George (1842-1906); 139, 141.
Matthews, Timothy Richard (1826-1910); 259.
Maxwell, Mary E. (20th Century); 169.
Medley, Samuel (1738-1799); 49.
Mendelssohn, Felix (1809-1847); 256, 258.
Merrill, William Pierson (1867-1954); 210.
Messiter, Arthur Henry (1834-1916); 26.
Miles, C. Austin (1868-1946); 196.
Miller, Edward (1731-1807); 70.
Mohr, Joseph (1792-1848); 268.
Monk, William Henry (1823-1889); 275.
Monsell, John Samuel Bewley (1811-1875); 222.
Moody, May Whittle (1870-1963); 184.
Moore, Thomas (1779-1852); 191.
Morris, Leila Naylor (1862-1929); 166, 239.
Mote, Edward (1797-1874); 92.
Mountain, James (1844-1933); 104, 188, 194.
Mozart, Wolfgang Amadeus (1756-1791); 49, 214, 228.
Murray, Robert (1832-1910); 171.

n

Neale, John Mason (1818-1866); 63, 262, 263, 270,
   276.
Neander, Joachim (1650-1680); 19.
Netherlands Melody, Anonymous; 254.
Neumeister, Erdmann (1671-1756); 55.
Newell, William Reed (1868-1956); 117.
Newton, John (1725-1807); 108, 186, 208.
Nichol, Henry Ernest (1862-1928); 230.
North, Frank Mason (1850-1935); 220, 229.
Norwegian Melody, Anonymous; 111, 253.

o

Oakeley, Frederick (1802-1880); 265.
Olivers, Thomas (1725-1799); 38.
Orr, J. Edwin (b. 1912); 148.
Ovens, W. G. (19th Century); 124.

index of authors, composers, and sources

index of tunes

index of tunes

m

Madrid, 30
Man of Sorrows, 73
Maori, 148
Margaret, 259
Marion, 26
Martyn, 78
Maryton, 211
Materna, 283
McAfee, 193
McDaniel, 120
Mendelssohn, 258
Mercy, 173
Message, 230
Miles Lane, 35
Minerva, 58
Mit Freuden Zart, 9
Montreat, 86
Moody, 76
More Love To Thee, 150
Morecambe, 175
Morning Hymn, 50
Morris, 166
Moscow (Italian Hymn), 28
My Saviour's Love, 112

n

National Hymn, 280
Near the Cross, 127
Need, 149
Nettleton, 2
Neumeister, 55
New Hampton, 249
Nicaea, 8
Nun Danket, 256

o

O Store Gud, 1
Oh, How I Love Jesus, 90
Okmulgee, 113
Old Hundredth, 51
Old, Old Story, 96
Old Rugged Cross, 77
Olivet, 167
Once for All, 119
Orleans, 158

p

Paradoxy, 141
Passion Chorale, 34
Pax Tecum, 192
Peoples Church, 110
Pine Street, 62
Pisgah, 247

Plagal, 22
Promises, 202

q

Quebec (Hesperus), 7
Quietude, 168

R

Rathbun, 72
Redeemed, 99
Rescue, 227
Revive Us Again, 156
Rockingham Old, 70
Rondinella, 146
Russian Hymn, 282
Rutherford, 244

s

Sagina, 74
St. Agnes, 25
St. Andrew, 125
St. Anne, 12
St. Catherine, 207
St. Christopher, 151
St. Dunstan's, 212
St. George's, Windsor, 255
St. Gertrude, 217
St. Hilda, 65
St. Leonards, 135
St. Louis, 266
St. Margaret, 139
St. Petersburg, 140, 229
St. Stephen, 240
St. Theodulph, 270
St. Thomas, 27
Salvatori, 278
Sanctuary, 164
Sandon, 187
Satisfied, 107
Schuler, 236
Scott, 153
Second Coming, 239
Seraph (Bethlehem), 204
Showalter, 190
Sine Nomine, 245
Slane, 147
Snead, 134
Solid Rock, 92
Something for Thee, 161
Sovereignty, 241
Stephanos, 63
Stille Nacht, 268
Story of Jesus, 91
Surrender, 177

t

Tack, O Gud, 257
Talmadge, 114
Te Deum, 11
Teach Me, 137
Terra Beata, 44
The Sweetest Name, 21
Tidings, 237
To God Be the Glory, 3
Toccoa, 243
Ton-Y-Botel, 85
Tours, 269
Tranquillity, 194
Trentham, 155
Trust and Obey, 181
Trust in Jesus, 109
Trusting Jesus, 183
Truett, 176
Tryggare Kan Ingen Vara, 189

v

Veni Emmanuel, 262
Victory, 275
Ville Du Havre, 200
Voluntas Dei, 174
Vox Dilecti, 56

w

Wakefield, 129
Waltham, 276
Warrington, 13
Webb, 226
Whitfield, 84
Whittle, 184
Wimby, 234
Winona Lake, 145
Wonderful Grace, 106
Wondrous Story, 94
Woodworth, 57
Words of Life, 101
Wye Valley, 188

z

Zeruiah, 61
Zuversicht, 277

topical index

topical index

topical index

topical index

alphabetical index of scripture readings

GeneRaL inðex

Titles are in small CAPS; first lines in lower case type

a

165 A CHARGE TO KEEP I HAVE — reminds the Christian of his obligation to live victoriously and to serve God faithfully.

32 A MIGHTY FORTRESS IS OUR GOD — the Battle Hymn of the Reformation, is Martin Luther's free adaptation of Psalm 46.

54 A ruler once came to Jesus by night (see YE MUST BE BORN AGAIN)

179 A wonderful Saviour is Jesus my Lord (see HE HIDETH MY SOUL)

88 Alas, and did my Saviour bleed? (see AT THE CROSS)

16 ALL CREATURES OF OUR GOD AND KING — says that all creation praises the Creator; written by Francis of Assisi, "the patron saint of animals."

270 ALL GLORY, LAUD, AND HONOR — Tradition says the singing of this Palm Sunday hymn won its 8th century author, Theodulph of Orleans, freedom from prison.

35 ALL HAIL THE POWER — calls all ransomed men of earth and all angels, to crown Jesus Christ "Lord of all."

178 ALL IS WELL! — is an adaptation of an early American text and tune, and breathes utter confidence in the providence of God.

107 ALL MY LIFE LONG — speaks of the soul's thirst, hunger and poverty, and of Jesus Christ who is a "well of water," "bread of life" and "untold wealth."

51 ALL PEOPLE THAT ON EARTH DO DWELL — is a poetic version of Psalm 100, one of the oldest hymns in the English language.

113 ALL THINGS IN JESUS — is a testimony that man's deepest longings and needs are satisfied only by Christ.

177 All to Jesus I surrender (see I SURRENDER ALL)

219 AM I A SOLDIER OF THE CROSS? — calls us to "endure hardness as a good soldier of Jesus Christ." (II Timothy 2:3)

108 AMAZING GRACE! HOW SWEET THE SOUND — is the testimony of John Newton, by the grace of God, a slave trader who became a clergyman.

241 Amid the fears that oppress our day (see OUR GOD IS SOVEREIGN STILL)

74 AND CAN IT BE THAT I SHOULD GAIN? — expresses abject wonder and humble confidence in the salvation bought and wrought by our Lord.

260 ANGELS WE HAVE HEARD ON HIGH — is in both words and music a traditional French carol based on the song of the angels in Luke 2:14.

278 ANOTHER YEAR IS DAWNING — is a prayer that in the year ahead we may "grow in grace and knowledge" and serve God faithfully. (II Peter 3:18)

63 ART THOU WEARY, HEAVY LADEN? — is an ancient Greek "question and answer hymn" based on Matthew 11:28; it may be sung antiphonally.

117 AT CALVARY — is a testimony of the love, grace and mercy shown in Jesus' death; words and music were written by men associated with Moody Bible Institute, Chicago.

88 AT THE CROSS — Isaac Watts' verses speak our sorrow and wonder as we contemplate the cross; Ralph Hudson's refrain expresses the joy of our salvation.

50 AWAKE, MY SOUL, AND WITH THE SUN — is a morning hymn of praise, which commits the day to God; it was written by an Anglican bishop of Winchester, Thomas Ken.

B

284 BATTLE HYMN OF THE REPUBLIC — a purely American hymn written during the Civil War, was sung at the funeral of England's Sir Winston Churchill.

182 Be not dismayed whate'er betide (see GOD WILL TAKE CARE OF YOU)

197 BE STILL, MY SOUL — says that in the middle of life's problems, our strength comes from "quietness and confidence" in God. (Isaiah 30:15)

147 BE THOU MY VISION — is an ancient Irish poem dating probably from the 8th century; the tune is a traditional Irish melody.

60 BELIEVE ON THE LORD JESUS CHRIST — is the answer to the question "What must I do to be saved?", and is based on Paul's experience in the jail at Philippi. (Acts 16:24-34)

151 BENEATH THE CROSS OF JESUS — expresses all that the believer feels as he thinks about the cross of Jesus Christ.

97 BLESSED ASSURANCE — a theme song of a Billy Graham Crusade, tells of the unending joy of the person who knows God accepts him.

205 BREAK THOU THE BREAD OF LIFE — is a prayer that God's Spirit will help us understand the Bible; it is based on Jesus' feeding the multitude. (John 6:1-14)

155 BREATHE ON ME, BREATH OF GOD — based on John 20:22, speaks of the Holy Spirit's work in salvation, in making us holy, and in our full consecration.

233 Brightly beams our Father's mercy (see LET THE LOWER LIGHTS BE BURNING)

80 BY FAITH IN CHRIST WE LIVE — is a new hymn submitted in a 1961 contest conducted by the National Church Music Fellowship.

page 278

GENERAL INDEX

C

169 **CHANNELS ONLY** — is a prayer that we may be used of God to bring His message and His blessings to others.

189 **CHILDREN OF THE HEAVENLY FATHER** — written by Lina Sandell ("The Fanny Crosby of Sweden"), tells of God's loving care of us, His children.

271 **CHRIST AROSE** — was written by Robert Lowry, Baptist minister and professor, in 1874; note the dramatic contrast between the stanzas and the refrain.

42 **Christ has for sin atonement made** (see WHAT A WONDERFUL SAVIOUR!)

126 **CHRIST LIVETH IN ME** — explains what we mean when we say, "A Christian is a person in whom Christ lives."

55 **CHRIST RECEIVETH SINFUL MEN** — An old German hymn has been translated and given a gospel song melody; it is based on I Timothy 1:15.

251 **CHRIST RETURNETH** — a favorite hymn on Christ's second coming, was written by James McGranahan, a songleader in evangelism from 1876 to 1887.

274 **CHRIST THE LORD IS RISEN TODAY** — refers to many scripture passages which teach us what the resurrection means.

30 **COME, CHRISTIANS, JOIN TO SING** — urges us to sing praise, because God demands it and because He is worthy of it.

178 **Come, come, ye saints** (see ALL IS WELL!)

58 **Come, every soul by sin oppressed** (see ONLY TRUST HIM)

186 **COME, MY SOUL, THY SUIT PREPARE** — compares our praying to the case or "suit" that a lawyer presents in court.

28 **COME, THOU ALMIGHTY KING** — is a prayer to each member of the Trinity in turn — Father, Son, and Holy Spirit — and finally to the "One in Three."

2 **COME, THOU FOUNT** — sings praise to God, from whom every blessing flows, as streams from a fountain.

59 **COME TO THE SAVIOUR NOW** — is a gentle call to the sinner, the "backslider" and the burdened Christian to "come to the Saviour."

27 **COME, WE THAT LOVE THE LORD** — explains why no true Christian can refuse to sing about His experience with God.

191 **COME, YE DISCONSOLATE** — a hymn of comfort written by the Irish poet Thomas Moore, has been altered by Thomas Hastings, an American church musician.

53 **COME, YE SINNERS, POOR AND WRETCHED** — a historic, theological hymn of invitation, was penned by Joseph Hart, a contemporary of the Wesleys.

255 **COME, YE THANKFUL PEOPLE, COME** — by Henry Alford, Dean of Canterbury, is a harvest hymn which also teaches the second coming and God's final judgment.

114 **COMPLETE IN THEE** — is based on Col. 2:10, "and ye are complete in Him;" the refrain outlines our total salvation, in this world and in the next.

31 **CROWN HIM WITH MANY CROWNS** — is a hymn about Christ the King; the text was contributed by two 19th century Anglican rectors, Matthew Bridges and Godfrey Thring.

D

118 **Deep in my heart there's a gladness** (see WHY DO I SING ABOUT JESUS?)

160 **DRAW ME NEARER** — was written by Fanny Crosby after a conversation (with musician W. H. Doane) about the nearness of God.

184 **Dying with Jesus, by death reckoned mine** (see MOMENT BY MOMENT)

E

145 **Earthly pleasures vainly call me** (see I WOULD BE LIKE JESUS)

F

246 **FACE TO FACE** — an "Eternal Life" hymn, is based on I Cor. 13:12. "For now we see through a glass, darkly; but then face to face . . . ."

39 **FAIREST LORD JESUS** — despite the title "Crusader's Hymn," first appeared in a German hymnal in 1677. This tune was first published in the 19th century.

207 **FAITH OF OUR FATHERS!** — originally Roman Catholic in emphasis, has been altered to speak of our common and historic faith in Christ.

231 **Far and near the fields are teeming** (see THE CALL FOR REAPERS)

245 **FOR ALL THE SAINTS** — a memorial hymn of saints now departed, is set to a famous tune by the English composer, Vaughan Williams.

132 **For salvation full and free** (see JESUS ONLY, LET ME SEE)

18 **FOR THE BEAUTY OF THE EARTH** — speaks our gratitude for the common things of life, as well as for the fellowship of the Church.

22 **FOREVER** — reminds us that, in the midst of life's uncertainties, God's love and peace and help are eternal.

GeneRaL inDex

180 **HOW FIRM A FOUNDATION** — mentions (vs. 2, 3, 4) three promises in Scripture in which we trust; the tune is an early American folk melody.

1 **HOW GREAT THOU ART** — First written in Sweden in 1886, this hymn of praise became popular around the world through Billy Graham Crusades.

52 **HOW GREAT THY LOVING KINDNESS IS** — This new hymn uses an Old Testament phrase "loving kindness" to recount God's providence in life and in eternity.

169 **How I praise Thee, precious Saviour** (see CHANNELS ONLY)

I

104 **I AM HIS, AND HE IS MINE** — is an exquisite expression of the joy of the believer who has not left his first love — Jesus Christ.

83 **I AM NOT SKILLED TO UNDERSTAND** — is a folk-like hymn which echoes repeatedly our wonder at the work of "Christ — my Saviour."

160 **I am Thine, O Lord** (see DRAW ME NEARER)

102 **I AM TRUSTING THEE, LORD JESUS** — is an intimate expression of trust in Christ, by Frances Ridley Havergal, one of Britain's leading women hymnists.

131 **I BELONG TO JESUS** — Like many other children's hymns, this simple expression of commitment will be enjoyed by older persons as well.

196 **I come to the garden alone** (see IN THE GARDEN)

235 **I GAVE MY LIFE FOR THEE** — is the author's response to a motto under a picture of the crucified Christ: "I did this for thee; what hast thou done for me?"

105 **I have a song that Jesus gave me** (see IN MY HEART THERE RINGS A MELODY)

56 **I HEARD THE VOICE OF JESUS SAY** — is based on John 1:16; each stanza gives first a call of Christ, and then the believer's response.

123 **I know not why God's wondrous grace** (see I KNOW WHOM I HAVE BELIEVED)

273 **I KNOW THAT MY REDEEMER LIVETH** — quotes and expounds the words of Job 19:25, 26 and John 14:2, 3 pertaining to our hope of eternal life.

123 **I KNOW WHOM I HAVE BELIEVED** — The stanzas list many things about God which are a mystery; the refrain counters with the positive note of II Timothy 1:12.

37 **I LOVE THEE** — is a simple expression of praise whose author and composer are unknown; the pentatonic melody signifies a true "folk hymn."

95 **I LOVE TO TELL THE STORY** — taken from a long poem on the life of Christ, expresses the universal appeal of the oft-repeated gospel story.

149 **I NEED THEE EVERY HOUR** — a confession of dependence on God written about 1870 by Annie S. Hawks; the refrain and melody are by Robert Lowry, her pastor.

84 **I SAW THE CROSS OF JESUS** — a meditation on the cross by Anglican rector Frederick Whitfield; the tune is adapted from an ancient Greek melody.

89 **I serve a risen Saviour** (see HE LIVES)

249 **I shall see the King in His beauty** (see THE KING IN HIS BEAUTY)

5 **I SING THE MIGHTY POWER OF GOD** — expresses the glory of God in creation, His universal presence and His perfect providence.

98 **I stand all amazed at the love** (see OH, IT IS WONDERFUL!)

112 **I stand amazed in the presence** (see MY SAVIOUR'S LOVE)

177 **I SURRENDER ALL** — written by J. W. Van DeVenter about 1895, tells of his long struggle against a call to Christian service, and his final surrender.

133 **I WAS A WANDERING SHEEP** — identifies the author and the singer with the lost sheep, for which the Shepherd sought, at great sacrifice. (Luke 15:4-7)

93 **I WILL SING OF MY REDEEMER** — was found in the effects of P. P. Bliss after he died in a train wreck in 1876. Try it with this Welsh tune.

94 **I WILL SING THE WONDROUS STORY** — A narrative testimony written by Rev. Francis Rowley in 1886, when conducting a mission in his church at Fall River, Mass.

279 **I WITH THEE WOULD BEGIN** — A Swedish hymn of "beginnings" — for each new day, or for each new experience of commitment to Christ.

145 **I WOULD BE LIKE JESUS** — is a personal expression of a desire to "be conformed to the image of Jesus Christ." (Rom. 8:29)

143 **I'LL LIVE FOR HIM** — one of our simplest hymns of commitment was written about 1880, by Ralph E. Hudson, Methodist lay preacher, music teacher and publisher.

122 **I'VE FOUND A FRIEND** — recounts the attributes and ministries of Jesus Christ, "a friend who sticketh closer than a brother." (Prov. 18:24)

115 **I'VE HEARD THE KING** — written during World War II, was inspired by a broadcast of England's King George VI, heard in this country.

62 **If you from sin are longing to be free** (see LOOK TO THE LAMB OF GOD)

43 **IMMORTAL, INVISIBLE, GOD ONLY WISE** — speaks of God in terms of transcendent "light," which reveals all things but obscures itself.

253 **IN HEAVEN ABOVE** — is a Scandinavian hymn, both words and music, telling of blessedness "where God the Father dwells."

105 **IN MY HEART THERE RINGS A MELODY** — is based on Eph. 5:19 ("making melody in your heart to the Lord.") It is the heart's song that God hears!

121 **IN TENDERNESS HE SOUGHT ME** — a song of Christian witness, recalls the stories of the lost sheep (Luke 15:4-7), and the good Samaritan (Luke 10:30-37).

72 **IN THE CROSS OF CHRIST I GLORY** — is based on Paul's words: "God forbid that I should glory, save in the cross of our Lord Jesus Christ." (Gal. 6:14)

196 **IN THE GARDEN** — allows the singer to share the experience of Mary Magdalene, as she met Jesus outside the tomb on Easter morning. (John 20:11-18)

69 **IS MY NAME WRITTEN THERE?** — The Bible suggests that all who know Jesus Christ as personal Saviour are recorded in "The Book of Life." (Rev. 20:12, 15)

159 **IS YOUR ALL ON THE ALTAR?** — Using Old Testament imagery, the author likens a full consecration of self to a sacrifice on God's altar. (Rom. 12:1, 2)

200 **IT IS WELL WITH MY SOUL** — an expression of faith in God's inscrutable providence, was written after the author H. G. Spafford had lost four daughters at sea.

251 **It may be at morn** (see CHRIST RETURNETH)

86 **IVORY PALACES** — was written by a Presbyterian layman (Henry Barraclough) at Montreat, North Carolina, after hearing J. Wilbur Chapman preach on Psalm 45:8.

J

47 **JESUS, GENTLEST SAVIOUR** — A children's hymn, suitable also for adults, tells of the transcendence and the immanence of our Lord.

194 **JESUS, I AM RESTING, RESTING** — is a devotional hymn expressing the joy of intimate fellowship between the Christian and his Saviour.

68 **JESUS, I COME** — suggests the many needs of those who come to Christ; verse one alone lists "freedom," "gladness," "light," "health" and "wealth."

214 **JESUS, I MY CROSS HAVE TAKEN** — is the answer of a true disciple (Mark 10:28) to Jesus' challenge — to take up our cross and follow Him. (Luke 9:23)

130 **JESUS, I WILL TRUST THEE** — says that to trust in Christ is the only rational decision we can make; the final stanza translates the decision into action.

100 **JESUS IS ALL THE WORLD TO ME** — was written (ca. 1900) by Will Thompson, renowned composer and publisher in East Liverpool, Ohio and Chicago, Illinois.

239 **Jesus is coming to earth again** (see WHAT IF IT WERE TODAY?)

243 **JESUS, JESUS, WE ARE WAITING** — was written by a former teacher of Bible at Toccoa Falls Institute (Georgia), and was harmonized by a music teacher there.

127 **Jesus, keep me near the cross** (see NEAR THE CROSS)

277 **JESUS LIVES, AND SO SHALL I** — by a German Reformed pastor, Christian Gellert, is based on Jesus' words, "Because I live, ye shall live also." (John 14:19)

79 **JESUS, LOVER OF MY SOUL** — called by hymnologist Louis F. Benson "the best-loved hymn in the language," was written soon after Charles Wesley's conversion.

140 **JESUS, MASTER, WHOSE I AM** — set to a brilliant Russian melody by Dimitri Bortniansky, is a prayer to "Jesus, Master" — "King of my life."

103 **Jesus my Lord will love me forever** (see NOW I BELONG TO JESUS)

199 **JESUS, MY SAVIOUR, LOOK ON ME** — may be based on the story in Matt. 9:36. Note the climax phrase of each stanza.

132 **JESUS ONLY, LET ME SEE** — was written by Oswald J. Smith, the famous pastor and missionary statesman of Toronto, Canada.

87 **JESUS SAVES** — a missions poem, was first written for a Sunday School missions anniversary, and first sung to Meyerbeer's "Vive le Roi!"

232 **JESUS SHALL REIGN** — looks forward to the day when "every knee shall bow and every tongue confess that Jesus Christ is Lord." (Phil. 2:10, 11)

25 **JESUS, THE VERY THOUGHT OF THEE** — is taken from **Jesu, dulcis memoria,** a long Latin poem of devotion written in the twelfth century.

7 **JESUS, THOU JOY OF LOVING HEARTS** — from the same Latin source as the previous hymn, is attributed by some scholars to Bernard of Clairvaux.

82 **JESUS, THY BLOOD AND RIGHTEOUSNESS** — written by the Moravian leader Count Zinzendorf, reveals the source of our confidence before a holy God.

4 **Jesus! what a Friend for sinners** (see OUR GREAT SAVIOUR)

17 **JOIN ALL THE GLORIOUS NAMES** — insists that all the names given to Christ are inadequate to express His true character.

66 **JUST AS I AM, THINE OWN TO BE** — A "youth" version of the earlier invitation hymn (listed next), by Marianne Hearn, a leading Sunday School writer of Britain.

57 **JUST AS I AM, WITHOUT ONE PLEA** — perhaps the most famous and most biblical of invitation hymns, is used often in Billy Graham Crusades.

K

67 **King of my life, I crown Thee now** (see LEAD ME TO CALVARY)

GeNeRaL inдex

L

67 **LEAD ME TO CALVARY** — teaches that true devotion to Christ results from a contemplation of His passion, death and resurrection.

218 **LEAD ON, O KING ETERNAL** — first written for a seminary graduation, is a challenge to follow Christ in His struggle with sin and evil.

190 **LEANING ON THE EVERLASTING ARMS** — was written as a hymn of comfort for two bereaved families; it is based on Deut. 33:27.

36 **Let all the world in every corner sing** (see MY GOD AND KING!)

138 **LET ME COME CLOSER TO THEE, JESUS** — is a very personal and intimate expression of love and devotion to our Lord Jesus Christ.

233 **LET THE LOWER LIGHTS BE BURNING** — was inspired by the story of a boat lost on the rocks, because the "lower" shore lights were not burning.

276 **LIFT UP, LIFT UP YOUR VOICES NOW** — tells the story of Christ's resurrection, and relates it to the Christian's own victory over sin and death.

188 **LIKE A RIVER GLORIOUS** — suggests that a remedy for today's personality conflicts is a heart "stayed upon Jehovah."

152 **LIVING FOR JESUS** — is a favorite youth hymn of consecration. The words were written by an insurance agent, Thomas Chisholm; the tune by music editor C. Harold Lowden.

62 **LOOK TO THE LAMB OF GOD** — An invitation hymn, inspired by John the Baptist's words: "Behold the Lamb of God, which taketh away the sin of the world." (Jn. 1:29)

69 **Lord, I care not for riches** (see IS MY NAME WRITTEN THERE?)

164 **LORD, I HAVE SHUT THE DOOR** — is based on Jesus' suggestion for effective privacy in prayer. (Matt. 6:6)

142 **LORD, SPEAK TO ME** — shows the progression of discipleship. God speaks; we are taught by Him and filled with His Spirit; then we are ready to serve as He directs.

171 **LORD THOU LOV'ST THE CHEERFUL GIVER** — is a call to full stewardship which begins with the pocketbook.

170 **LOVE DIVINE, ALL LOVES EXCELLING** — sets forth Charles Wesley's teaching of sanctification; this tune is a favorite in Great Britain.

250 **Love divine, so great and wondrous** (see HE THE PEARLY GATES WILL OPEN)

104 **Loved with everlasting love** (see I AM HIS, AND HE IS MINE)

271 **Low in the grave He lay** (see CHRIST AROSE)

m

236 **MAKE ME A BLESSING** — dedicated to the choir of the famed Moody Memorial Church, says that each believer is an ambassador of Jesus Christ.

141 **MAKE ME A CAPTIVE, LORD** — as indicated by the tune name, sets forth the seeming paradoxes of a life which is given wholly to God.

73 **"Man of Sorrows," what a name** (see HALLELUJAH, WHAT A SAVIOUR!)

76 **Marvelous grace of our loving Lord** (see GRACE GREATER THAN OUR SIN)

135 **MAY THE MIND OF CHRIST, MY SAVIOUR** — is a prayer growing out of the admonition in Phil. 2:5, "Let this mind be in you, which was also in Christ Jesus . . . . "

284 **Mine eyes have seen the glory** (see BATTLE HYMN OF THE REPUBLIC)

184 **MOMENT BY MOMENT** — a poem by the evangelist D. W. Whittle, is set to music by his daughter May, who married Will R. Moody, son of D. L. Moody.

157 **MORE LIKE THE MASTER** — says that Jesus was a perfect example of what we should be, and that His death makes it possible for us to be like Him.

150 **MORE LOVE TO THEE** — as suggested in the third stanza, was written at a time when its author Elizabeth Prentiss was experiencing both physical and mental anguish.

281 **MY COUNTRY, 'TIS OF THEE** — written by Baptist seminary student Samuel F. Smith, was first sung in Park Street Church, Boston, at a 4th of July celebration in 1831.

111 **My faith has found a resting place** (see NO OTHER PLEA)

167 **MY FAITH LOOKS UP TO THEE** — was written when Ray Palmer its author was only 22 years old, and has been called the greatest American hymn.

36 **MY GOD AND KING!** — a poem by one of the earliest English hymnwriters, is set to music by the late Robert McCutchan, a leading Methodist hymnologist.

92 **My hope is built on nothing less** (see THE SOLID ROCK)

129 **MY HOPE IS IN THE LORD** — one of the best new congregational hymns of salvation, was written by Norman Clayton, a brick layer turned musician!

163 **MY JESUS, I LOVE THEE** — though written when Wm. Featherstone was still a teenager, is the sort of hymn no adult Christian dare sing carelessly!

143 **My life, my love I give to Thee** (see I'LL LIVE FOR HIM)

86 **My Lord has garments so wondrous fine** (see IVORY PALACES)

248 **MY SAVIOUR FIRST OF ALL** — is blind Fanny Crosby's attempt to say that in heaven our joy will center in our Lord, not in harps or golden streets!

112 **MY SAVIOUR'S LOVE** — was written by Charles H. Gabriel (1856-1932), one of the most prolific gospel song composers, who excelled in both lyrics and music.

GENERAL INDEX

N

78 NAILED UPON GOLGOTHA'S TREE — a hymn of Christ's passion and final victory over death, is a favorite of the fellowship called "Plymouth Brethren."

127 NEAR THE CROSS — was first a tune written by the manufacturer-musician Wm. Howard Doane, for which his friend Fanny Crosby wrote these words.

193 NEAR TO THE HEART OF GOD — was written in 1901 by a pastor of Chicago's First Presbyterian Church, to express his faith in spite of personal tragedy.

166 NEARER, STILL NEARER — can be said to be a companion hymn to "Nearer, My God, to Thee," because it breathes the same prayer of intense devotion.

111 NO OTHER PLEA — emphasizes that the basis of our eternal salvation is nothing more nor less than the atoning death of Jesus Christ.

125 NOT WHAT THESE HANDS HAVE DONE — says that good works and even suffering can not bring peace with God; it comes only through His love and grace.

103 NOW I BELONG TO JESUS — is a testimony which follows the truth, "ye are not your own; for ye are bought with a price." (I Cor. 6:19, 20)

256 NOW THANK WE ALL OUR GOD — a chorus of praise for God's blessings, was written during the Thirty Years War (1618-1648), one of Europe's darkest hours.

O

283 O BEAUTIFUL FOR SPACIOUS SKIES — was written by Katherine Lee Bates in 1893, after a visit to the summit of Pike's Peak in Colorado.

265 O COME, ALL YE FAITHFUL — latest research says, was written by John Francis Wade, a Catholic layman who sold music in the 18th century at Douai, France.

262 O COME, O COME, EMMANUEL — derived from 12th century Latin antiphons, anticipates the coming of Jesus Christ. See Isa. 7:14; Luke 1:78; Isa. 22:22.

49 O COULD I SPEAK THE MATCHLESS WORTH — suggests that human words and melodies are inadequate to express the glory of our Lord Jesus Christ.

24 O FOR A THOUSAND TONGUES TO SING — was inspired by these words spoken to Charles Wesley, "Had I a thousand tongues, I would praise Him with them all."

12 O GOD, OUR HELP IN AGES PAST — is Isaac Watts' poetic version of Psalm 90:1, 2, 4; it was first sung in 1719.

128 O HAPPY DAY THAT FIXED MY CHOICE — describes conversion as "a choice," "a bond," "a great transaction," and "rest for my long-divided heart."

172 O JESUS, I HAVE PROMISED — originally written for a confirmation service, is a much-loved hymn of dedication to discipleship.

65 O JESUS, THOU ART STANDING — is our response to the words of Christ, "Behold, I stand at the door and knock." (Rev. 3:20)

266 O LITTLE TOWN OF BETHLEHEM — was written by the eminent Episcopalian minister Phillips Brooks, as he remembered his visit to Jesus' natal city in 1866.

1 O Lord my God, when I in awesome wonder (see HOW GREAT THOU ART)

139 O LOVE THAT WILT NOT LET ME GO — by the blind Scot George Matheson, says that the Christian's cross brings him fullness of love, light and joy.

211 O MASTER, LET ME WALK WITH THEE — is a modern disciple's prayer that we may be more like Christ in His character and His service to men.

229 O MASTER OF THE WAKING WORLD — voices the cry of all restless, hungry and oppressed people in our day, whose needs are only completely met in Christ.

34 O SACRED HEAD, NOW WOUNDED — is a translation of part of a medieval poem of devotion, directed to the crucified Christ; the tune has a secular origin.

252 O THAT WILL BE GLORY — was inspired by the radiant life of a rescue mission director, Ed Card of St. Louis. He often used the word "glory," was called "Old Glory Face," and always ended his prayers with "and that will be glory for me."

85 O THE DEEP, DEEP LOVE OF JESUS — repeats, in glowing phrases, that the love of Christ is boundless, resistless, changeless and endless.

71 O THOU THAT HEAR'ST WHEN SINNERS CRY — is based on David's prayer of contrition after his great sin, as found in Psalm 51.

48 O WORSHIP THE KING — based on Psalm 104, maintains that the God of cosmic infinity is concerned with us "frail . . . . feeble children of dust."

237 O ZION, HASTE — is a call to the church to "hurry up" with its challenge to bring the message of Christ to all the world.

90 OH, HOW I LOVE JESUS — a hymn written in an Anglican rectory, is here wedded to a tune and a refrain that originated in an early American camp meeting.

98 OH, IT IS WONDERFUL! — uses words like "amazed," "confused," "tremble" and "marvel" to express our wonder at the sacrifice of Christ.

146 OH, TO BE LIKE THEE — is a prayer that we may more resemble Christ, in our service to men and our personal holiness.

GeNeRaL InDeX

GeneRaL InԀex